MUA1940067

Ecology, Climate and Empire

Ecology, Climate and Empire

colonialism and global environmental history, 1400–1940

Richard H. Grove

Australian National University

The White  Horse Press

Copyright © Richard H. Grove 1997

First Published 1997 by The White Horse Press, 10 High Street, Knapwell, Cambridge CB3 8NR, UK

Set in 11 Point Adobe Garamond
Printed and Bound in Great Britain by Biddles Ltd, King's Lynn

All rights reserved. Except for the quotation of short passages for the purpose of criticism and review, no part of this book may be reprinted or reproduced or utilised in any form or by any electronic, mechanical orother means, including photocopying or recording, or in any information storage or retrieval system, without permission from the publisher.

A catalogue record for this book is available from the British Library

ISBN 1-874267-18-9 (HB); 1-874267-19-7 (PB)

For Vinita

Contents

Richard Grove was born in Cambridge in 1955. After a schooling in Ghana and England he graduated in Geography from Hertford College Oxford in 1979. Following a graduate schooling in Conservation at University College London he took a PhD at Cambridge University in History and was subsequently a British Academy Research Fellow and a Fellow of the Woodrow Wilson International Center for Scholars in Washington DC. Currently he is a Senior Fellow of the Institute of Advanced Studies at the Australian National University, and a life member of Clare Hall, Cambridge. He is founder-editor of the international journal *Environment and History*. His books include *The Cambridgeshire Coprolite Mining Rush* (1976), *The Future for Forestry* (1983), *The SSSI Handbook* (1985), *Conservation in Africa: People, Policies and Practice* (1987) *Green Imperialism: Colonial Expansion, Tropical Island Edens and the Origins of Environmentalism 1600–1800* (1995) and *Nature and the Orient: the Environmental History of South and Southeast Asia* (1997). Major parts of this book were created while he was a Fellow of the National Humanities Center, North Carolina and a Leverhulme Trust Award-holder at the University of Cambridge and the Ancient India and Iran Trust, Cambridge, U.K.

Acknowledgements

This book represents a long period of my research life, but is particularly the fruit of my associations with the Australian National University and the History of Science Department at Cambridge. During the course of it I have incurred many personal and intellectual debts most of which I cannot hope to repay. The work originated in my own environmental activism. In that respect I should like to pay tribute to the work of Chris Rose, Charles Secrett and Andrew Lees. Andrew, sadly, died in tragic circumstances in Madagascar, while he was, characteristically, confronting major logging and mining interests in the region.

In the last few years Polly Hill has been a great friend and mentor and I hope that she will like this book. Her work on economic anthropology in West Africa, begun while at the University of Ghana, is unparalleled. Moreover, her sharp awareness of the signficance of the forest environment and the history of land use change in the context of cocoa and dry land farming in Ghana and Nigeria inspired me to take up an interest in West Africa, the results of which appear as a chapter in this book. Peter Herbst, another emeritus academic of the University of Ghana, has also inspired me with his historical insights and commitment to the cause of forest protection in New South Wales. In Canberra I would particularly like to thank Janet Copland, a prominent green activist who made my transition to Australia much easier than it might have been. The book was originally started while I was a Fellow of the National Humanities Center in Durham, North Carolina in 1996. In that congenial place I drew richly from the great knowledge of Wayne Pond, Mario Klarer, Tim Breen and many others. At the Forest History Society in nearby Durham I was greatly helped by Pete Steen and Cheryl Oakes, and their staff, as well as by the great resources of the Book Exchange, the 'greatest bookshop in the South'. As usual, John Richards and Betsy Flint were my friends and intellectual guides at Duke University. Many of the ideas in this book were first tried out at seminars at the Cabinet of Natural History in the History of Science Department in Cambridge, as we began to build up the Global Environmental History Unit. At Cambridge too, Clare Hall has been a great source of scholarly support, principally through the agency of Gillian Beer and Wenda, who knows everything that goes on. In Malawi John Killick was a most hospitable host, and a great raconteur of the myths of the Mulange forests. William Beinart and Barry Supple have, as ever, been wonderfully constant friends and guides. At the Australian National University, which has now become a major world centre for environmental history, I have benefited greatly from the enjoyable but rigorous intellectual company of Graeme Snooks, Barry Smith, Mark Elvin, Tim Bonyhady and John Dargavel.

I should also like to thank James Cormack, Nick Jardine, Simon Schaffer, Ranabir Chakravarti, Mahesh Rangarajan, Ravi Rajan, Colyer Dawkins, Jeff Burley, Quentin Cronk, Richard Tucker, Deepak Kumar, Satpal Sangwan, Sita Damodaran, Martin Abdullahi, Richard Drayton, Ajay Skaria, Robert Anderson, Peggy Harper, Vera White, Ann Chivers, Adrian Walford and Piers Vitebsky. I owe a great deal to Andrew and Alison Johnson for pulling the book together so efficiently.

I am grateful to Manchester University Press for permission to include Chapters 1 and 6. A version of the former appeared as 'Imperialism and the discourse of desiccation' in M. Bell, R. Butlin and M. Heffernan, eds, *Geography and Imperialism, 1820–1940* (Manchester University Press, 1995); the latter was first published in John Mackenzie, ed., *Imperialism and the Natural World* (Manchester University Press, 1990). Cambridge University Press kindly gave permission to reprint Chapter 2, which first appeared in *Comparative Studies in Society and History,* XX (1993), pp. 318–351. Chapter 3 originally appeared in *Journal of Southern African Studies,* 15 (1989), pp. 163–187; this journal is now published by Carfax Publishing Company, PO Box 25, Abingdon, Oxfordshire, whose permission to reproduce the chapter is duly acknowledged.

Finally, I should like to thank the Australian National University, the Leverhulme Trust and the British Academy for their financial support of research published here.

Canberra Day, March 17th 1997

Ecology, Climate and Empire

The gorge of the Torakudu river, as it was drawn by Captain D. Hamilton on Hugh Cleghorn's expedition to the Annamalai Mountains, South India, in 1851. (From Cleghorn, The Forests and Gardens of South India)

Introduction

This book aims to serve as an introduction to a relatively new area of research on the environmental history of the European colonial empires. There are at least two major reasons why the history of the colonial periphery is now emerging as vital to an understanding of the development of perceptions of the global environment, both for historians and historians of science. Firstly, it was in the tropical colonies that scientists first came to a realisation of the extraordinary speed at which people, and Europeans in particular, could transform and destroy the natural environment. Above all the environments of tropical islands played a very prominent part in this development of mental perceptions. Secondly, the colonial context also stimulated a dramatic growth in scientific and state interest in the apparent links between climate change and deforestation. This led directly to a series of state programmes directed at large scale forest conservation, especially in the French and British colonial empires and then, more latterly, in the western 'frontier empire' of the United States and its colonies. Many of the 'experts' involved in this process were what we might now term 'environmentalists', at least from a post-hoc perspective, with all the limitations that involves. Nevertheless, the depth and sophistication of their concerns considerably pre-dated the emergence of comparable notions in Europe. Their preoccupations are especially topical to the climatic and environmental worries of today.

The structure of the book is essentially chronological. It will soon be apparent to the reader that I have placed considerable emphasis on the critical importance of India to the course of developments in climatic and conservation thinking in the rest of the world. The story of the involvement of the British East India Company in natural history and then in forest management was of particular importance. This may come as a surprise when one considers the undoubted commercial priorities of an organisation that was, in some senses, a forerunner of the major transnational companies that emerged in the late nineteenth century. But the East India Company was also an intrinsically Indian institution and one that placed far more value on indigenous expertise than its Raj successor. As a result its experts were able to absorb a great deal of significant local knowledge about the tropical environment and to suggest strategies for its management based on local precepts. The fear of famine and gross agrarian failure was a vital factor in bringing about structures for forest, soil and water conservation, as the first two chapters of the book make clear. The spectre of famine, particularly after the disastrous drought episode of 1862, was also a major factor in the advent of state conservation in South Africa, the story told in chapter three. Although conservation and climatic thinking in Southern Africa were heavily derivative of concepts first thought through in India and Mauritius the colonial environmental discourse in Africa owed a great deal to the maverick campaigning and writing of one man, John Croumbie Brown. In particular Brown successfully propagandised the idea of regional and global desiccation and climate change brought about by the 'evils' of deforestation.

However, it fell to scientists in Indian and then Australian colonial employ to collect evidence for global teleconnections in climate change, a concern that arose initially out of failures in the Indian monsoon. We now know that these were often closely related to severe El Niño current events, periodic climatic episodes triggered by unusually warm ocean currents off the coast of Peru. The history of the discovery of distinct patterns and correlations involved in global climate change by scientists operating at the colonial periphery is detailed in chapter four. This account should help to finally put paid to the idea popularised by some historians that science in the colonies was inherently secondary and far from the cutting edge of fundamental discovery. In fact, the reverse seems to have been the case in many of the medical, field and meteorological sciences. Indeed, the idea of a monolithic colonial scientific mentality is one that needs to be seriously questioned. The links between metropolitan 'centres of calculation' and the activities of colonial scientists were often of a tenuous and ambivalent kind. Instead, the relations between local colonial experts and local colonial administrations were probably more important than researchers have previously thought. Where indigenous people were employed as scientists by the colonial state, as happened as early as the 1830s in India and by the 1880s in Nigeria, the picture was an even more complex one.

However, there is no doubt that the introduction of often draconian colonial forest and land management structures, albeit designed to check climate change and promote sustainable resource use, actually brought about frequent clashes and contests over land use. These typically involved the colonial state, private companies and local people as separate and competing actors in contests of governance, protest and manipulation. In some instances colonised peoples succeeded in blocking the advent of state forest or soil conservation and then turning the colonial programmes to their own ends. This is the picture presented in chapter five. More frequently, as I make clear in the concluding chapter, the enforcement of colonial attempts at environmental control resulted in a whole typology of resistance and reaction by indigenous peoples and colonial inhabitants. These reactions were often the catalyst to violent and significant political changes, ranging right through from the American Revolution to the Mau-Mau revolt.

In many ways the business of empire, for most of the colonised, had far more to do with the impact of different modes of colonial resource control and colonial environmental concepts, than it had to do with the direct impact of military or political structures. Some groups gained from the new forms of control, while many others clearly lost out. Some colonial officials favoured indigenous environmental knowledge and criticised the application of western methods, while other officials preferred to see the 'native' as uniformly profligate and possessed of no useful environmental insights. By and large the latter perception tended to win the day, but it was by no means always the case.

Why is it worth studying these past struggles over land use and environmental meaning and mechanism? There are many reasons, practical and academic. But not least is the fact that in the post-colonial period, many 'independent' governments, most of them actually run by isolated social elites, have tended to repeat, sometimes even more crudely and brutally, the arrogant environmental mistakes made by their colonial predecessors. Frequently they have displayed the same disdain and disrespect for indigenous and traditional knowledge. Large-scale prestige projects for dam-building, irrigation, land development and afforestation or deforestation have proved to be just as seductive to post-colonial as to colonial governments, and past mistakes have simply been re-run on much larger scales. Some of them might have been avoided, given sufficient historical insight. Moreover, current and fashionable worries about climate change and global warming actually have a very long pedigree that might well repay careful study, especially with respect to the ambivalent and difficult relations between scientists and the state.

Current preoccupations with a 'global' environmental crisis about pollution, climate change and resource over-use are now the problem of everyman and everywoman and of all states. But they were foreshadowed in the early days of empire by the dramatic globalisation of economic and natural transformations that was enabled during the colonial period. The often (although not always) grievous ecological impact of westernisation and empire, which took centuries to take effect, is now felt almost everywhere, and is probably irreversible. It is this fateful globalisation which has forced an environmental agenda upon historians, among many others. But it has, I think, also forced a new historical agenda upon the scientists. These people, no longer always seen favourably as the harbingers of an unalloyed progress and prosperity, now find themselves needing to seek insights in historical pattern and analysis. To take one example, we can only understand the complex dynamics and undoubt-edly profound impact of the El Niño current on world climate and economies by a sophisticated interpretation of archival sources. As yet, this task has barely been commenced.

It is probably a measure of the growing relevance of environmen-tal history to human affairs that its academic centre of gravity has now shifted firmly away from North America and Europe to South and Southeast Asia and Africa. Perhaps not surprisingly it is particularly in India that the historiography of the subject has become especially rich and well developed. Indeed much of the environmental history of South Asia (and elsewhere) is being written by individuals who started their careers as environmental activists. But this is really nothing new. William Roxburgh, the pioneer of climatology in India, and Hugh Cleghorn, the pioneer of forest protection, were themselves early environmental histo-rians, ever ready to irritate authority and break with orthodoxy. I believe that they would have appreciated and thoroughly understood the growing importance of environmental history in the tropics today. This book is intended to encourage that development.

1

The Evolution of the Colonial Discourse on Deforestation and Climate Change, 1500–1940

Concepts of artificially induced climatic change have a much longer history than one might imagine.[1] Nowadays, of course, they have become a part of our popular culture, and part of a widespread and possibly justifiable environmental neurosis. They are especially familiar and useful in providing the justification for new plans to prevent tropical deforestation and reduce outputs of carbon dioxide into the atmosphere.

It is, moreover, not well known that the fear of artificially caused climate change, and much of the modern conservation thinking which that anxiety stimulated, developed specifically in the tropical colonial context.[2] These fears and these connections attained their most vigorous forms, in terms of deliberate state policy, during the heyday of imperialism. After about 1750 a few learned societies at the metropolitan centre had begun to play a major role in formulating and then propagandising ideas about deforestation, desiccation and climate change, often as a basis for proposing large scale forest conservation. The Royal Society, the Royal Society of Arts, the Académie des Sciences and, above all, the Royal Geographical Society were pre-eminent in this activity. However, the antecedents of this institutional advocacy have to be sought very early on in the history of colonialism. This chapter seeks to narrate the development of ideas about climate change and 'desiccationism' through from their earliest emergence to their current prominence in our own times.

An awareness of the detrimental effects of colonial economic

---

[1] For more specific regional details of this see Chapter 2.

[2] See R.H. Grove, 'The origins of environmentalism', *Nature* (London), 10 May 1990, pp. 5–11.

activity and, above all, of capitalist plantation agriculture (the potential profits from which had stimulated much early colonial settlement) developed initially on the small island colonies of the Portuguese and Spanish at the Canary Islands and Madeira.[3] It was on these islands that the ideas first developed by the Greek naturalist Theophrastus in his essays on deforestation and climate change were revived and gradually gathered strength. as his works were translated and widely published during the Renaissance.[4] For example Columbus, according to one of his biographers, feared, on the basis of his knowledge of what had happened after deforestation in the Canaries, that similar devastation in the West Indies would cause major rainfall decline.

Certainly these ideas were already fashionable by 1571 when Fernandez Oviedo, in Costa Rica, soon followed by Francis Bacon and Edmund Halley in England, began to theorise about the connections between rainfall, vegetation and the hydrological cycle.[5] Edmund Halley's fieldwork on this subject, carried out in 1676 on the island of St Helena during a summer vacation, while he was a student at Queen's College Oxford, showed remarkable insight. Furthermore it was on St Helena that some of the earliest and best documented attempts were made to prevent deforestation and control soil erosion, both of which were serious by the end of the seventeenth century. These attempts were elaborately recorded by officials of the English East India Company, which controlled the island. However the early conservation methods and local environmental thinking developed before 1750 on islands such as St Helena, and also in a similar fashion on Barbados and Montserrat, were purely empirically based, localised and often unsuccessful in

---

[3] There is no single useful work on the environmental impact of colonial rule. However see the useful secondary summaries in Clive Ponting's *A green history of the world* (London, 1991); and the useful regional study by David Watts, *The West Indies: patterns of development, culture and environmental change, since 1492* (Cambridge, 1987). *A plague of sheep*, by Elinor Melville (Cambridge, 1994) tackles the environmental impact of Spanish colonisation and horse-culture in 16th century Mexico.

[4] The most useful contextualisation of Theophrastus is in C. Glacken, *Traces on the Rhodian shore* (Berkeley, 1967).

[5] See Edmund Halley, 'An account of the watry circulation of the sea, and of the cause of springs', *Philosophical Transactions of the Royal Society*, 192:17 (1694), pp. 468–472.

application.[6] Indeed they were not based on any coherent body of climatic theory, despite the knowledge of Theophrastus' desiccationist hypotheses that already existed in some intellectual circles in Europe and South America.

The increasingly complex infrastructures of colonial rule under the British and French after the mid-eighteenth century provided the basis for the kinds of information networks needed to systematically collate environmental information on a global basis and to respond to perceived environmental crises with effective forms of environmental control based on unitary climate theories. These information networks were based primarily on the botanic gardens of Europe and the colonies and were a direct consequence of the rapid growth in interest in economic plant transfer and agricultural development which took place between 1750 and 1850.[7] But these networks were not sufficient on their own. As I shall argue in this paper the development of conservationist ideas and early environmental concern was also critically dependent on the diffusion of desiccation concepts, or the formulation of a desiccationist discourse linking deforestation to rainfall reduction. Developing notions of species rarity, extinctions and endemism also played a significant although secondary part in early environmentalism.[8] To some extent it seems that the colonial networks of botanical exchange and the botanic

---

[6] Detailed information on the environmental history of the West Indies and on early conservation thinking on the islands can be found in Watts, *The West Indies*. For an excellent case study of Montserrat see Lydia M. Pulsipher, *Seventeenth century Montserrat: an environmental impact statement* (London, Institute of British Geographers, Historical Geography Research Series no. 14, 1986).

[7] Unfortunately there is as yet no coherent account of the growth of these networks on a global basis. For a sketchy and doctrinaire but still useful account of colonial botanic gardens see Lucille M. Brockway, *Science and colonial expansion: the role of the British Royal Botanic Garden* (New York, 1979). Richard Drayton, *Nature's Government* (New Haven, Yale University Press, in press) deals with the ideology and politics behind the rise of the Kew system. The origins of the Dutch colonial system of plant exchange are usefully covered for the seventeenth century by J. Heniger in *Hendrik Van Reede tot Drakenstein and the Hortus Malabaricus: a contribution to the study of colonial botany* (Rotterdam, 1986).

[8] My interpretation of the origins of western environmentalism clearly differs in its emphasis on the importance of the periphery from such orthodox explanations as that

gardens themselves acted as social institutions that encouraged the slow development of an environmental consciousness.[9]

The linking of deforestation to climatic change and rainfall reduction (the essence of desiccationism) laid the basis for the initiation and proliferation of colonial forest protection systems after the Peace of Paris in 1763, particularly in the West Indies. The intense interest which developed during the eighteenth century, particularly in France, in theories linking climate to theories of cultural 'degeneration' and human evolution assisted this process.[10] But after about 1760 empirical observations of deforestation and the impact of droughts in the colonies were now complemented by the widespread promulgation of desiccationist theories by metropolitan institutions in Britain and France, and especially by the Académie des Sciences in France and the Society of Arts in Britain. While deforestation in temperate countries, especially in North America, tended to be seen as beneficial, quite the opposite view pertained in many of the tropical colonies by the late eighteenth century.[11] Climatic change, it was believed, threatened not only the economic well-being of a colony but posed hazards to the integrity and health of the settler populations of the plantation colonies of the

given in David Pepper, *The roots of modern environmentalism* (London, 1986). More recent work has been far more insightful than that of Pepper in its stress on the significance of Rousseau's circle in provoking a new environmental consciousness, see, for example, G.F. Lafrenière, 'Rousseau and the European roots of environmentalism', *Environmental History Review,* 14 (1990), pp. 241–273. Even Lafrenière, however, does not recognise the direct impact of Rousseau's thinking on the beginnings of conservation in the French colonial context. Perhaps the best regional work to date on the early history of conservation is L. Urteaga, *La Tierra Esquilmada; las ideas sobre la conservacion de la naturaleza en la cultura espanola del siglo XVIII* (Barcelona, Serbal\CSIC, 1987).

[9] The best study to date on the working and social influence of a single colonial scientific institution is probably J. E. Maclellan, *Colonialism and science: Saint Dominique in the Old Regime* (Baltimore, Johns Hopkins University Press, 1992).

[10] Emma Spary, 'Climate, natural history and agriculture, the ideology of botanical networks in eighteenth century France and its colonies', unpublished paper presented at the International Conference on Environmental Institutions, St Vincent, West Indies, April 1991. See also Emma Spary, 'Making the natural order: the Paris Jardin du Roi, 1750–1795' (Ph.D. thesis, University of Cambridge, 1993).

[11] See K. Thompson, 'Forests and climatic change in America: some early views', *Climatic Change*, 3 (1983), pp. 47–64.

Caribbean and the Indian Ocean.[12]

The business of forest protection and tree-planting had thus acquired, by the late eighteenth century, far more acute meanings in the colonial setting than it had in contemporary Europe.[13] The timing of the development of colonial forest protection actually depended both on the existence and complexity of institutions with an intellectual involvement in the colonies and on the pattern of diffusion of desiccationist ideas. Whilst the Royal Society had taken an early interest in forest preservation, colonial deforestation was not a concern of the Society, even though it played a part in the development of the desiccationist discourse in the late seventeenth century. Instead the institutional connection between desiccation ideas and the colonial environment was made in the wake of the foundation of the Society of Arts in 1754.[14] Simultaneously the Académie des Sciences developed an interest in the matter, so that the intercourse between French and British intellectuals became of prime importance in the development of colonial environmentalism and indeed remained so until the mid nineteenth century.

The elaboration of early desiccation ideas into complex physical and biological theories depended at first on the work of John Woodward at Gresham College in London (the founder of the first chair in geology at Cambridge University) in establishing the basic principles of transpiration.[15] In his *Vegetable Staticks* of 1726 Stephen Hales of Corpus Christi College, Cambridge refined this work further in estimating the amount of moisture contributed by trees to the atmosphere.[16] Buffon's

---

[12] For a typical contemporary expression of these views see Edward Long, *A history of Jamaica*, (London, 1777), vol.3, pp. i–iv.

[13] For the significance of tree-planting in Britain at this time see K. Thomas, *Man and the natural world: changing attitudes in England 1500–1800* (London, 1983); F. Perlin, *A forest journey: the role of wood in the development of civilization* (New York, 1989); and S. Daniels, 'The political iconography of woodland', in D. Cosgrove and S. Daniels, *The iconography of landscape* (Cambridge, 1988).

[14] For the early programmes and ideology of the Royal Society of Arts see D.G.C. Adams, *William Shipley: founder of the Royal Society of Arts, a biography with documentation* (London, Scolar Press, 1979); and Henry Trueman Wood, *A history of the Royal Society of Arts* (London, John Murray, 1913).

[15] J. Woodward, 'Some thoughts and experiments concerning vegetation', *Philosophical Transactions of the Royal Society*, 21 (1699), pp. 196–227.

subsequent translation of Hales's work came to the attention of Duhamel du Monceau, the great French meteorologist and arboriculturist. In a popular work on tree-planting, published in 1760, du Monceau developed the connections between trees and climate at length.[17] These ideas were then transferred across the channel once again and were widely discussed at meetings of the new Society of Arts, which included the Marquis de Turbilly, the Comte d'Abeille and other members of the Académie des Sciences among its members.[18] However the whole matter might have remained academic had it not been for the fact that at least two members of the Society of Arts also served as members of the powerful Lords Commissioners for Trade in the Colonies, the body responsible for planning land-use in the new West Indies possessions.

The most significant of these figures was Soame Jenyns, the MP for Cambridge.[19] It seems to have been due to his influence that the Lords Commissioners were apprised of desiccation ideas at some point between 1760 and 1763. With the signing of the Peace of Paris in 1763 the Ceded Isles of St Vincent, St Lucia, Grenada and Tobago all came under British rule. As part of their plans for the survey and division of lands on the isles, all of them still inhabited by substantial numbers of Carib Indians, the Lords Commissioners made provision for the gazetting of large areas of mountain land as forest reserve, for 'the protection of the rains'.[20] These were the first forest reserves ever to be established with a view to preventing climate change. The most extensive of them, on the highlands of north-western Tobago, is still in existence. In 1769 some very similar

---

[16] A. Clark-Kennedy, *Stephen Hales, DD, FRS: an eighteenth century biography* (Cambridge, 1929). See Stephen Hales, *Vegetable Staticks* (London, 1727), p. 20. Hales owed a great deal to the pioneering chemical work of the Leiden establishment and cited Hermann Boerhave's *New Method of Chemistry* translated into English in 1727 by P. Shaw and E. Chambers.

[17] Duhamel du Monceau, *Des semis et plantations des arbres et de leur culture* (Paris, 1760).

[18] Royal Society of Arts Archives, John Adam Street, London W1, Members' Files.

[19] R. Rompkey, *Soame Jenyns* (Boston Mass., Twayne Publishers, 1984); and 'Soame Jenyns, M.P., a curious case of membership', *Journal of the Royal Society of Arts*, 120 (1972), pp. 532–542. See also PRO/CO/102/1, beginning 'representations of the commissioners', Public Record Office, Kew, UK.

[20] Public Record Office, Kew, UK. Ref. No. CO106/9; CO101/1 No. 26

reserves, based on the same theory and with the same intellectual precedents, were established on Mauritius (then known as the Isle de France) by Pierre Poivre, the Commissaire-Intendant of the colony.[21] We know that Poivre had been an advocate of colonial forest protection for some time and that he had given, in 1763, a major speech in Lyons on the climatic dangers of deforestation.[22] This speech may go down in history as one of the first environmentalist texts to be based explicitly on a fear of widespread climate change.

Poivre's forest conservation programmes on Mauritius were encouraged by a government of physiocratic sympathies and by the botanists of the Jardin du Roi in Paris.[23] In the British Caribbean colonies on the other hand, the more autonomous institutional influence of the Society of Arts remained critical to promoting tree planting and, to a lesser extent, forest conservation. The Society had been instrumental in founding the botanic garden at Kingstown on St Vincent, the first such garden in the western hemisphere.[24] It was the existence of this garden and the activities of its superintendents, particularly those of Alexander Anderson, a Scottish physician, that ensured institutional support for further forest protection measures in the Caribbean, especially on St Vincent and the other islands of the Grenada Governorate.[25] On St

---

[21] See J.R. Brouard, *The woods and forests of Mauritius* (Port Louis, Mauritius, Government Printer, 1963).

[22] Lecture to the Agricultural Society of Lyons, MS no. 575, folio 74, pp. 27–29; Archives of the Bibliothèque Centrale du Muséum National d'Histoire Naturelle, Paris.

[23] Louis Malleret, *Pierre Poivre* (Paris, 1974). Physiocracy was an economic philosophy developed after about 1757 in France by François Quesnay and the Marquis de Mirabeau and their colleagues. It attempted to relate economic systems to the workings of natural systems. It was an economic philosophy that was very hostile to the unrestricted activity of speculative bullion and investment markets and to absentee landlordism. Physiocracy encouraged the application of science to agriculture and commerce but saw agriculture as the most important economic activity.

[24] See *Premiums by the Society established at London for the encouragement of Arts, Manufactures and Commerce,* issue dt 10 June 1760. The society offered large cash prizes for tree planting and in this case for the establishment of a botanic garden, which it advocated in 1760. The garden was actually founded in 1763 by Robert Melville, the first Governor of the Grenada Governorate. See R. Dossie, *Memoirs of agriculture,* vol. 3 (London, 1789), p. 800.

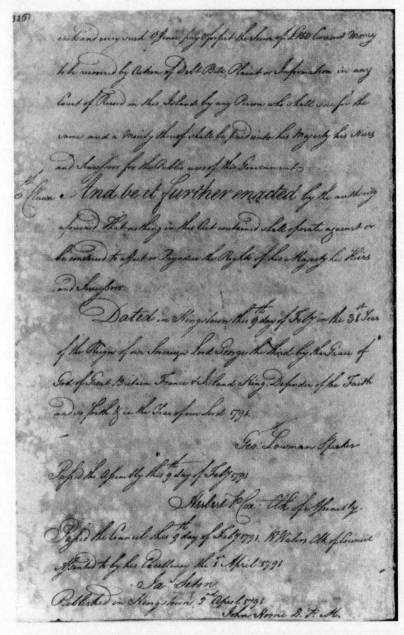

A section of the King's Hill Forest Act of 1791, delineating the bounds

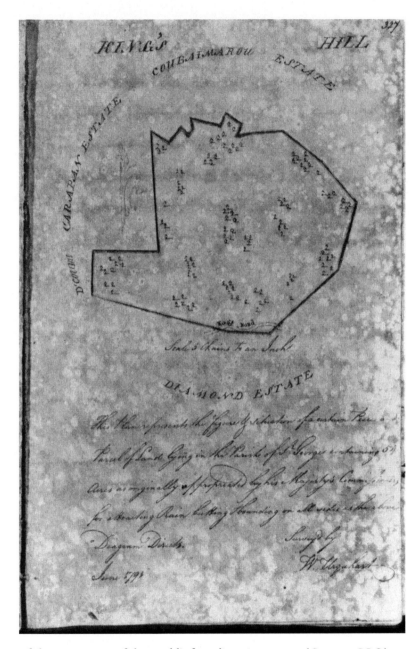

of the reserve, one of the world's first climatic reserves. (Courtesy PRO)

Vincent a comprehensive law was passed in 1791 to protect the Kings Hill Forest with the specific intention of preventing rainfall change.[26] This legislation was subsequently imitated on St Helena and subsequently in India.[27] Incidentally a major stimulus to forest protection activities in 1790 and 1791 was the occurrence of droughts in tropical regions on a global scale.[28] These events appear to have been caused by an unusually strong El Niño current in those years, which caused severe drought in Southern India, Australia, St Helena and the West Indies as well as at locations in central America, especially in Mexico.[29]

Once colonial forest protection ideas, based on desiccation theo-

---

[25] There is as yet no useful of comprehensive biography of Alexander Anderson's extraordinary life. But see Lancelot Guilding, *An account of the botanic garden in the island of St Vincent* (Glasgow, 1825) for some biographical details.

[26] The act was proclaimed at St Vincent on 2 April 1791. The second reading of the bill for the Act had taken place in the St Vincent Assembly on 13 November 1788. PRO CO263\21.

[27] See Chapter 2.

[28] For case-studies of the way in which the El Niño current has historically had a global impact see Michael Glantz, ed., *Teleconnections linking worldwide climate anomalies: scientific basis and social impact* (Cambridge, 1991).

[29] For details of the unusual strength of the El Niño current in the years 1790–1792 (as well as for details of evidence of other major El Niño events see W.H. Quinn and V.T. Neal, 'El Niño occurrences over the past four and a half centuries', *Journal of Geophysical Research*, vol. 92 no. C13 (1987), pp. 14449–14461. The strength of the 1791 El Niño was recorded by J. H. Unanue in *El clima de Lima* (Madrid, 1815)

In the West Indies detailed records of the 1791 droughts appear in the Proceedings of the Legislative Assembly of Montserrat for the year 1791, dt 13 August 1791 (Petition of the Council to the Governor of the Leeward Islands), Archives of the Colony of Montserrat, Public Library, Plymouth, Montserrat, BWI. On St Helena the 1791 droughts are recorded in H.R. Janisch, *Extracts from the St Helena Records* (Jamestown, 1908), p. 202, entry dt 25 June 1791. Bad as the drought was in St Helena in 1791–1792 it was 'much more calamitous in India' (Alexander Beatson, *Tracts relative to the island of St Helena, written during a residency of five years* [London, 1816], p. 198). Beatson recorded that 'owing to a failure of rain during the above two years, one half of the inhabitants in the northern circar had perished by famine and the raminder were so feeble and weak that on the report of rice coming up from the Malabar coast five thousand people left Rajamundry and very few of them reached the seaside although the distance is only fifty miles'. Beatson had culled this information from a letter written by Dr James Anderson, Curator of the Madras Nopalry Garden, to Robert Kyd, curator of the Calcutta botanic garden. The evidence for the 1791 drought in Australia is impression-

ries, were firmly installed, notably on Tobago, St Vincent, St Helena and Mauritius, they acquired a momentum of their own, assisted by emerging colonial botanic garden information networks, and particularly the lines of communication between the gardens at St Vincent, St Helena, Cape Town, Mauritius and Calcutta.[30] The influence of the metropolitan centres in these networks was actually relatively weak. This remained the case even after Sir Joseph Banks began his period of dominance of botanical science in Britain and Kew began to achieve pre-eminence. Although aware of the possibilities of environmental change, not least on St Helena, Banks cannot be counted among the major environmentalist pioneers. The Royal Botanic Gardens at Kew only became a significant player in colonial conservation after Sir William Hooker became Superintendent in the 1830s.

Probably the first environmental theorist in the British colonial context to parallel the pioneering work of Pierre Poivre and his colleague Bernardin de St Pierre on Mauritius was Alexander Anderson. His *Geography and History of St Vincent*, written in 1799, and his *Delugia*, an early geological history of the world, mark him out as a visionary environmental thinker and the pioneer of a generation of surgeon-conservationists and geographers.[31] The colonial expertise of men such as Anderson and Poivre meant that the role of metropolitan institutions in initiating 'centres of environmental calculation' (to adapt the terminology of Bruno Latour)[32] remained relatively unimportant and derivative. Even much later, after 1800, the emergence of a school of environmentalists in India in the ranks of the East India Company medical

---

istic but decisive. By the end of 1791 the Tank Stream, the main water supply for the convict colony at Port Jackson, had dried up and 'tanks' were cut in the bed of the stream to conserve water. Drawings of the colony in early 1792 show that the stream was still empty, while in later pictures of Sydney the stream is always full; see T. McCormick, *First views of Australia 1788–1825* (Sydney, 1987).

[30] This emerges in the correspondence of Sir Joseph Banks; see W. R. Dawson, ed., *The Banks letters: a calendar of the manuscript correspondence of Sir Joseph Banks preserved in the British Museum, London* (London, 1958).

[31] Alexander Anderson, 'Geography and History of St Vincent', and 'Delugia', book manuscripts, Archives of the Linnaean Society, London.

[32] Bruno Latour, *We have never been modern* (Cambridge, Mass., 1993).

service, long after desiccationist forest protection policies had emerged on the island colonies, was largely an internal and indigenous matter, drawing heavily on Indian environmental knowledge and tree-planting practice, and the desiccationist ideas put into practice on St Vincent and St Helena. [33] However, the influence of the Society of Arts remained important for a while. For example, William Roxburgh, the second superintendent of the Calcutta Botanic Garden, promoted extensive tree-planting policies in Bengal with the active encouragement of the Society of Arts.[34] Indian forest conservation practice and environmentalism after 1842 also drew on the climatic theories of Alexander von Humboldt and Joseph Boussingault, as well as on the forestry methods inspired by French physiocracy and its German physiocratic imitator [35]

Initially local colonial scientific societies in India provided the impetus and professional authority necessary to establish the first forest conservation agencies in India to be based on desiccationist notions (specifically the Bombay Forest Department and the Madras Forest Department).[36] In the early 1850s, however, the proponents of forest conservation on an all-India basis found it necessary, in the face of state reluctance to finance such an establishment, to resort once more to a source of metropolitan scientific authority, namely the British Association for the Advancement of Science. In 1851 the BAAS commissioned a full report on the 'physical and economic consequences' of tropical deforestation.[37] This helped to legitimate the theoretical and environmental basis for the subsequent development of an all-India forest

---

[33] See R.H. Grove, *Green imperialism: colonial expansion, tropical island Edens, and the origins of environmentalism, 1600–1860* (Cambridge, 1995).

[34] British Library, India Office Library and Records (IOL) ref no. F4\4\427. For details of Roxburgh's tree-planting experiments in Bengal and Bihar see Home Public Consultations letters, National Archives of India, New Delhi; especially letters dated 31 Jan 1798 and 23 May 1813, and 'Botanic garden' letters, 1816–1817. His methods are detailed in HPC, NAI Letter dt. 23 October 1812, E. Barrett (Acting Collector of Bauleah) to Richard Rocke, Acting President and member of the Board of Revenue, Fort Willliam, Calcutta.

[35] Alexander von Humboldt, 'Sur les lines isothermes et de la distribution de la chaleur sur le globe', Societé d'Arcueil, *Memoires,* 3 (1817), pp. 462–602.

[36] See Chapter 2.

administration. Seven years later the BAAS became the forum for discussions on 'the general and gradual desiccation of the earth and atmosphere' in the wake of a paper delivered by J. Spotswood Wilson.[38] This paper can be said to mark the onset of a truly international environmental debate in which processes operating at a global scale were being considered.

In the ensuing two decades the BAAS continued to serve as a forum for advocates of forest and species preservation. Professor Alfred Newton and Alfred Russell Wallace both utilised the BAAS for launching their conservationist opinions and programmes and evoking discussions on extinction and deforestation.[39] To some extent, however, the BAAS proved unsatisfactory as an institutional setting for the airing of environmentalist views, partly because it only met for a limited time, once a year, and partly because its influence in the colonial context was relatively weak. As a result the Royal Geographical Society displaced the BAAS, during the 1860s, as the most prominent institutional setting for the discussion of the desiccationist and conservationist discourses that were receiving so much attention from botanists and policy-makers in the colonies. At this period, it should be pointed out, the construction of environmental agendas and local land use policies in the British colonies, in contrast to the French case, did not yet receive any backing or guidance at all from governmental institutions at the centre. In other words, there was no imperial environmental 'centre of calculation' sponsored by the state in Britain itself (and this remained the case until the establishment of the Imperial Forestry Institute at Oxford in 1924).[40]

---

[37] H. Cleghorn, F. Royle, R. Baird-Smith and R. Strachey, 'Report of the Committee appointed by the British Association to consider the probable effects in an economical and physical point of view of the destruction of tropical forests', *Report of the British Association for the Advancement of Science*, 1852, pp. 78–102.

[38] J.S. Wilson, 'On the general and gradual desiccation of the earth and atmosphere', *Report of the British Association for the Advancement of Science (Transactions)*, 1858, pp. 155–156.

[39] Both Newton (the originator and drafter of Britain's first bird protection legislation passed in 1868) and Wallace used their respective presidencies of sections of the BAAS meetings as platforms for propagandising their own conservationist agendas. Both men linked global deforestation and desiccation with species extinctions.

*Professor Alfred Newton, pioneer conservationist. Newton linked global
deforestation and desiccation to species extinctions.*

Instead any government centres of calculation were all situated at the imperial periphery, especially in Madras, Bombay, Port Louis, Cape Town and, more latterly, at Dehra Dun, the headquarters of the Indian Forest Service and training schools.

In France, on the other hand, the imperial forest school at Nancy had served as a centre of environmental ideas and training, much of it desiccationist in nature, since 1824.[41] The Royal Geographical Society, therefore, was effectively required to fulfil a centralising role and did so in a very important sense, particularly with respect to the transfer of forest conservation and desiccation ideas between India, where they had become well established, and the rest of the British colonies, above all those in Africa. In the course of being utilised in this way the RGS effectively played a role in the globalisation of desiccation concepts and hence a major part in the diffusion of a particularly exclusionist and hegemonic forest conservation ideology. In the course of acquiring this environmental role the RGS began to undergo a significant transition in terms of its own raison d'etre and in terms of the influence which it exerted over the emerging agendas of academic geography.

The publication of Charles Darwin's *Origin of Species* in 1859 had set the scene for a decade of existential and religious crisis in which old assumptions about birth and death, time and chronology, religion and generation, already much fractured, were finally broken. These anxieties were mirrored, or coped with, in an unprecedented wave of environmental concern throughout the 1860s. Thus the decade saw the foundation of the all-India forest department, the founding of the Commons Preservation Society, the passing of the first British bird protection legislation and the publication of G.P. Marsh's *Man and Nature* and the publication of Dr Hugh Cleghorn's *Forests and Gardens of South India.*[42]

---

[40] To some extent the forestry school founded at Cambridge in 1904 could be seen as a centre of environmental calculation and was certainly responsible for much innovation in colonial forest policy. It was more autonomous in some respects than the later Oxford Institute which replaced it in 1924. See Cambridge University Library Archives; files on the Forestry school.

[41] For a period Indian foresters were trained at Nancy. See E. P. Stebbing, *The forests of India* (Edinburgh, 1922), vols 1 and 2.

The main focus of academic geography soon reflected this shift in the emergence of 'evolutionary physical geography' and in the birth of 'denudation chronology'. Indeed the RGS *Proceedings* of 2nd May 1869 advertised Sopwith's geological models in wood, one of which was called 'Valleys of denudation'. And it was in the field of denudation and desiccation that the RGS and early environmentalists such as Hugh Cleghorn, John Croumbie Brown and George Bidie found much in common.

The intellectual ground had been well prepared by Livingstone's reports of what he believed to be evidence of chronic and irreversible desiccation in parts of the Kalahari and northern Bechuanaland. It was this data that first stimulated the writing in 1858 of a paper by J. Spotswood Wilson on 'the general and gradual desiccation of the earth and atmosphere'.[43] This is one the earliest papers on the 'greenhouse' effect and held out the stark promise of an early extinction of humanity as a result of atmospheric changes brought about by natural desiccation and augmented by the upheaval of the land, 'waste by irrigation', and the destruction of forests. Wilson quoted liberally from the works of Livingstone and other travellers, giving descriptions of desiccated land-scapes in Australia, Africa, Mexico and Peru, all of which had 'formerly been inhabited by man', as Wilson put it. On March 13 1865 a paper remarkably similar in theme, especially in its references to Southern Africa and to Livingstone's writings, was given at the RGS.[44] Significantly an earlier version of the paper had first been given at the BAAS.[45] One may surmise that the fact that the same paper was then delivered at the RGS was due to the intervention of Colonel George Balfour of the

---

[42] There is no general work as yet on the 'environmental decade' of the 1860s. Separate works on and from the period are Lord Eversley (George Shaw-Lefevre), *Forests, commons and footpaths* (London, 1912); George Perkins Marsh, *Man and nature: or physical geography as transformed by human action* (New York, 1864); H. F. Cleghorn, *The forests and gardens of South India* (Edinburgh, 1861). For a very limited treatment, confined to Britain itself see J. Sheail, *Nature in trust* (London, 1976).

[43] Wilson, 'On the general and gradual desiccation of the earth and atmosphere'.

[44] J.S. Wilson, 'On the progressing desiccation of the basin of the Orange river in Southern Africa', *Proceedings of the Royal Geographical Society*, IX (1865), pp. 106–109.

[45] J.S. Wilson, 'On the increasing desiccation of inner Southern Africa', *Report of the British Association for the Advancement of Science (Transactions)*, 1864, p. 150

Indian Army, a member of the RGS Council. George Balfour was a brother of Dr Edward Green Balfour, then deputy Inspector-General of Hospitals, Madras Presidency (and later Surgeon-General of India) and one of the earliest and strongest advocates of forest protection in India.[46]

At meetings of the RGS in 1865 and 1866 Colonel Balfour spoke at some length on developments in forest conservation that were then taking place in several different colonies. This display of his unrivalled knowledge was no mere vanity. George Balfour clearly saw it as his task to propagandise what he saw as the merits of forest protection in stemming the threat of global desiccation. By 1865 the terms of a debate about the causes of desiccation in the tropics had been set far more clearly. While in 1858 it had remained acceptable to attribute the process to tectonic upheaval (which David Livingstone favoured, for example,) RGS discussions by March 1865 saw the appearance of an entirely new interpretation of global processes of degradation. Desiccation was not natural, James Wilson argued, 'but was entirely the consequence of human action'. Wilson felt that one could demonstrate this well in the case of South Africa. 'The human inhabitants (of the Orange river basin) are a prime cause of the disaster' he wrote, and 'the natives have for ages been accustomed to burn the plains and to destroy the timber and ancient forests...the more denuded of trees and brushwood, and the more arid the land becomes, the smaller the supply of water from the atmosphere'. Thus 'the evil advances', Wilson went on apocalytically, 'in an increasing ratio, and, unless checked, must advance, and will end in the depopulation and entire abandonment of many spots once thickly peopled, fertile and productive'.[47]

He followed this warning with a global survey of locations in which climatic changes had followed on deforestation. The lessons were clear, Wilson thought, where

> in our own British colonies of Barbadoes, Jamaica, Penang, and the Mauritius, the felling of forests has also been attended by a diminution of rain. In the island of Penang, the removal of the jungle from the

---

[46] See especially Edward Green Balfour, 'Notes of the influence exercised by trees in inducing rain and preserving moisture', *Madras Journal of Literature and Science*, 25 (1849), pp. 402–448.

[47] Wilson, 'On the progressing desiccation'.

summits of hills by Chinese settlers speedily occasioned the springs to
dry up, and, except during the monsoons, no moisture was left in the
disforested districts. In the Mauritius it has been found necessary to
retain all lands in the crests of hills and mountains in the hands of
government to be devoted to forest, the fertility of the lower lands having
been found by experience to depend upon clothing the hills with wood.[48]

Only draconian controls, it was implied, could stop a world-wide
ruination of the forests of the British colonies and indeed the entire
economic demise of large areas of country. Wilson was especially
concerned with South Africa,

> it being a matter of notoriety ....that the removal piecemeal of forests,
> and the burning off of jungle from the summits of hills has occasioned
> the uplands to become dry and the lowlands to lose their springs........it
> becomes of extreme importance to our South African fellow-subjects,
> that the destruction of the arboreal protectors of water should be
> regarded as a thing to be deplored, deprecated and prevented; and that
> public opinion on the matter should be educated.....but we must not
> stop there. The evil is one of such magnitude and likely to bear so
> abundant a harvest of misery in the future, that the authority of law,
> wherever practicable, should be invoked in order to institute preventive
> measures. Not only should fuel be economized, but the real interests of
> the British colonies and Dutch republics, for many long years to come,
> would most certainly be represented by the passage of stringent enactments
> which should in the first place forbid, at any season or under any
> circumstances whatsoever, the firing of grass on field or mountain. The
> absolute necessity which exists for keeping as large a surface of the
> ground as possible covered with vegetation, in order to screen it from the
> solar rays, and thus to generate cold and humidity, that the radiation
> from the surface may not drive off the moisture of the rain-bearing
> clouds in their season, ought to compel the rigid enforcement of such a
> legal provision. Those colonial acts on this subject which are already in
> existence – for the Colonial Parliament at the Cape has found it necessary
> to pass restrictive measures – are not sufficiently stringent to be of much
> service, inasmuch as they are not entirely prohibitory, permitting the
> burning of the field at certain times of year.[49]

The main discussants of Wilson's seminal paper at the March

---

[48] Ibid.
[49] Ibid.

1865 RGS meeting were, on the one side, Drs Livingstone and Kirk, who both contested social explanations of deforestation in favour of non-anthropogenic explanations of continental desiccation, which both believed to be taking place in Africa. Ranged on the other side of the argument were Francis Galton, the secretary of the RGS, (and a cousin of Charles Darwin), Colonel George Balfour and Lord Stratford de Redcliffe. Sir Roderick Murchison, chairing the discussion, also declared himself in favour of the interpretations offered by Wilson and in favour of his radical interventionist solutions. Livingstone, for his part, pointed out that 'the author of the paper did not seem to know that many of his suggestions had already been adopted at the Cape, where immense quantities of *Eucalypti* were grown in the botanic garden for distribution among those who wished to plant trees. In four years the trees grew to a height of twenty feet.' Such exchanges of basic information serve to indicate the role which could be played by the RGS. However the discussion following the Wilson paper also exposed, in a somewhat embarrassing fashion, the very slow nature of the diffusion of environmental information and ideas between colonies and, even more, between colonies and the imperial centre.

This was particularly apparent to George Balfour who, in successive RGS debates, saw it as his duty to advertise the efforts made in particular colonies, above all in India, Mauritius and Trinidad, to protect forest and thereby forestall climatic change. Possibly as a result of Balfour's lobbying two further papers given at the RGS, at meetings in June 1866 and in March 1869, dealt very specifically with the issue of state responses to deforestation and desiccation. The paper given by Clements Markham in 1866, ('On the effect of the destruction of forests in the western Ghauts of India on the water supply'), seems to have been intended to demonstrate and publicise the contemporary efforts being made to control deforestation in upland India.[50] The ensuing discussion took on much the same format as that of 1865, bringing together a whole variety of self-confessed experts and travellers from several different colonies. Initiating the discussion of Markham's paper Murchison

---

[50] Clements Markham, 'On the effects of the destruction of forests in the western Ghauts of India on the water supply', *Proceedings of the Royal Geographical Society,* X (1866), pp. 266–267.

commented that the subject of the destruction of forests 'was one of very
great interest to all physical geographers'.[51] Murchison added that it was
a subject upon which he had himself much reflected in reference to other
countries, 'even our own country'. He was happy, he said, to see many
gentlemen present connected with India; and he would, in the first
instance, call upon Sir William Denison, late Governor of Madras, to
make some observations upon the subject.

Under Denison's able administration, Murchison informed the
gathering, some of those very forest protection operations had been
undertaken to which Mr Markham had alluded. A three-cornered
discussion then followed which fiercely debated the culpability or
otherwise of the 'native' for deforestation. Denison believed that Indians
'cut down trees without hesitation, and no-one ever dreamt of planting
a tree unless it were a fruit tree'. George Balfour, reflecting the anti-
establishment attitudes of his conservationist brother, Edward Balfour,
countered that it was 'the practice of rich Hindoos to sink wells and plant
topes of trees'.[52] Another discussant, Mr J. Crawfurd, pronounced it his
opinion that 'the presence of immense forests had proved one of the
greatest obstacles to the early civilization of mankind' and made the
assertion that Java, free from forest, was 'incomparably superior to all the
other islands of the Indian Archipelago'. Balfour's unusual advocacy of
the significance of indigenous knowledge reflected the beliefs of the first
generation of (East India Company) colonial conservationists in India,
in stark contrast to Denison's comments which typify the more racist,
harsh and counter-productive exclusionism of much post-Company
Indian forest policy after 1865.[53]

Sir Henry Rawlinson, in his contribution to the RGS debate,
opined that 'it was a matter patent to every traveller, and it might be
adopted as a principle in physical geography, that the desiccation of a
country followed upon the disappearance of its forests'. It was this

---

[51] Report of discussion, *Proceedings of the Royal Geographical Society*, X (1866), pp. 267–
269.

[52] Ibid., p. 268

[53] This is the later policy usefully characterised by R. Guha in 'Forestry and social protest
in British Kumaon, 1893–1921', *Subaltern Studies*, 4 (1985), pp. 54–101.

realisation that the emerging discipline of physical geography could be enlisted in the cause of global forest protection that seems to have persuaded the core of the Indian forest service establishment to patronise the meetings of the RGS in the late 1860s. Furthermore, in the absence of any other imperial institution, at least in London, showing any significant interest in the pressing issue of colonial deforestation, the RGS provided a sympathetic oasis in what was otherwise an institutional desert. Thus it was that on 25th January 1869 that Hugh Cleghorn, the Inspector-General of the new Indian forest department, attended a meeting of the Society addressed by Dr George Bidie on the subject of 'the effects of forest destruction in Coorg'.[54] Murchison claimed on this occasion that 'it was highly gratifying to geographers to see various branches of natural history combined in illustration of a great subject in physical geography'.

Introducing Dr Cleghorn, Murchison suggested that 'we were more indebted than to any other gentleman in reference to this important question'.[55] Deforestation could best be understood, Cleghorn believed, in terms of an analysis of the amount of capital being invested in forest areas, principally by British planters. The native population in the Western Ghats, he pointed out, were almost universally of the opinion that the climate was drier on account of the changes that Europeans were gradually introducing. The Madras Forest Department, he added, was a new one, initiated only 13 years before. It was gradually increasing in usefulness and it was now receiving the official attention that it deserved.[56]

Attempts to prevent deforestation in other colonies had, as late as the 1860s, received virtually no support from the imperial centre. Instead important propaganda for conservation was being created at the periphery, not only in India but, in particular, in South Africa. Thus some of the most strenuous extra-Indian efforts to promote forest protection and

---

[54] G. Bidie, 'On the effects of forest destruction in Coorg', *Proceedings of the Royal Geographical Society*, XIII (1869), pp. 74–80.

[55] Report of discussion, *Proceedings of the Royal Geographical Society*, XIII (1869), pp. 80–83.

[56] Ibid.

tree-planting and restrict grass-burning had been made by John Croumbie Brown, a missionary and the Colonial Botanist of the Cape Colony from 1862 to 1866. [57] However, local funding for these pioneer efforts had been removed, without protest from Whitehall, in 1866 and a resentful Brown had had to return to Scotland. [58] From there he proceeded to publish a stream of works on hydrology and forest conservation, many of which soon came to the attention of the colonial authorities in the Cape, Natal and elsewhere. The two most important of these works were *A Hydrology of South Africa* published in 1875 and *Forests and Moisture* published in 1877.[59] These works, far more influential on policy in the colonial context than the writings of G. P. Marsh, drew heavily on the debates which had taken place at the RGS during the 1860s, and derived authority from them. In Brown's books the discourse of desiccationism was refined and made, in a sense, into an environmental article of faith. Furthermore his dicta on deforestation and climate were repeated and developed throughout the colonial context during the ensuing 40 years.[60]

Brown's frequently expressed proposals for an Imperial School of Forestry (the idea itself was largely of his authorship) were ultimately developed at Cooper's Hill in Surrey and Dehra Dun in India and eventually in the form of the Imperial Forestry Institute at Oxford in 1924, exactly a century, incidentally, after the foundation of the French Imperial Forestry school at Nancy.[61] In the long interregnum between the establishment of forest conservation in India and the establishment of forestry training in Britain the RGS had acted as a highly formative

---

[57] See Chapter 3.

[58] R.H. Grove, 'Early themes in African conservation; the Cape in the nineteenth century', in D. Anderson and R.H. Grove, eds, *Conservation in Africa: people, policies and practice* (Cambridge, 1987), pp. 21–39.

[59] J.C. Brown, *A hydrology of South Africa* (Edinburgh, Oliver and Boyd, 1875); *Forests and moisture* (Edinburgh, Oliver and Boyd, 1877).

[60] See W. Beinart, 'Soil erosion, conservationism and ideas about development; a southern African exploration, 1900–1960', *Journal of Southern African Studies,* 11 (1984), pp. 52–83.

[61] Stebbing, *The forests of India,* vols 2 and 3. See also Ravi Rajan, 'Colonial science and imperial environmental history: the case of forestry in the British Empire'; chapter 1 of 'Imperial environmentalism: the agendas and ideologies of natural resource management in British colonial forestry, 1800–1950 (D.Phil Thesis, University of Oxford, 1994).

centre of debate and calculation and as a centre of academic authority of great practical use to such fervent early environmentalists as John Croumbie Brown. Above all, the society had served to legitimate a notion of global environmental crisis, articulated in a desiccationist discourse of remarkable political power, and the subject of a wide degree of consensus. The warnings against the 'evil' consequences of deforestation which were expressed at the RGS in the 1860s were closely connected with an emerging contemporary consciousness of the possibility of extinction which Darwin had sharply focussed in 1859.[62] A sense of existential crisis and sense of impending loss was translated, through the RGS, into a highly empirical debate about deforestation and the possibilities of intervention and environmental institution-building.

The hegemonic prescriptions for colonial forest control which the new consciousness stimulated and which the RGS encouraged can be interpreted, perhaps, as a desire to re-assert control over a new existential chaos and over environmental processes that might threaten the existence of humanity itself. Prescriptions for forest conservation, for grass-fire prevention and for irrigation can be seen in this sense as redemptive or in terms of atonement. Brown had originally been a Congregationalist missionary. He had found it logical and congenial to adapt the dire warnings of such desiccationists as Wilson and Bidie as a kind of environmental gospel. His otherwise 'scientific' accounts are sprinkled with references to Old Testament texts. The publication of *The Origin of Species* had simply helped to make the threat of desiccation more dire. Darwin made extinction a necessary part of natural selection and evolution. This gave deforestation and desiccation a much strengthened meaning, necessitating human and conservationist intervention. New scientific theory could not, however, immediately displace religious meaning in the environment. Desiccation continued to be associated with an expulsion from the Garden of Eden and with evil. If society failed to make conservationist amends for the evils of deforestation, extinction and ruin would follow. In the circumstances of this new thinking

---

[62] The background to this emerging consciousness of the possibility of extinctions is discussed by Mario di Gregorio in 'Hugh Edwin Strickland (1811–1853) on Affinities and Analogies or, the case of the missing key', *Ideas and Production*, 7 (1987), pp. 35–50.

colonial conservation acquired the overtones of a kind of redemptive and confessional doctrine.[63]

For this purpose the evidence of desiccation needed, of course, to be global or cosmological, while its prescriptions needed to be universalist. It need hardly be said that practical policy prescriptions for counteracting desiccation, principally through forest reservation and soil conservation, would turn out to be highly palatable to the agendas of colonial rule, particularly when it came to controlling the landscape, and manipulating a 'chaotic' subject population. Those who attended the RGS debates during the 1860s probably did not fully appreciate that. Instead, placed at the centre of such transitions, it is not surprising that geography itself should soon have been affected by a redemptive cosmology. The redemptive element was reflected particularly in the new discipline of physical geography as it developed after 1870 and is best understood in the writings of Archibald Geikie. 'Evolutionary Geography', he wrote,

> traces how man alike unconsciously and knowingly has changed the face of nature........ it must be owned that man in most of his struggle with the world had fought blindly for his own immediate interests. His contest, successful for the moment, has too often led to sure and sad disaster. Stripping forests from hill and mountain, he had gained his immediate object in the possession of abundant supplies of timber; but he has laid open the slopes to be parched by drought or to be swept down by rain. Countries once rich in beauty and plenteous in all that was needful for his support are now burnt or barren or almost denuded of their soil. Gradually he had been taught by his own experience that while his aim still is to subdue earth he can attain it not by setting nature and her laws at defiance but by enlisting them in his service.........he has learnt at last to be a minister and interpreter of nature and he finds in her a ready and uncomplaining slave.[64]

The final lines of Geikie's text indicate that, even while it assumed an environmentalist guise, geography continued to exhibit some of the attributes of a discourse of domination. However it was a discourse that was ultimately contradictory. Thus the efforts made by colonial conser-

[63] I discuss these issues at greater length in Chapter 2.
[64] Archibald Geikie, 'On evolutionary geography', *Journal of the Royal Geographical Society*, 2 (1870), pp. 232–245.

vationists and metropolitan geographers to understand the mechanisms of environmental degradation could hardly fail to touch on the uncomfortable and dynamic connections between the kinds of economic development unleashed by imperial expansion and annexation and the alarming patterns of global environmental change that had become apparent to audiences at RGS debates after 1860. In the concluding part of this narrative I make a short survey of the way in which fears of artificially-induced impacts on climate and environment developed into the patterns of propaganda and environmental discourse with which we are so familiar today.

After the 1860s desiccation and 'desertification' fears, incorporated particularly into the forestry and land management policies of the French and British colonial empires, continued to exert a sporadically powerful impact. It was an impact that was reinforced after extreme climatic events and in periods of rapid political change. The initial thrust to this policy in the British context was given by Sir Joseph Hooker, the Director of Kew Gardens, when he pressed for a more systematic application of forest policies in a series of lectures published in 1872.[65] The environmental texts and propaganda of particular individuals were highly influential in this story. Like those of John Croumbie Brown and Archibald Geikie the new narratives of environmental alarmism were frequently evangelical and even millennial in their tone. Their prescriptive ambitions held out the promise of increased status for scientists as well as increased funding. Partly as a result of this, desiccationist and conservationist ideas, in which considerable claims were made for the virtues of state land control, became a major feature of the technical agendas of French and British colonial rule, not least during the expansionist phase of the late nineteenth century. This tendency was magnified as governments consolidated their rule in climatically marginal areas that were highly vulnerable to droughts. Soon after the publication of J. C. Brown's first two texts India, Southern Africa and Australia were all affected by droughts in 1877–1880 of an almost unprecedented severity, the result of the strongest El Niño episode since

---

[65] Reported in J.D. Hooker, 'On the protection of forests', *Journal of Applied Science*, 1 (1872), pp. 24–25.

1791–2. In India the droughts resulted in especially high mortality, and led to a wholesale re-examination of the evidence for deforestation-rainfall links in the the reports of the Famine Commission of 1880.[66] This led in turn to a strengthening and effective militarising of the powers of the forest department in India. It also stimulated the systematic investigation of global teleconnections between climatic events at the colonial periphery, research that led eventually to an understanding of the Southern Oscillation and the mechanism of the monsoon[67]. Communications between Indian and Australian scientists were especially important in this respect.[68] Meanwhile, roving experts from the Indian Forest Department travelled throughout the newly expanded British Empire, reproducing the models of forest management that had been developed in the previous 40 years in India. Indian precedents were adopted in Southern Africa (particularly in Natal and the Cape), Cyprus, Central America, South-East Asia, Australia and elsewhere. Even in coastal West Africa the desiccationist message began to diffuse, not least in the work of Alfred Moloney, the Governor of the Lagos Colony.[69]

By the late 1880s the typologies of anti-desiccation forest policy in the French and British colonial states were so closely inter-related that they can be said to have constituted a single ruling philosophy rather than two separate traditions. French and British forestry journals were alert and imitative of the experiences of their rival services, while many British foresters were actually trained at the French Imperial School at Nancy.[70] French foresters were even employed directly by the British colonial

---

[66] Government of India, *Reports of the famine commission* (4 vols, Calcutta, 1880).

[67] The Southern Oscillation is a recognised large-scale meteorological feature made up of high-altitude air currents and jetstreams, connecting the climates of South America, Australia and the Indian Ocean. It is a geographically and seasonally oscillating phenomenon dynamically connected with the timing and strength of ocean currents such as the El Niño. As such it is fundamental to the timing of periodic droughts and to alterations in the strength of the monsoon.

[68] See Chapter 4.

[69] A. Moloney, *Sketch of the forestry of West Africa* (London, 1887); and see Olufemi Omosini, 'Alfred Moloney and his strategies for development in Lagos colony and hinterland', *Journal of the Historical Society of Nigeria*, 7 (1975), pp. 657–672.

[70] Perhaps the most famous of these was Charles Lane-Poole, eventually appointed

services; the employment of the Count Vasselot de Regne in the Cape Conservancy in South Africa being a notable example of this. Similarly, German-trained foresters were widely employed by both French and British colonial governments, above all in the higher echelons of the Indian Forest Service. In the colonial context this resulted in an intermixing of German forest science methods and an Anglo-French tradition of desiccationism. The sheer vigour of the Anglo-French forest 'movement', as one might legitimately term it (which reached its apogee in the remarkable 1934 Anglo-French Boundary Forest Commission) began even to influence the very tardy development of conservationism in the United States.[71] Thus Franklin Benjamin Hough, one-time director of the United States census (and a local historian and evangelical preacher), who was a keen student of colonial forestry methods as well as a close friend of John Croumbie Brown, wrote a series of reports after 1873 that led to the foundation of the United States Forest Service.[72]

The years immediately prior to 1900 saw a renewed interest developing in somewhat millennial theories of global desiccation. Significantly perhaps, these were preoccupied with regions that lay outside the areas of Anglo-European and American colonial control. In particular, they posed a post-glacial desiccation of the environments of Central Asia and China based on the twin tenets that wet conditions characterised the glacial phases of the Pleistocene and that aridity had increased in the Holocene since the warming of the Pleistocene icesheets. Travellers in Central Asia pointed to the occurrence of dry water courses and lakes

---

Conservator of Australia; see Lane-Poole papers, Nancy files, MSS Collection, Australian National Library, Canberra.

[71] The Anglo-French Boundary Forest Commission was set up at the instance of colonial forest department officials in the Ivory Coast, the Gold Coast and Nigeria. It commenced an ambitious and partially successful programme of tree-planting, mainly of eucalypts, in the semi-arid Sub-Saharan zones on the northern boundaries of Anglo-French West Africa. The onset of the Second World War brought it to an unfortunate and premature end. For details see National Archives of Nigeria (Ibadan), Forest Department AFBF Files.

[72] E.g., see Franklin B. Hough, *On the duty of governments in the preservation of forests* (Salem, 1873), and *Report upon forestry; from the committee appointed to memorialise Congress … regarding the preservation of forests* (Salem, 1878).

and abandoned settlements as evidence of this desiccation and suggested that deteriorating environmental conditions had spurred successive nomadic invasions of their more civilised neighbours during periods of increased aridity.[73] The work of Kropotkin (1904) and Ellsworth Huntington (1907) are conspicuous examples here.[74] However, like the work of G.P. Marsh, the ideas of Americans such as Huntington had only a limited effect in the European colonial context. Similarly, Theodore Roosevelt's famous Conservation Conferences exerted, at first, only a limited effect outside North America, even though Roosevelt's main advisers, and speech-writers, Gifford Pinchot and William McGee, were well informed themselves about Anglo-French colonial forest conservation initiatives, and admired them.[75]

Moreover these progressivist American initiatives were made at precisely the period when British colonial administrations in West Africa were encountering formidable and effective indigenous opposition to the imposition of their own surprisingly enlightened forest policies from chiefs and other interests in the Gold Coast and Nigeria.[76] This was a problem that, in general, was not encountered at this stage by the French in West Africa; although German forest administrations in Tanganyika and Togo found it necessary to implement their forest regulations through the use of draconian punishments.[77] In the Gold Coast and Nigeria colonial governments were forced to abandon their Indian-derived forest management programmes entirely, only replacing them with policies sanctioned by the chiefs after the First World World War, at a time when the word 'development' started to appear in colonial

---

[73] Not all investigators of the time agreed with these views, however. Sven Hedin, the Swedish explorer, for example, thought that much of the apparent desiccation could be explained by rivers shifting their courses; see S. Hedin, *The wandering lake* (New York, 1940).

[74] P. Kropotkin, 'The desiccation of Eur-Asia', *Geographical Journal*, 23 (1904), pp. 722–741; and E. Huntington, *The pulse of Asia* (London, 1907).

[75] See Michael Lacey, 'The Washington scientific community in the nineteenth century' (Ph.D. thesis, George Washington University, 1979).

[76] See Chapter 5.

[77] For details see Robert Cornevin, *Histoire du Togo* (Paris, Editions Berger-Levrault, 1969), pp. 182, 249, 353.

government publications.[78] Some of the anxieties and the military language of the period leading up to the First World War encouraged a continued doom-laden interest in global desiccation that was especially apparent in William Macdonald's widely-read *Conquest of the Desert*.[79]

It seems quite possible that a generalised revulsion at the human destructiveness of the Great War was reflected in a strengthened awareness of the possibilities of human environmental destructiveness on a world scale. This would help to account for the flurry of colonial publications and commissions on the connections between drought and human activity that appeared in the early 1920s. In 1920 it was the turn of the French to voice their desiccation fears, above all in an influential article by H. Hubert, entitled 'Le déssechement progressive en Afrique Occidentale'.[80] However it was in semi-arid South Africa that the gospel of desiccation found its most pronounced and didactic post-war expression. Here, in 1919, E.H.L. Schwartz published an article entitled 'The progressive desiccation of Africa; the cause and the remedy'.[81] Even the wording of the title echoed that of J. Spotswood Wilson's seminal article of 1865 on 'the progressing desiccation of inner Southern Africa', which had been based on the text of an address to the Royal Geographical Society. [82] Schwartz followed the article with a book published in 1923 on *The Kalahari or Thirstland Redemption*, a title which surely gives us a clue to a critical crusading element of the desiccation discourse. In many ways this book reinforced an implicitly religious and redemptive (and even Calvinist) element that had been present in environmentalist writing in Southern Africa since the time of John Crombie Brown. A zeal for the spreading of an environmental message was seen as a vital and even evangelical task. Schwartz's texts was directly transmuted into govern-

---

[78] See F.M. Oliphant, *Report on the commercial possibilities and the development of forests of the Gold Coast* (Accra, 1934).

[79] W. Macdonald, *Conquest of the desert* (London, 1914).

[80] *Bulletin Comité d'Etudes Historiques et Scientifique de l'Afrique Occidentale Francaise*, 1920, pp. 401–437.

[81] E.H.L. Schwartz, 'The progressive desiccation of Africa; the cause and the remedy', *South African Journal of Science*, 15 (1919), pp. 139–190.

[82] Wilson, 'On the progressing desiccation'.

ment policies through the 1922 report of the South African Drought Commission, a highly alarmist document. This alarmism revealed, for the first time, the beginnings of a North American influence on British colonial soil and forest conservation, at least in South Africa. Two of the Afrikaner members of the Commission had worked in the United States as refugees after the South African war (1899–1902). H.S.D. du Toit, its chairman, trained there as an agronomist, and he later became head of South Africa's agricultural extension service. R.J. Van Renen studied civil engineering and worked on irrigation projects in Nebraska before returning to the Transvaal civil service. T.D. Hall, one of the first South Africans to write systematic historical studies of pastures, studied agriculture in Illinois in the 1910s.

During the 1920s, too, the experience of Central Asia continued to exert an influence on the desiccationist school. C. Coching, in 1926, summarised much of this thinking in a paper entitled 'Climatic pulsations during historic times in China'.[83] Geographical periodicals and institutions were, as in the previous century, important fora for the desiccation debate. In Africa this meant that the concerns of the 1920s now began to embrace some colonial territories that had not featured at all in the earlier environmental literature of the years before the Great War but which were now the subject of considerable colonial interest and infrastructure investment. This was especially the case in the Anglo-Egyptian Sudan, about which some of the first literature on desert-spreading or 'desertification' now began to be written. A pioneer in this area was E.W. Bovill, who echoed Schwartz in South Africa in his 1921 paper on 'the encroachment of the Sahara on the Sudan'[84] His arguments were further followed up in an article entitled 'The Sahara' in 1929.[85] Bovill's arguments were, in turn, taken much further by G.T. Renner in one of the first articles to paint Africa as a potentially famine-ridden continent, under the title 'A famine zone in Africa; the Sudan'.[86]

The impact of North American 1930s 'Dustbowl' thinking on

---

[83] *Geographical Review*, 16 (1926), pp. 274–282.

[84] *Journal of the Royal African Society*, 20 (1921), pp. 175–185, 259–269.

[85] *Antiquity*, 3 (1929), pp. 4–23.

[86] *Geographical Review*, 16 (1926), pp. 583–596.

African colonial conservation thinking has been extensively explored by
scholars such as William Beinart and David Anderson.[87] In America the
droughts that characterised the period and devastated so much of the
mid-west and southern states brought about an irrevocable shift in
agrarian thinking away from expansionist optimism and towards a
rigorous interventionist conservationism in practical and policy terms.
However, the impact of the Dustbowl ideology in Africa may have been
over-exaggerated, since it actually had little effect on forest policy and far
less on French than British colonial policy. Although influential in the
semi-arid parts of East and Southern Africa, the American ideas also
received far less attention in the wetter colonies of Central Africa (such
as Nyasaland) and West Africa. In West Africa, however, Indian concerns once more made themselves felt. Soil erosion had become a
prominent issue in India during the 1920s and huge investments were
being made in anti-erosion schemes in such regions as the Etawah district
of the United Provinces of northern India, long before scientific reactions were articulated to the American 'Dustbowl'. In 1934 E.P. Stebbing,
a very prominent Indian forester (and early historian of Indian forestry)
visited West Africa for a few weeks during the dry season. His perceptions
of the dry season Sahelian landscape provoked him into writing a feverish
warning on what he saw as the dangers of desertification. The title of the
essay ('The encroaching Sahara; the threat to the West African colonies')
leads one to suspect that he had read Bovill's similarly titled 1921 article
on 'the encroachment of the Sahara'. Stebbing's alarmism contributed
directly to the founding of the Anglo-French Boundary Forest Commission. This commission, initiated in 1934, soon found that Stebbings'
warnings were largely unfounded; and his analysis was decisively dismissed by B. Jones, a member of the Commission, in a 1938 article
published, as Stebbing's had been, in the *Geographical Journal.* Nevertheless, the damage had been done and Stebbing's alarums were soon
echoed by much more popular writers, and above all by Jacks and Whyte
in their inflammatory, semi-racist and inaccurate account entitled *The*

---

[87] Beinart, 'Soil erosion'; D,M. Anderson, 'Depression, dustbowl, demography and
drought: the colonial state and soil conservation in East Africa during the 1930s', *African
Affairs*, 83 (1984), pp. 321–244.

Rape of the Earth; A World Survey of Soil Erosion.[88] This book set the scene for the post-war British colonial obsession with soil erosion and gullying in its 'second colonial occupation', as well as for the desertification myth of the 1970s and 1980s.[89] It may have owed at least some of its desiccationist obsession to the prevailing and well-rooted anxiety about the fascist threat. One might well argue on present field evidence that the fascist threat was a good deal more real than the desiccation danger sketched out by Jacks and Whyte, and initially engineered by Stebbing and his American dustbowl colleagues.[90] Nevertheless the profound influence of *The Rape of the Earth* on global environmental policy in subsequent decades can be firmly attributed to its roots in what we can now recognise as a very long-standing desiccationist tradition.

---

[88] G.V. Jacks and R.O. Whyte, *The rape of the earth: a world survey of soil erosion* (London, 1939).

[89] I use the term 'myth' here advisedly. While very real aridification and vegetation change did actually take place in the Sahelian and Sub-Saharan regions during the drought periods of 1913–1920 and 1969–1985, especially in West Africa, the stereotype of 'desertification' has been used both to construct an image of a hopeless agrarian Africa and to ensure a constant flow of research funds to the many researchers who have now 'discovered' desertification throughout Africa, Asia and even Southern Europe. For a highly effective critique of these notions see D.S. Thomas and S.J. Middleton, *Desertification: exploding the myth* (Chichester, 1994).

[90] Jacks and Whyte were not the only scholars who may have articulated their geo-political anxieties in environmental terms. Sir Aurel Stein embarked on a similar exercise in 1938 in a essay called 'Desiccation in Asia, a geographical question in the light of history', *Hungarian Quarterly*, 13 (1938).

2

Conserving Eden: The (European) East India Companies and their Environmental Policies on St Helena, Mauritius and in Western India, 1660–1854

The history of tropical forest change over the last millenium is difficult to chart with any confident degree of accuracy. Indeed, systematic attempts even for the last hundred years have been made only recently. In general, more is known at present about the history of tropical forests in Asia and Southeast Asia than forests in Africa or South America.[1] This lack of knowledge is partly due to the fact that the causal factors behind the erosion of tropical forests area are particularly difficult to disentangle. However, important connections can be made between European expansion, the penetration of capitalist economic forces, and the transformation of tropical environments.[2] Above all, the spread of market relations in the tropics has served to encourage the rapid clearance of forests for agriculture. The history of global deforestation has probably

[1] See J. F. Richards, J. R. Hagen, and E. S. Haynes, 'Changing land-use in Bihar, Punjab and Haryana', *Modern Asian Studies,* 19 (1985), pp. 699–752. In some respects a reliance on official sources produced between 1870 and 1970 has led to a neglect of the critical but little understood period of forest clearance between 1780 and 1850, colonial perceptions of which led to the developments described in this chapter.

[2] For some initial attempts in this direction, see I. Wallerstein, *The modern world system* (New York, 1974). There remain, of course, some major problems to be encountered in equating any expansion of the 'European world system' with processes of ecological change. It is now well established that the activities of indigenous peoples in Australia and East Africa, for example, caused widespread ecological change long before the advent of the European. The same was true in many Pacific islands; see the chapter on Easter Island in Clive Ponting's *A green history of the world* (London, 1991).

been closely associated at many of its fastest stages with the dynamics of
the forces of industrialisation and the expansion of a European-centred
world-system. Nevertheless, there have also been phases of rapid change
in zones as yet unaffected by the dynamics of capitalist transformation as
they are normally understood. The conceptual problem that arises has
less to do with the difficulties of explaining the dynamics of rapid
ecological change than with the problems entailed in using a monolithic
and Eurocentric world system theory to describe patterns of proto-
capitalist and indigenous consumption. Thus, at various times the
relatively rapid clearance of large areas of forest in much of the Pacific
area, in tropical Africa, and in Northern India has taken place outside the
context of the expansion of any world system. Significantly, some phases
of non-European clearance have led to the development of important
and ambitious state initiatives in forestry and environmental control,
although very few have ever been properly investigated.[3]

Since the Second World War, tropical deforestation has taken
place so rapidly that the prospect of the disappearance of the remaining
core areas of continental forest has led to a widespread contemporary
apprehension about its consequences. This is frequently expressed in
terms of anxieties about global climatic change and the likely disappearance of a high proportion of existing species of fauna and flora. Such
concerns are, in fact, not new and, in their essentials, constitute a re-
statement of anxieties expressed for more than two centuries.[4] Furthermore, interventionist responses to rapid forest destruction have a long
and coherent intellectual history. Many emerged from the specific
circumstances of colonial expansion and associated ecological change,
although there have been some important exceptions. In particular,
western anxieties about the possible connections between deforestation
and climatic change emerged quite specifically in the colonial rather than
the metropolitan European context. This essay intends to identify,
briefly, some of the main milestones in the history of early western

---

[3] An outstanding exception is found in Conrad Totman's survey of forest conservation
in Japan in the seventeenth century, *The green archipelago* (Berkeley, 1989).

[4] See R. H. Grove, '*Green imperialism: colonial expansion, tropical island Edens and the
origins of environmentalism, 1600–1800* (Cambridge, 1995), and 'The Origins of
Environmentalism', *Nature*, 3 May 1990, pp. 6–11.

conservationist responses to the ecological effects of the colonial transformation of the landscape and to the destruction of tropical forests in particular.

Some historians have suggested that the environmentally destructive effects of colonialism were not only economic but had their roots in ideologically imperialist attitudes towards the environment.[5] This does not seem an extraordinary thesis to advance, particularly because the evidence seems to indicate that the penetration of western economic forces (not all necessarily synonymous with colonialism) did indeed promote a rapid ecological transformation in some instances,[6] which was especially true in the early nineteenth century in India and Southern Africa.[7] On closer inspection, however, the hypothesis of a purely destructive environmental imperialism constituting a complete break with the pre-colonial past does not stand up well at all. Indeed this notion apparently arose out of a misunderstanding about the contradictory, heterogeneous, and ambivalent nature of the colonial state's workings. Above all, a number of scholars have been generally unaware of the extent to which colonial governments were peculiarly open to the pressures of a contemporary environmental lobby during the first half of the nineteenth century, a time of great uncertainty about the role and long-term security of the colonial state. Thus, although it undoubtedly promoted widespread ecological destruction, colonial enterprise also helped to create a context conducive to rigorous analytical thinking about the processes of ecological change and to the formation of a conservation ideology.[8]

---

[5] This argument is put forward in D. Worster, *Nature's economy: a history of Western ecological ideas* (Cambridge, 1985).

[6] For a useful survey, see R. P. Tucker and J. R. Richards, eds, *Global deforestation and the world economy* (Durham, N.C., 1983).

[7] See R. H. Grove, 'Early themes in African conservation: The Cape in the nineteenth century', in D. Anderson and R. H. Grove, eds, *Conservation in Africa: people, policies and practice* (Cambridge, 1987), pp. 22–47.

[8] For discussions of the later development of conservation ideologies, see Chapter 3; and W. Beinart, 'Soil erosion, conservationism and ideas about development: a Southern African exploration, 1900–1960', *Journal of Southern African Studies*, 11 (1984), pp. 52–83.

Ironically, too, the colonial state in its pioneering conservationist role provided a forum for controls on the unhindered operations of capital for short-term gain which, it might be argued, constituted a fundamental contradiction to what is normally supposed to have made up the common currency of imperial expansion and profit maximisation.[9] Moreover, the absolutist nature of colonial rule made it possible to introduce interventionist forms of land management that would have been very difficult to impose in Europe, even though many of them provoked active indigenous resistance. Colonial expansion also promoted the rapid diffusion of new scientific ideas and environmental concepts among colonies and between metropole and colony over a large area of the world. Such ideas sometimes acquired a potent momentum of their own independent of the apparatus of colonial rule while still exerting influence on its actors.

Conservation in its more modern sense has often been perceived as a phenomenon with antecedents in late nineteenth- or early twentieth-century North America.[10] This interpretation regards Henry D. Thoreau, John Muir, and George Perkins Marsh as the leading originators of modern environmentalism. In contrast, scholars dismiss colonial conservation and forestry regulation, especially in India, as mere disguises legitimised by a subordinate colonial science for resource exploitation and land seizure by the state.[11] Although some elements of truth in such doctrinaire accounts are normally coupled with doubtful notions of pre-colonial Golden Ages of ecological balance, they have all tended to overlook the remarkably innovative nature of early colonial conserva-

---

[9] For a useful analogous discussion of colonial state hostility to capital interests, see D. Washbrook, 'Law, state and agrarian society in colonial India', *Modern Asian Studies*, 15 (1981), pp. 648–721.

[10] E.g., Worster, *Nature's economy;* S. Hays, *Conservation and the gospel of efficiency: the Progressive Conservation Movement, 1880–1920* (Cambridge, Mass., 1959); D. Lowenthal, *George Perkins Marsh, versatile Vermonter* (New York, 1958).

[11] See especially R. Guha, *The unquiet woods: ecological change and peasant resistance in the Himalaya* (Delhi: Oxford University Press, 1989), and M. Gadgil, 'Towards an ecological history of India', *Economic and Political Weekly*, XX (1985), 1909–18. Similar interpretations appear in V. Shiva, 'Afforestation in India: problems and strategies', *Ambio*, 14 (1985), pp. 21–41; and M. Gadgil, *Deforestation: problems and prospects* (New Delhi: Society for Promotion of Woodlands Development, 1989).

tionism, the characteristics of which have been very much neglected until recently. They also tend to underplay the highly developed trend towards exclusionist forms of state forest control developed in pre-colonial states in South Asia, as well as the well-established history of rapid, and often state-sponsored, deforestation in the centuries before the onset of East India Company rule in the sub-continent.[12]

As a result the notion of North American primacy in conservation thinking has remained unquestioned. In fact, a good deal of evidence indicates that complex notions of state intervention in natural resource protection, many of them strongly connected with new and highly anthropomorphic valuations of the environment, emerged and were extensively promulgated in the colonial context more than a century before George Perkins Marsh published his famous *Man and Nature* in 1864.[13] What is more, Marsh apparently drew much of his inspiration from a detailed knowledge of the history of important colonial experiments in environmental intervention. Indeed, the very speed of degradation induced by colonisation helped to evoke such experimentation.[14] Colonial conservationism probably did emerge not so much because colonial annexation and capitalisation brought about extensive ecological changes as because the conditions inherent in early Dutch, French and British colonial rule promoted the rapid rise of a distinctive group of professional naturalists and scientists to disproportionate influence. Many of these early experts constructed an effective critique of the environmental effects of colonial rule, often as a surrogate for more direct but less politically palatable social commentaries on colonialism itself. Pre-eminent among these professional naturalists, especially in India

---

[12] For some details of early phases of pre-colonial deforestation, see Makhan Lal, 'Iron tools, forest clearance and urbanisation in the Gangetic Plains', *Man and Environment*, 10 (1984), pp. 83–90. Widespread deforestation in the Ganges valley during the fourteenth century led to water-table declines and extensive soil deterioration.

[13] G. P. Marsh, *Man and nature* (New York, 1864).

[14] Marsh was well aware of the deforestation history of St Helena and early attempts to control the process. He was largely unaware, however, of the history of Indian conservation with which he became acquainted only through correspondence with Dr. Hugh Cleghorn during the late 1860s. See Cleghorn/Marsh correspondence (Marsh Papers, Archives Department of Vermont, Burlington, Vt., 1865–82).

before the 1851 rebellion, were the medical surgeons of the East India
Company, whose relatively influential status permitted a very rapid
diffusion of their environmental diagnoses and interventionist prescriptions. Their outlook was strongly influenced by Hippocratic and
Physiocratic ways of thinking. Both of these medically based philoso-
phies dealt implicitly with the relations between the external environment and the health of man.[15] Their impact was, in environmental terms,
more keenly felt in the tropics than in contemporary Europe, where
vegetational changes in more temperate conditions were generally much
slower and less easily observed in their effects. Although the Hippocratic
interpretation of environmental processes was innate to the training of
all western physicians, the Physiocratic environmental critique (itself
derived from medical antecedents), was much more narrowly confined,
at first, to the response of French colonial science to tropical conditions
in the late eighteenth century. By the 1760s in Mauritius (and a little later
in India and the Cape Colony), these two environmental discourses had
been translated into a set of highly interventionist conservation policies,
preceding the emergence of conservationism in either Europe or the
United States.[16]

   Thus, as early as 1840, one can clearly distinguish the emergence
of fully developed environmental concerns and conservation policies
strongly reinforced by what were considered to be scientific interpretations of environmental interactions. These interpretations were based
largely on the writings of French and German Romantic scientists and,
later, on the work of Alexander von Humboldt.[17] Such concerns had not
developed in isolation. From the late eighteenth century, particularly in
Mauritius (the Isle de France), environmentalist theories developed in

[15] For an extended introduction to the evolution of Hippocratic environmental
psychology see Clarence Glacken, *Traces on the Rhodian shore* (Berkeley, 1969).

[16] See Grove, *Green imperialism*, ch. 5. It has to be said that the more utopian and
transcendental elements in conservationism during the period were partly suppressed, for
fairly obvious reasons. Nevertheless a careful inspection of the writings of Hugh
Cleghorn in particular indicates similar underlying preoccupations, reinforced by the
Humboldtian antecedents of much of early conservation thinking in colonial India.

[17] For a specific characterisation of this genre of science, see A. Cunningham and N.
Jardine, eds, *Romanticism and the sciences* (Cambridge, 1990).

close association with political or even revolutionary radicalism, anti-slavery, and overt anti-colonial sentiment, as well as with a naturalistic Orientalism. Such interconnections have been a characteristic feature of the early history of conservationism. Along with Alexander von Humboldt, other thinkers also serve to exemplify the apparent dualism of environmental and social reform in the critically formative years between 1770 and 1870. Pierre Poivre, Jean Jacques Rousseau, Ernst Dieffenbach, P. E. Strzelecki, Hugh Cleghorn, Edward Balfour, John Croumbie Brown, and Henry David Thoreau all stand out as exemplars of this phenomenon. Only in its later stages of development did conservationism, as a highly bureaucratised justification for state control of land use, start to enforce its own inflexible and alienating logic. Moreover. conservationism then evoked widespread popular resistance in the context of the development of the more narrowly defined interests of late nineteenth-century imperialism.[18] By then the original reformist ideologues of colonial conservation had almost all long since faded in influence. Their ideological successors were, instead, to be found at work far more in the metropolitan context, where state conservationism developed much more slowly in response to the pressures of urban growth and industrialisation.[19]

Early European Colonial Expansion and the Origins of Western Conservationism

The essential precepts of modern conservation actually arose from the conditions of colonial rule and colonial notions of the state's role. Indeed conservationist ideas developed almost in tandem with the growth of the material demands of nascent capitalism, whether in its European form or in indigenous forms in, for instance, pre-colonial India, China, or Japan. The growth of market relations and urbanisation had, of course, long

---

[18] See Chapter 6.

[19] For details of the growth on early metropolitan environmental lobby groups, see J. Sheail, *Nature in trust* (London, 1976). The most important of these was the Commons Preservation Society founded by Octavia Hill, Robert Hunter, John Stuart Mill, T. H. Huxley, and George Shaw-Lefevre. See Lord Eversley (G. Shaw-Lefevre), *Forests, commons and footpaths* (London, 1912).

been associated with deforestation in Europe and the Middle East, particularly in the more southern margins of these regions.[20] Indeed, it was in the course of the deforestation of classical Greece that Theophrastus of Erasia, an early ecologist, as well as the keeper of Aristotle's botanic garden and his archivist, first put forward his precocious theories of desiccation. These linked deforestation and declines in rainfall with the destruction of trees around the perimeters of the Greek city-states.[21] In temperate northern Europe, anxieties about the impact of deforestation developed much later than this and for reasons more straightforwardly connected with timber depletion. During early medieval phases of European expansion eastward into the forests of Germany and central Europe, some pioneer attempts were made to limit agricultural clearance under the German kings. Sometimes these involved very clear-sighted notions of sustainable timber use and, in very rare instances, an awareness of the value of forest protection in preventing soil erosion.[22] More systematic insights into the mechanisms of environmental degradation had to await the circumstances of the much more extensive deforestation and soil erosion episodes associated with the rise of the great European maritime empires. In particular, the mercantile and colonial expansion of Venice gave rise to a phase of very rapid and destructive deforestation in Northern Italy, Dalmatia, and Crete.[23] The military and strategic demands of the empire implied a need for a continuous supply of wood for ship and barge building, most of which was carried out at the *Arsenale* in Venice itself.[24] One of the first signs of the progressive deforestation of the Venetian hinterland, the movement of the barge-building industry inland from Venice, was well under way in the second quarter of the fifteenth century. During the 1450s, the high rate of deforestation

[20] See J. Perlin, *A forest journey: the role of wood in the development of civilization* (New York, 1989), pp. 35–145.

[21] J D. Hughes, 'Theophrastus as Ecologist', *Environmental Review,* 4 (1985), pp. 291–307. See also remarks on Theophrastus in Glacken, *Traces on the Rhodian shore*; and H. Rubner, 'Greek Thought and Forest Science', *Environmental Review,* 4 (1985), pp. 277–296.

[22] See E. Mummenhoff, *Altnürnberg* (Bamberg, 1890), pp. 55–57.

[23] Ellen C. Semple, *The geography of the ancient Mediterranean* (London, 1932).

[24] For a wider discussion of these matters, see F. C. Lane, *Venetian ships, shipbuilders and the Renaissance* (Baltimore: University of Baltimore, 1934).

apparently became recognised as a danger to the Venice lagoon because it increased the amount of silt brought down by the rivers. To prevent the lagoons from filling up, the Council of Ten ordered the re-planting of all cut over woods at the edges of streams of flowing water.[25] A definite policy designed to conserve and increase the supply of oak from state woodlands was formulated between 1470 and 1492. Although innovative, these measures failed almost entirely to conserve or replenish the timber supply or to curb the ruinous destruction of the oak woods, which continued unabated until the sixteenth century. This failure contributed in no small measure to the decline of Venice and its trading and military displacement by maritime powers with easier access to relatively undepleted forests.[26] However, while the Venetian experience of contending with soil erosion was certainly important, far more holistic or comprehensive speculations about the processes of environmental degradation were taking shape on the new European island colonies. These speculations eventually focussed on the connections between deforestation and climatic change.

From the twelfth century onwards the Spanish and Portuguese colonisation of the Canary islands, Madeira, and, after 1492, the West Indies started to lead to a developing awareness of the capacity of the colonist to decimate both indigenous populations and forest cover. The high rate of deforestation in Madeira and the Canary islands was directly related to the remarkable growth in the emergent European urban market for sugar products and the opportunities for profits presented by the development of sugar plantations. Faced with the consequences of deforestation and the loss of hydraulic storage capacity, the colonists and planters had to resort to a wholesale development of artificial irrigation systems constructed by Genoese engineers but based on the designs of Moorish irrigation systems in Spain.[27] The new level of deforestation also

---

[25] See Venice Archives (Arsenale), basta 8, fl./9/10

[26] The Venetian records show that local peasant opposition to state conservation, featuring even active sabotage and incendiarism, contributed to this policy. The phenomenon of popular resistance to colonial forest policy was repeated over and over again in the context of much later colonial conservation policy, especially in Africa and India. See Chapter 6.

[27] R. Bryans, *Madeira, pearl of Atlantic* (London, 1954), p. 30; and A.M. Watson, *Agricultural irrigation in the early Islamic world* (Cambridge, 1983).

gave rise to a more generalised theoretical response. In particular, Theophrastus' classical theories were circulated once more with the Renaissance, while the publication of his works in Latin in 1483 assured their wider dissemination.[28] Christopher Columbus, for example, is reported by his son, Ferdinand, to have warned constantly of the dangers of forest clearance on West Indian islands, such as a decline in rainfall.[29] Such notions may have arisen from the explorer's own observations of the acute water shortages in the Canary islands after the forests were cut over. These observations are likely to have been coupled with a knowledge of Theophrastus' theories.

Thus on the earliest European island colonies the destructive effects of capital-intensive economic activity first became fully apparent and elicited an environmental critique. Significantly too, at about this time the classical idea of the island as an Eden or social refuge was revivified, much as Theophrastus' ideas had received a new lease of life at the time of Columbus. Indeed the conviction that an Eden might be found across the ocean may have sustained Columbus in his transatlantic exploit.[30] Long before this, in *Purgatorio,* Dante had already transferred classical notions of Paradise or the Hesperides to the Atlantic in the form of an 'earthly paradise' or an 'island in the Southern Ocean'.[31]

During the fifteenth century too, the developing Renaissance conception of the botanic garden as a symbolic location for the recreation of Paradise took firm root, displacing the simpler apothecarial connotations of the early medieval herbal gardens.[32] In this way the Italians (and shortly afterwards the Dutch, French and English) adapted and elabo-

---

[28] Theophrastus' *Historia Plantarum* was translated into Latin in 1483, according to I.H. Burkill, (*Chapters in the History of Indian Botany* [Delhi: Government of India Press, 1965]).

[29] K. Thompson, 'Forests and climatic change in America: some early views', *Climatic Change,* 3 (1983), pp. 47–64.

[30] For a detailed discussion of this, see Ernst Bloch, 'Geographical Utopias', ch. 2 of *The principle of hope* (Oxford, 1986).

[31] See A. Keymer, 'Plant imagery in Dante', (M.Phil. dissert., Faculty of Modern Languages, University of Cambridge, 1982).

[32] J. Prestt, *The Garden of Eden: the botanic garden and the recreation of paradise* (New Haven, 1981).

rated upon Arabic, Persian, and Mughal garden models, thus structurally incorporating notions of *Paradaeza* (meaning, literally, in Farsi/Ancient Iranian, an enclosed garden) associated with the gardens of, for example, Mesopotamia and Moorish Spain.

All these changes formed part of an important Renaissance shift in attitudes away from identifying earthly Nature with the fallen state of man and towards a new conception of nature as an intended and beneficent part of divine purpose. By about 1550, therefore, many of the major intellectual and metaphorical themes had emerged which were later to form the infrastructure for a new kind of environmentalist response to evidence of the Europeans' destructive capabilities in tropical climates. Although the conditions of European protocapitalism (with its nascent urban market for luxury products from the tropics) stimulated the onset of tropical plantation agriculture and the tropical timber trade, a new valuation of nature (symbolised at first in the re-creation of Paradise in the botanic garden and closely associated with the geographical search for the Garden of Eden) provided a philosophical and quasi-theological basis for an interventionist response to environmental destruction. As a part of this response, it is noteworthy that two European precedents for land management, new irrigation technology and the antecedents of the botanic garden, played a significant part. More important, the paradise metaphor, particularly in its stereotyped association with newly colonised and previously uninhabited desert islands. acquired a transitional symbolic role in the more complex use of the image of island as a device for representing religious or social utopias. Although Thomas More had pioneered the use of this utopic form as the basis for social critique, it received a new lease of life with the spread of a distinctively Calvinistic willingness to perceive and create earthly paradises, a development reflected in the emergence of a whole genre of desert island literature in English and French. Bishop Francis Godwin's *The man in the moone* is a case in point. The book conceived of the island of St Helena as a paradise and pointed to the limitations of its resources in sustaining visiting Europeans. By fictionally representing his hero, Diego Gonzales, as a man who moves physically away from the island (a convenient metaphor for the world), circles the world in a flying machine, and then views the world from the moon, Godwin underlined the new physical and interpretative power of man relative to the world and the cosmos. Implicitly, then, Godwin portrays man as having acquired both a new capacity for destructiveness and a capacity, in the terms of the seventeenth-century scientific revolution, to understand and control his actions. Appropriately, both these new capacities began to be displayed on St Helena in the late seventeenth century. However, the development of a utopic, yet empirically based, literary genre became of great consequence in conceptualising the growing human impact, especially among the adherents of such utopian writers as Defoe and his devotee, Jean-Jacques Rousseau.

The rapid expansion of European plantation agriculture in the West Indies did promote some attempts at conservation during the seventeenth century. Often, however, the response to environmental degradation involved a progressive westward displacement from one Caribbean island to another as these environments were successively exhausted by plantation cropping. It soon became clear that the very destructive and visually dramatic impact of plantation agriculture on the soils of a tropical island required either outmigration and relocation of the whole plantation economy or the development of a systematic conservationist response. Proximity to other islands and to South America meant that the former course was often adopted in the West Indies. The Dutch, for example, in a number of instances, shifted their plantation activities from island to island and then, eventually, to Brazil.[33] As David Watts has recently shown, conservationist forms of soil erosion control did develop in the West Indies during the seventeenth century.[34] However, they were devoted more to ensuring the continuation of plantation activity than the survival of any forest cover. Those colonial officials, such as the Governor of Barbados in the 1670s, who expressed more comprehensive concerns and plans for conservation, were generally ignored by their masters at the metropole.[35]

---

[33] J. Edel, 'The Brazilian sugar cycle of the seventeenth century and the rise of West Indian competition', *Caribbean Studies*, 9 (1969), pp. 24–44.

[34] D. Watts, *Environmental change, slavery and agricultural development in the Caribbean since 1492* (Cambridge, 1985).

[35] This stood in stark contrast to the official response developing outside the European

The emergence in the seventeenth century of a new kind of capitalist structure, the joint stock trading company, as a new, flexible, and more capital-intensive element in European expansion helped to promote plantation and trading activities at a much greater distance from Europe than before. This provided, too, the conditions for further far-reaching environmental changes. The new companies, often reinforced by the growing ambitions of European states, began to transform some of the often uninhabited oceanic islands, earlier treated simply as stopping places for the ships of many nations, into the locations of more permanent kinds of settlement for military and plantation development, as well as timber extraction. By 1670 St Helena, Mauritius, and Formosa had all been colonised by the Dutch or the English. It was on these islands, located along the main trading routes to India and China, that sophisticated forms of state conservation first emerged. In some respects the Cape of Good Hope can also be treated physiographically as an island, with a parallel and early growth in the state's awareness of environmental constraints.[36]

The tropical island colonies were generally small and the consequences of deforestation, especially in terms of streamflow decline, could be quickly observed and thus acted upon. In this way insular environments stimulated both innovative interventionist responses and theorisation in environmental terms. The history of St Helena illustrates this particularly well.[37] Annexed by the English in 1659, the island was extremely isolated. This extreme isolation, combined with its central importance as a secure watering and provisioning point for the East India Company ships, placed the island's resources under heavy pressure. By

---

domain, particularly in Japan. Here, as Conrad Totman has recently revealed, rapid population increases, urban growth, and fuelwood demand had led to a widespread ecological crisis by the mid-seventeenth century. The Tokugawa Shogunate responded by initiating an elaborate forest conservation and reafforestation programme designed both to safeguard timber reserves and prevent soil erosion. These measures, however, do not appear to have become known to European contemporaries. See C. Totman, *The green archipelago* (Berkeley, 1989).

[36] See Grove, 'Early Themes in African Conservation', pp. 21–39.

[37] For an overall historical treatment, see P. Gosse, *St Helena, 1502–1938* (London, 1938).

A map of St Helena, published shortly after the time of the English settlement.

1700 St Helena had become extensively deforested, and soil erosion and deep gullying were widespread. The history of this progressive degradation is recorded in minute detail in Company diaries and in correspondence between the governor and the EIC Court of Directors in London,[38] which also elaborately record the story of the innovative early attempts made to impede further deterioration.[39]

In less remote locations the island would have been quickly abandoned. Indeed, in 1716, a newly arrived Governor of St Helena

---

[38] For a detailed compilation of the St Helena records, see H. R. Janisch, ed., *Extracts from the St Helena records* (Jamestown, St Helena: Government Printer, 1908).

[39] For a detailed account, see Grove, *Green imperialism*, ch. 3; see also Q.C.B. Cronk, 'The Historical and Evolutionary Development of the Plant Life of St Helena,' (Ph.D. thesis, University of Cambridge, 1985), pp. 53–88.

Late seventeenth-century engraving of the Dodo, taken from Strickland,
The Dodo and its kindred. *The Dodo lived in the dry lowland ebony
forest and persihed as much from disappearance of its habitat as from the
depredations of visiting sailors.*

canvassed the possibility of resettling the inhabitants on Mauritius,
which the Dutch had recently vacated.[40] The continuing importance of
St Helena to the Company as a replenishment point meant that this
could not realistically be allowed to happen. Between 1670 and 1770,
therefore, almost every successive governor on the island attempted to
control the ecological changes which were taking place. The most
ambitious efforts were those made by Governor Roberts in 1709, who set
up forest reserves and afforestation programmes, introduced an irriga-

---

[40] Letter, St Helena Council to Court of Directors, dt 19 February 1715, in Janisch, *St
Helena records*, p. 113.

tion system, and attempted to exterminate the goat population, which he had identified as peculiarly destructive.[41]Furthermore, he and his successor attempted to transplant specimens of the increasingly rare St Helena redwood in the fear that it was about to become extinct.[42] The efforts of the Governors, amongst the earliest made in recognition of the likely extinction of an endemic species, were successful. Later Governors, particularly John Byfield in the 1730s, imitated Roberts' conservationist methods and philosophy.[43] In so doing they found themselves constantly at odds, as Roberts had been, with the relatively unschooled opinion of the East India Company's Court of Directors. Indeed, throughout the eighteenth century the Company seemed quite incapable of understanding the environmental consequences of introducing plantation schemes into the island and was especially unwilling to support the Governors in their efforts to regulate the environment of the island through protecting the forests and corralling animals. Each succeeding Governor quickly found himself siding with the settler freeholders against the Company on a wide variety of land-use issues, not the least being the recognition of the need for communal land-use practices, to which the islanders had consistently adhered despite all the efforts of the Court of Directors.[44] Despite the conservation policies pursued by Roberts and his successors, the sheer scale of the erosive processes at work on St Helena and the lack of any relevant environmental insights derived from the outside world meant that, when Sir Joseph Banks visited the island in 1771, he was shocked at what he saw and contrasted it unfavourably with the situation at the Cape Colony. There, he asserted, the Dutch colonists had made a 'Paradise of a desert,' while the Company had allowed the 'Paradise' of St Helena to 'become a desert.'[45]

The central difficulty for the Governor-conservationists of St Helena was that they had to deal with a Company hierarchy that, before

---

[41] Council to Court of Directors, dt November 1708, in Janisch, *St Helena records*, p. 85.

[42] Ibid., p. 88.

[43] St Helena Council Diary, dt 23 October 1745, in Janisch, *St Helena records*, p. 183.

[44] Ibid., pp. 105–106.

[45] Sir Joseph Banks, diary entry, dt May 1771, in J.C. Beaglehole, ed., *The 'Endeavour Journal' of Sir Joseph Banks, 1768–1771* (Sydney: Sydney University Press, 1968), vol. 6.

the 1790s, possessed no insights into the impact of European capital-intensive and slave employing agricultural methods on a tropical land-scape or into the destructive hydrological consequences of tropical deforestation. In direct contrast to the French state at the same period, the EIC had not at this stage yet developed any serious commitment to the commercial or practical cultivation of scientific expertise.[46] A further problem related to the divergent traditions of the state's involvement in forestry in England and France. In England the state's role in forest regulation, particularly during and after the Commonwealth period, became severely restricted. As a result, that country was forced increasingly to rely upon timber supplies from the Baltic region and North America.[47] In France, by contrast, the state itself acquired a more direct role in forest control under Colbert's direction.[48] Thus in the period from 1660 to 1760, as a consequence of these differences, two quite separate models of tropical forest management developed on St Helena and Mauritius respectively. A distinctive forest conservation system was also developed at the Cape but was cut short by the onset of British rule. In France, the provisions of the 1669 Forest Ordinance ensured that forest management was treated in conjunction with water management and administered by Inspecteurs des Eaux et Forêts.[49] Thus, from the outset, French approaches to the environment of Mauritius involved a well-developed awareness of the possibility of ecological regulation and control. The Dutch had already exploited intensively the ebony for the market in luxury island woods during the earlier period of Dutch rule.[50] By contrast, the Dutch management of the Cape environment, at least

---

[46] Probably the East India Company's earliest formal scientific appointment was that of Dr. Johann Koenig as 'Company Naturalist' at Madras in 1778. Koenig had earlier held a post as 'Naturalist' to the Nawab of Arcot. The much earlier instance of patronage by the Company represented by the sponsorship of Edmund Halley on his St. Helena expedition in 1676 should perhaps be discounted for this purpose.

[47] J. Thirsk, ed., *Agricultural history of England and Wales* (Cambridge, 1985), vol. 5, pp. 375–376.

[48] John Croumbie Brown, *The French Forest Ordinance of 1669* (Edinburgh, 1876).

[49] Jean-Claude Wacquet, *Les Grandes maîtres des eaux et forêts de France de 1689 à la Révolution* (Paris: Librarie Droz, 1978).

[50] J.R. Brouard, *The woods and forests of Mauritius* (St Louis, Mauritius: Government Printer, 1963), pp. 1–12.

on paper, was highly regulated and cautious, mirroring the careful organisation needed to husband and manage the limited resources of the Netherlands.[51] Dutch Mauritius, on the other hand, had been treated merely as a source of high-value timber and was abandoned once the forests easily reached near the coast were depleted. Indeed, the exclusively depletionary management of Mauritius seems to have been the exception to the general rule of Dutch caution. Deliberate and systematic working of the teak forests in Java, on an apparently sustainable basis, had already been commenced by the Dutch East India Company (VOC) in 1677.[52] Such a policy clearly depended on a considerable degree of territorial control of a kind not yet achieved in Asia by the French or British during this period.

When the French annexed Mauritius in 1721, the commercial rivalry between Britain and France had begun to sharpen. This led directly to an intensive contest for control over sources of marine timber for the navies needed for the growing struggle for global trade and influence, particularly in the Indian Ocean.[53] It was in this setting that the financial collapse of the Compagnie des Indes after 1763 elicited the direct intervention of the French Crown in the government of Mauritius and a more direct attempt at intervention in the control of the strategically important forests.[54] The fact that the French possessed no equivalent to the vast forests of North America, which were now accessible to the British, further stimulated a cautious attitude towards timber resources, particularly on Mauritius (the Isle de France) and Réunion (Bourbon).

---

[51] T.R. Sim, *The forests and forest flora of the folony of the Cape of Good Hope* (Edinburgh, 1907), pp. 76–80.

[52] For an overall literature survey, see P. Boomgard, 'Forests and forestry in colonial Java, 1677–1942', in J. Dargavel, ed., *Changing tropical forests: historical perspectives on today's challenges* (Canberra: Australian National University, Centre for Resource and Environmental Studies Special Publication, 1989). Far more detailed accounts are contained in numerous articles by E.H.B. Brascamp, in particular 'Hourlevanties order de O.I. Compagnie. De Aate van 21 Juin desor de soeshanan aan de O.I. compagnie verleend tot het Kappen van hout-weiken in de bosschen van blora [uit het koloniaal Archief No. XLXII]', *Tijdschrift voor Indische taal, land en Volkenkunde van het Koninklijke Bataviaasch Genootschap van Kusten en Wettenschappen*, 52 (1932), pp. 108–112.

An analogous process had been taking place in India itself. From as early as AD 800 a gradual pattern of state forest control had been emerging.[55] Reinforced by the advent of Mughal rule, this shift away from communal forest use towards state intervention was actually accelerated by the ascendancy of the successor states to the Mughals, particularly on the West Coast of India, where timber harvesting was most intensive. Thus, as early as the 1740s, the rulers of the Maratha empire had found it expedient to acquire control over large tracts of coastal forest and to set up plantations, both for shipbuilding and revenue.[56] In Cochin and Travancore similar monopoly controls over forest were initiated.[57] However, the most extensive pre-colonial programmes for afforestation and forest protection were carried on, between 1770 and 1840, by the Amirs of Sind.[58] Such pre-colonial policies of state forest control in India are historically important, not least because the British used them extensively to legitimate new attempts at forest reservation in the Bombay Presidency during the 1840s.[59] Thus, by about 1770, throughout many regions of South Asia, the Mascarenes, and the East Indies, a widespread emergence of state forest controls had become clearly apparent. This phenomenon developed as relatively

---

[53] See R. C. Albion, *Forests and sea-power: the timber problem of the Royal Navy, 1652–1862* (Harvard, 1926).

[54] The dynamics of French naval timber demand are dealt with in P.W. Bamford, *Forests and French sea-power, 1660–1789* (Toronto, 1956), pp. 88–102.

[55] Some idea of the early stages of this process is contained in Diprakanjan Das, *Economic history of the Deccan* (Delhi: Munshiram, 1976), pp. 105–115.

[56] *Report of the Bombay Forest Commission*, 1887, vols. 1 and 2 (Bombay: Government Press, 1887). The taxation features of Maratha forest policy are an unexplored field in research terms; however, for a cursory survey, see H. B. Vashishta, *Land revenue and public finance in Maratha administration*, (Delhi, 1975), pp. 138–146.

[57] Until the end of the eighteenth century, the forests of Cochin were under the control of the feudal chiefs of Nadivazlis, who owed allegiance to the Rajah of Cochin. In 1813 a forest department was set up under a Mellei Melvicharappan (Mountain Superintendent); see H. Viswanath, ed., *Working plan for Chakakuan* (Trivandrum: Forest Department, 1958), pp. 12–13. For details of the Travancore timber monopolies and early forest conservancy, see F. Bourdillon, ed., *Report on Travancore forests (Trivandrum: Government Printer*, 1886), pp. 15–16.

[58] A short account of these is given by H.T. Lambrick in *Sir Charles Napier and Sind* (Oxford, 1952), pp. 22–24, 192–193.

integrated forces of economic penetration began to respond to new levels of trade and demand, particularly in the search for timber to satisfy the increasingly complex demands of both western and indigenous navies and growing urban centres.[60] In Mauritius the demands of the colonial state took a very distinctive form. A continuing timber shortage in France and the growing size of the French navy meant that Labourdonnais, Governor of Mauritius after 1731, found it worthwhile to construct and repair ships locally, utilising Mauritius teak. A fleet of these ships was then used, successfully, to attack Madras in 1746.[61]

However, naval demand was not the only destabilising factor on Mauritius. Under Labourdonnais the ecological distortions that had developed in an island environment subjected to the demands of a plantation economy gave rise, as they had on St Helena, to anxieties about the capacity of this climatically unreliable island even to produce sufficient food for its settler population and slave-labour force.[62] These fears led Labourdonnais to develop a new botanic garden with the specific objective of breeding drought-resistant crops to tide the population over the leaner years. This type of institutional concept was later imitated and elaborated by Colonel Robert Kyd as justification for founding a botanic garden at Calcutta in 1786, an innovation which later became vital in providing the infrastructure for the scientific monitoring of environmental changes in India.[63]

---

[59] See, for example, Alexander Gibson, 'Description of the System Adapted for the Forest Conservancy of the Bombay Presidency', in A. Gibson, ed., *A handbook for the forests of the Bombay Presidency,* (Byculla: Government Printer, 1863). Gibson states that 'Teak and "Junglewood" have been carefully preserved ever since this tract of country came under the rule of the Angria, and even, I think, dates from the taking of Sevendroog by Admiral Watkins.'

[60] A detailed account of the impact of new naval demand is found in R.A. Wadia, T*he Bombay Dockyard and the Wadia master builders* (Bombay, 1957).

[61] Brouard, *Woods and forests of Mauritius,* p. 12.

[62] R. Toussaint, ed., *Dictionary of Mauritian biography* (5 vols, Port Louis, 1941–84), p. 154. See also Grove, green imperialism, ch. 5.

[63] R. Kyd to Company Board, Fort William, Madras, dt 15 April 1786, quoted in 'Proceedings of the Supreme Council relative to the establishment of a botanic garden at Mackwa Tannah' (Calcutta). [In India Office Library, Home Miscellaneous, No. 799), pp. 1–207.]

The most significant intellectual departure in French environmental policy on Mauritius, the installation of a forest reservation
system, was explicitly based on the fear of the impact of deforestation on
rainfall and soil erosion. This was a direct consequence of the assumption
of direct political control by the Crown and the rise to political influence
in government, especially in the Navy ministry, of a group of men
strongly attracted by Physiocracy, a political and economic philosophy
which had originated in the writings of economist Richard Cantillon and
physician François Quesnay. Significantly, it attached particular importance to the working of the 'laws of nature' in economics.[64] The political
ascendancy of the Physiocrats facilitated the appointment of Pierre
Poivre as Commissaire-Intendant of Mauritius in 1766. Poivre had
evolved a conservationist approach to the environment essentially as
matter of moral economy in a manner characteristic of the Physiocrats.
A proper understanding of the basis of the environmental moral economy
which he advocated necessitates an appreciation of the antecedents of the
man himself.[65] Poivre was at one time a Jesuit priest and had first visited
Mauritius in the 1740s. He then used the island as the base for a series
of expeditions to collect spice tree specimens from the Moluccas.[66] A
primary part of this exercise involved attempts to transplant imported
species of spices in Mauritian soil. This had led Poivre directly to an
interest in soil conditions, soil humidity, water table levels, and the
desirability of maintaining an extensive protective tree cover so that
agriculture on the island might prosper. He had become especially
appreciative of the attempts made by the Dutch at the Cape in soil
erosion prevention and in planting shelter belts.[67]

---

[64] H. Higgs, *The Physiocrats: six lectures on the French économistes of the eighteenth century* (London, 1897).

[65] For biographical details of Poivre, see L. Malleret, *Pierre Poivre* (Paris: L'Ecole Français d'Extrême Orient, 1974).

[66] These journeys are detailed in Madeleine Ly-Tio-Fane, *Mauritius and the spice trade: the Odyssey of Pierre Poivre* (Port Louis: Mauritius Archives Publication Fund, 1958), and 'Pierre Poivre et l'expansion franc,ais dans l'Indo-Pacifiques', *Bulletin de l'Ecole Français d'Extrême Orient*, 1967, Extrait du Tome L111 Fasc. n. 2.

[67] Pierre Poivre, *Travels of a philosopher: or observations on the manners of the various nations in Africa and Asia* (Dublin, 1770).

Poivre became very critical of what he saw as the profligate and destructive felling of trees on Mauritius, maintaining that the lack of control contrasted badly with Dutch practices at the Cape. Poivre had, furthermore, made himself familiar, during a period of enforced detention in Canton, with Chinese horticultural methods.[68] Later, too, he became acquainted at Pondicherry and in Malabar with indigenous Indian techniques for irrigation and planting trees and referred extensively to this knowledge in his writings.[69] Poivre's return to France coincided with the rise in prominence of the *agronomes* and a period of intense activity in Enlightenment science. After his arrival, he added to his unrivalled knowledge of tropical land-use practices in a wide-ranging survey of travel and scientific literature on the Americas in which he probably first encountered desiccation theories.[70] Significantly, many of his writings during this period contained biting critiques of the Europeans' treatment of indigenous peoples in the Americas, and his extensive lectures on tropical land use and agriculture aimed particularly scathing criticism at colonial land-use methods.[71] These criticisms soon came to the attention of the Physiocratic political circle surrounding the Duc de Choiseul, who was himself closely associated with Physiocratic thinking and attracted by a philosophy which set great store by notions of the moral superiority of agricultural versus financial prosperity and by the virtues of scientific agriculture versus short-term profitmaking.[72] The Duc de Choiseul had, however, found it politically impossible to assert his reforming Physiocratic zeal in any substantial way in France itself, so he increasingly turned to the colonies in the hope of exercising his reforming ideals, much as Lord Dalhousie did in India in the next century.

---

[68] On the value of empirical observations of the Orient, see P. Poivre, 'Utilité d'un voyage dans l'Orient', in P. Poivre, *Citoyen du monde; ou lettres d'un philosophe à ses amis dans l'Orient* (Amsterdam, 1763), p. 172.

[69] L. Malleret, ed., *Un manuscrit de Pierre Poivre: les memoires d'un voyageur* (Paris: Ecole Français d'Extrême Orient, 1968), pp. 113–114.

[70] P. Poivre, *D'Amerique et des Americains* (Berlin, 1771).

[71] Poivre's seminal metropolitan interlude is covered in Y. Laissus, 'Note sur les manuscrits de Pierre Poivre (1719–1786) conservés à la bibliothèque centrale du Muséum National d'Histoire Naturelle', *Proceedings of the Royal Society of Arts and Sciences of Mauritius, vol. 4*, part 2 (1973), p. 37 and p. 37, n. 2.

[72] H Higgs, *The Physiocrats*, p. 78.

The encounter with Mauritius gave both de Choiseul and Poivre the opportunity to experiment with their ideas. Choiseul could exercise the role of the state in reform by putting Physiocracy into practice, and Poivre could carry out a programme of transplantation and conservation. 'If the forests do not regenerate in the island,' Choiseul wrote in his instructions to Poivre,

> rain will be less frequent, the over-exposed soil will be burnt by the sun…timber shall be your particular attention…. Complaints have been made that this very important matter has not received all the care and attention which it deserves. Messrs Dumas and Poivre should hasten to control it with a good policy; they will exercise the existing regulations on the subject, study the exact conditions of the forests, exploit and utilise them in the most economical way possible and only allow people to cut them if they ensure their conservation.[73]

On his arrival in Mauritius in 1767 Poivre immediately made a series of speeches and proclamations to the French colonists, many of which specifically emphasised the high priority attached to preserving the island forests.[74] This, he asserted, would assure the colony a reliable level of rainfall. A morality expressed in land use, Poivre implied, would complement the religious morality of the individual. These environmental homilies were later published as revolutionary tracts in Paris in 1797. probably less for their revolutionary environmentalism than for their class-based critique of colonial absentee landlordism.[75] The desire to make a clean sweep of colonial conventions did not stop with plans for environmental reform. Poivre also took initial steps in a campaign to abolish slavery on the island, a cause which he was unable to carry through. Indeed, he experienced much opposition both in this respect and in his conservation programmes, not least from a succession of island Governors who felt threatened by his attempts to stamp out timber and property speculation by colonial officials for private gain. At the end of

---

[73] R. Brouard, *Woods and Forests of Mauritius,* 10.

[74] *Discours prononcés par M. Poivre, Commissaire du Roi, l'un à l'assemblée générale des habitans de l'Isle de France lors de son arrivée dans la colonie, l'autre à la première assemblée publique du Conseil Superieur nouvellement etablié dans l'isle* (Port Louis: Imprimerie Royale, 1768, 50 pp.). This publication is very rare, but a copy is at the Auguste Brunet Library, Toulon.

[75] See I. Salles, ed., *Oeuvres complètes de Pierre Poivre* (Paris, 1797).

1768 the departure of Governor Dumas, disgraced for his corrupt involvement in land sales, allowed Poivre to carry on his conservation programmes unhindered. The first Forest Conservation Ordinance, or *Reglement Economique,* passed in November 1769,[76] proved to be a model of its kind. During the next century, its essential elements were incorporated in future statutes in, for example, St Vincent (West Indies), the Cape Colony, Natal, and India.[77]

In his pioneering conservation efforts, Poivre enlisted the aid of two men in particular, Philibert Commerson and J. H. Bernardin de St Pierre. Poivre contrived to secure an appointment on the island as a government scientist for Commerson, who had arrived in Mauritius in November 1768 as the naturalist on the Bougainville expedition. Officially Commerson was intended to carry out a pharmacological and timber resource survey of the Mauritius forests.[78] These surveys provided the justification for Poivre's far-reaching conservation legislation of 1769, who was also backed.in his efforts against the anti-conservation interests on the island and in Paris by the Chief Engineer of the colony, Bernardin de Saint Pierre. Later better known as one of the first French romantic novelists and orientalists, Saint Pierre was a pioneer figure in campaigns against slavery, a practice which he had first witnessed on Mauritius.[79] It was Saint Pierre who first pointed out to Poivre the extent to which deforestation on the island was contributing to the rapid siltation of the main rivers and harbours of the island. This observation led Poivre to develop the twin concepts of the mountain reserve and the

---

[76] The separate articles are compiled in (Anon.) Règlement économique *sur le défrichement des terres et la conservation des bois de l'Isle de France* (Port Louis: Imprimerie Royale, 1769) [Auguste Brunet Library, Toulon]. The rules were signed by Governor Desroches as well as Poivre himself.

[77] Details of this transference are found, for example, in Government of Natal, *Report of the committee enquiring into the extent and condition of the forest lands of the colony* (Pietermaritzburg: Government Printer, 1880) [Natal Provincial Archives, Pietermaritzburg]. Evidence of the diffusion of knowledge of Mauritius forest protection regulations into India as early as 1844 is provided in W. H. Sleeman, *Rambles and recollections of an Indian official* (London: J. Hatchard, 1844), p. 450.

[78] A certificate releasing Commerson to the service of Poivre's administration was delivered to him by Bougainville on 15 November 1768. For details, see Series designated 'Col-E.', Commerson's File, F1., Archives Nationales, Paris.

river reserve, the intellectual antecedents of ideas which were widely applied in India after 1846. These steps were only partially successful in inhibiting the rate of deforestation on the island which, towards the end of the eighteenth century and increasingly during the nineteenth century, came under exceptional pressure as a result of the activities of sugar plantation owners. However, had Poivre not introduced his conservation system, there is little doubt that deforestation would have proceeded at a much more rapid pace. Even today the boundaries of some of the reserves established by 1800 can still be seen, particularly along the west coast of Mauritius, adjacent to Black River and Tamarin.

Most of the conservationist initiatives taken by Poivre were essentially locally derived. The critical innovation contained in the new conservation measures, while based in a broad sense on Colbert's 1669 Forest Ordinance, consisted of the articulation of new insights into the relationship between forest cover, stream flow, soil erosion, and rainfall. Poivre's most effective argument to justify the sterilisation of forest capital as reserved land involved a conviction that deforestation would cause a decline in rainfall. However, in evolving a methodology for conservation in 1769, Poivre's precedents were only partly European. His tree-planting policies, for example, were based entirely on Indian precedents, and he utilised species imported from Malabar and Bengal, especially *bois noir*.[80]

Although for political purposes Poivre put forward economic and pharmacological reasons for preserving forests and contriving legislation, other motivations which were almost certainly more significant to the Intendant himself were also involved. These fell roughly into two kinds: the scientific and botanical and the unashamedly utopian. The presence of one of the largest and most elaborate botanical gardens in the world, sometimes known as a 'wonder of the East', and the presence of Commerson, one of the most experienced and well-travelled French botanists of the period, meant that the rich and endemic flora of the island was soon recognised as scientifically important in world terms,

---

[79] See J.H. Bernardin de Saint Pierre, *Voyage à l'Isle de France* (Paris, 1773). I have referred to the edition published in London in 1800 as *A Voyage to the Isle of France*.

[80] This was probably *Dalbergia latifolia*.

highly valued aesthetically and worthy of preservation.[81] This alone
constituted a significant impetus for the embryonic conservation lobby.
Further encouragement to protect the island in its natural state was
provided by the individual predilections of St Pierre and Commerson.
Both were avid field botanists steeped in the writings of Rousseau
(another contemporary botanist, who is better known in other roles).[82]
Both were also social rebels who valued the natural state of the island as
integral to their conception of the colony as a practical and mental refuge
from the political and, for them, moral turmoil of metropolitan France.
As a member of Bougainville's expedition, Commerson had the opportunity to observe the inhabitants of Tahiti (which he called *utopie*) and
believed their society idyllic in social and environmental terms. His
writings indicate that by 1768 he was already very critical of metropolitan
France and its prevailing social values. He had little desire to return to
France and, indeed, never did so before he died on Mauritius in 1773.
Bernardin de Saint Pierre, trained in botany by Poivre himself, returned
to France to write *Paul et Virginie* and to become the main confidant of
Rousseau, whom he had long admired and corresponded with. His
manifestly ecological views were set out in three major texts, *Journey to
the Isle de France, Studies in Nature* (in which *Paul et Virginie* formed the
fourth volume) and *Harmonies of Nature*. Poivre, Commerson, and Saint
Pierre all arrived in Mauritius at a time when the French preoccupation
with the 'Robinsonades' (imitations of Defoe's *Robinson Crusoe*) was
developing into a fully developed cult or mythology of the South Sea
tropical island. The desire of all three men to preserve an unspoilt utopian
island environment necessitated some form of environmentalism, simply to ensure the continuity of the Rousseauian return to nature to which
they were dedicated.[83] None of these motivations would have been
transmuted into the conservation policies pursued by Poivre had it not
been for the opportunity which the Physiocrats had provided to Poivre

---

[81] This valuing was of a very personal kind on Commerson's part: 'My plants,' he wrote,
'my beloved plants have consoled me for everything; I found in them, Nepenthes, curare,
dulce' (S. Pasfield-Oliver, *The life of Philibert Commerson* [London, 1909], p. 202).

[82] For details of Rousseau's botanical enthusiasms, see J.-J. Rousseau, *Letters on the
elements of botany addressed to a lady*, trans. T. Martyn (London, 1782).

[83] See Grove, *Green imperialism*, ch. 5.

in political terms. This permitted him free rein to pursue his environmental programme and his innovatory state patronage of scientific expertise.

The emergence of conservationism on Mauritius under Poivre might be considered of merely antiquarian interest, but it was not so. The Isle de France lay intellectually and geographically, as did Tahiti at the same period, at the very core of the outward-looking intellectual and Romantic projects of late-eighteenth-century France. One of the earliest major literary figures in the French Romantic reaction, Bernardin de Saint Pierre above all ensured that Mauritius became a central and symbolic focus of contemporary aesthetic and Orientalist-leaning perception.[84] As a product of this intellectual climate, Poivre's conservationism itself left an intellectual legacy of environmental attitudes both in Mauritius itself (which remained in the forefront of conservation ideas until the 1870s) and throughout a much wider colonial context.[85] After Poivre left the island for France in 1772, his legislation for forest conservation was strengthened in 1777 and 1795, then much further elaborated in 1804, at a time when the colony had acquired effective political autonomy under Governor Decaen.[86] Political isolation and naval blockade then encouraged the passing of additional pioneering environmental legislation in the fields of water pollution, fishery protection, and safeguarding watersheds. As was the case much later in India, the state botanic garden set up by Poivre at Pamplemousses provided an essential part of the intellectual and technical infrastructure needed for these innovations. Furthermore the notion of the colonial scientific *Academie*, first conceptualised in 1770 by Philibert Commerson, en-

---

[84] See B. de Saint Pierre, *Studies of nature* (5 vols, London, 1796); *Harmonies of nature* (3 vols, London, 1815); *Paul et Virginie* (London, 1841); *La chaumière indienne* (Calcutta, 1866).

[85] For specific details of the links between Poivre's conservation policy on Mauritius and the environmental philosophy of Edward Balfour, the original proponent of forest protection in the Madras presidency, see IOL, V/27/568/107 [Correspondence files on trees and the incidence of rainfall].

[86] The main articles were Arrêté of the 13th Messidor, Art. III (July 1795); and Arrêté of the 14th Vendemiaire, Art. XIII (October 1804). It was this last law which the British incorporated on their annexation of the island in 1810.

Enregistré par nous, greffier en chef du tribunal d'appel au désir de l'arrêt de ce jour, qui et ce requérant le Commissaire du gouvernement.

Au Port Nord-Ouest, le 12 Vendémiaire an 13.   CHASTEAU.

Extrait des registres des arrêtés du Capitaine-Général

AU NOM DE LA REPUBLIQUE.

DECAEN Capitaine-Général des Etablissemens français à l'Est du Cap de Bonne-Espérance.

SUR la représentation du Préfet Colonial, que, pour l'avantage de la colonie de l'Isle de France, il est important de remettre en vigueur les anciens réglemens sur la conservation des eaux et forêts, et sur la police de la chasse et de la pêche, et d'y ajouter les dispositions dont l'expérience et les circonstances font sentir chaque jour l'utilité,

ARRÊTE:

Administration Forestière.

TITRE PREMIER.

De la conservation des Bois.

ARTICLE PREMIER.

Aucun défrichement de bois debout ne pourra se faire, sans qu'auparavant le propriétaire du terrein n'ait fait, au bureau de la conservation des eaux et forêts, la déclaration de la quantité d'arpens qu'il voudra mettre en culture; cette déclaration ayant pour objet la conservation des eaux et forêts de cette Isle, ainsi que l'emploi économique des bois de construction.

II. Tout propriétaire réservera, en bois debout, le sixième au moins de sa propriété; et en outre ceux existans sur les lits, encaissemens et escarpemens des rivières et ruisseaux, si ces parties de terrein sont une dépendance de sa propriété.

Il est expressément défendu de défricher les mornes et pitons au-delà du tiers de leur hauteur à partir de la base.

III. Les bois seront conservés sur les bords des rivières et ruisseaux. Les lisières de bois sur chaque rive seront de cent vingt pieds de largeur, à partir du bord de la mer, jusqu'à deux lieues de distance en ligne directe, et de soixante pieds, au-delà de cette distance.

IV. Sur les habitations et autres lieux désignés en l'article II, qui devaient être réservées, où les bois ont été détruits, tout propriétaire sera tenu de rétablir, par des plantations ou semis, les réserves et lisières dépendantes de sa propriété, ci-devant déterminées.

Un dixième de la plantation prescrite devra être effectué chaque année.

V. Tout propriétaire limitrophe des réserves de la République vers le bord de la mer, sera tenu de conserver sur son terrein, un rideau de cent quatre-vingt pieds de largeur dans les parties où ces réserves sont déboisées.

Ceux dont les terreins se trouvent découverts dans les mêmes parties, seront tenus de rétablir la lisière par des semis ou plantations d'arbres, ainsi qu'il est prescrit par l'article IV.

VI. Les propriétaires qui ne se seront pas conformés aux articles IV et V, seront condamnés à une amende, qui ne pourra être moindre de vingt-cinq francs, ni en excéder deux cents: il sera en outre procédé à leurs frais et dépens, à la dili-

Conservation legislation published by Governor Decaen on Mauritius in 1804, based on the rules established by Pierre Poivre in 1769.

sured a continuity of scientific tradition developed further in the form of the Royal Society of Arts and Sciences of Mauritius.[87]

Both in Mauritius and later in India and Southern Africa the existence of such local scientific institutions proved a critical stimulus to the formulation of colonial responses to environmental change and provided a platform for conservation propagandists, such as Louis Bouton in Mauritius and Edward Balfour in Madras.[88] In contrast to the situation on St Helena until the 1780s, the environmental analysis of the consequences of deforestation on Mauritius was based not only on local observation but on insights derived from a whole range of intellectual concepts developed in regions as diverse as France, the Cape Colony, China, and Malabar. However, Poivre had synthesised a coherent body of environmental thought, stimulated largely by the specific conditions of colonial rule in the tropics. However, until the 1820s no comparable intellectual development of an environmental consciousness had yet emerged in metropolitan Europe. The first application of Poivre's ideas outside Mauritius itself took place, perhaps not surprisingly, on St Helena. Surveys carried out by Alexander Beatson, an army officer and subordinate of Arthur Wellesley in Mysore, on Mauritius in 1794 indicated that by then the scientific rationale behind forest reservation on Mauritius was becoming more widely known.[89] Thus, in that same year the EIC somewhat belatedly instructed the St Helena government to protect the forests on the island as a way of ensuring that the rainfall

---

[87] M. Ly-Tio-Fane, 'Notice historique' (Port Louis, Mauritius: Royal Society of Arts and Sciences of Mauritius, 150th Anniversary Commemorative Publication, 1986).

[88] Bouton's conservation ideas were put forward in such publications as: 'Sur le decroissement des forêts a l'Ile Maurice', *Le Cernien*, 12–14 April 1838; 'Note sur le décroissement des forêts', *Rapports de la Société d'Histoire Naturelle de l'Ile Maurice*, 1846, p. 10. For Balfour's views, see E. G. Balfour, 'Notes on the Influence Exercised by Trees in Inducing Rain and Preserving Moisture', *Madras Journal of Science and Literature*, 25 (1849), pp. 402–448. Balfour had been stimulated in his advocacy of forest protection by his observations of the efficiency of the Mauritius conservation ordinances and by his readings of the works of Joseph Priestley on the water-holding dynamics of the atmosphere (see IOL V27/560/107, pp. 1–11).

[89] A. Beatson, 'Account of Mauritius' (unpublished ms, British Museum, BM13868, London, 1784).

would not decline.[90] The establishment of botanic gardens at Calcutta and St Helena in 1788, which imitated the French establishment on Mauritius, may have heightened EIC sensitivity to the potential damage that desiccation might cause. Certainly the famines in Bengal between 1770 and 1784 had been a major anxiety to the Company, particularly to Captain Robert Kyd, who persuaded the EIC to fund a Calcutta Botanic Garden specifically to breed and test drought-resistant crops.[91] In 1808 Alexander Beatson was appointed Governor of St Helena, where his programmes to plant trees and prevent soil erosion became well known through his own publications, particularly the *Tracts on St Helena* (1816).[92] Knowledge of this activity and the improvements made by Beatson's programmes to the hydrological state of the island became important when the foundations were being laid for forest protection in India during the late 1840s.[93]

The Indian Medical Service and the Emergence of Conservationism in India

The employment of medical surgeons as superintendents of botanic gardens in India had already expanded the professional role of the surgeon outside the medical service and laid the foundations for a technical infrastructure of scientific expertise. This infrastructure relied not only on the diverse medical and botanical skills of the surgeons but on their high level of university education and the considerable social status conferred by the possession of medical knowledge in a disease-ridden tropical environment. In Mauritius, in a similar fashion, the ascendancy of the scientific lobby and its success in putting its preferred

---

[90] Letter, EIC Court of Directors to Governor, St Helena, dt 23 January1794, in Janisch, *St Helena Records*.

[91] IOL, Home Misc., no. 799, letters on pp. 1–201.

[92] A. Beatson, *Tracts relative to the island of St Helena, written during a residency of five years* (London, 1816).

[93] For details of J.D. Hooker's visit to Ascension island, see E. Duffey, 'The Terrestrial Ecology of Ascension Island', *Journal of Applied Ecology*, 1 (1967), pp. 219–236. A brief discussion of earlier afforestation programmes under the East India Company and the impact of tree-planting on rainfall in St Helena is found in the *St Helena Almanac*, vol. 1 (1848), p. 24.

policies into operation was based primarily on the ability to demonstrate convincingly that uncontrolled deforestation might threaten the security of the state itself. The high status afforded to science by the French Physiocratic interest in government facilitated this development.

On a much larger scale, but much more slowly, the views and influence of India's medical elite eventually acquires a similarly high status. Only gradually did this scientific lobby come to concern itself with the effects of forest clearance. However, when the medical surgeons did finally come to define deforestation as a matter requiring serious policy initiatives and an expansion in the role of the state, their opinions carried considerable weight. This was partly due to the long history of the medical service's consultancy to the state on all matters relating to health, water supply, scientific botany, and forest resources. The tours of Dr A.P. Hove in the Bombay presidency (1787–88) were an early exemplar of the performance of this consultancy role.[94] Moreover, as early as 1778 the Company had begun to employ eminent surgeon-botanists, such as J.G. Koenig, Patrick Russell, and William Roxburgh in official capacities as naturalists, with the active encouragement, after 1784, of Sir Joseph Banks, the president of the Royal Society.[95] The subsequent systematic development of links between the EIC medical service and the scientific and botanical establishment in Britain served to reinforce the authority of the surgeons as environmental commentators.

By 1830 the vast majority of the 800 Company surgeons in India were Scottish.[96] Many had been trained in botany by Professors John Hope in Edinburgh and William Hooker in Glasgow, both keen advocates of rigorous field observation, holistic approaches to nature, and tree-planting programmes.[97] Wherever attempts were made to establish conservancies or teak plantations in Malabar, in Bengal, or in Burma between 1805 and 1822 (in connection with war-time timber

---

[94] A.P. Hove, 'Tours for scientific and economical Research made in Guzerat, Kattiawar and the Conkans in 1787–1788', *Bombay Selections* XVI (Bombay: Government Printer, 1855), pp. 50–185.

[95] For biographical information on the surgeons employed by the EIC, see D.G. Crawford, *The roll of the Indian Medical Service* (Calcutta, 1930).

[96] H.H. Spry, *Modern India* (London, 1837), pp. 55–58.

[97] See I.H. Burkill, *Chapters in the history of Indian botany* (Calcutta, 1965).

shortage), the Medical Service quickly became involved. As early as the
1820s some of the surgeons lobbied heavily against the deforestation
taking place during that decade and argued in favour of plantation
programmes. Nathaniel Wallich, the director of the Calcutta Botanic

*Teak plantations established by Collector Conolly and Chatur Menon at
Nilumbur in Malabar. These trees, planted in the 1840s, were
photographed in 1994.*

Ships under construction by traditional methods using Malabar teak at Beypore south of Calicut in 1994. Shipbuilding has taken place at Beypore, according to local belief, since the first century AD. It expanded under the East India Company due to the efforts of Alexander Maconochie.

Garden, was pre-eminent among these early campaigners. 'Unless speedy provision is made,' he stated to a parliamentary committee in 1831, 'for the renewal of timber, we shall, within a very short time, find a most painful falling off. I should say it is quite time that means should be resorted to, to preserve the forests that are remaining, and new plantations should be made.'[98] In spite of these early efforts, a direct connection between decline in forest area and apparent regional increases in desiccation in India was not put forward as an argument for controlling deforestation until the end of the 1830s.

This delay can be partly attributed to a lack of evidence about rates of deforestation in India as a whole. Even so, throughout the 1820s and 1830s anxieties about deforestation were already frequently expressed. Bishop Heber, for instance, warned in 1824 that excessive deforestation, of the kind he had observed in the Siwalik foothills, might lead to a more general aridity.[99] A second reason for the delay may have been the paucity of articles in sufficiently authoritative technical publications on the links between deforestation and climate, despite the EIC's warning about desiccation to the St Helena government as early as 1794.[100] Moreover, at this stage Mauritius's experience was still not widely known. In both colonies the essential limitations of resources on an island undergoing visually apparent deforestation and soil erosion stimulated action as well as theorisation. In contrast, no comparably coherent or comprehensive evidence of the human environmental impact was available at a sub-continental scale in India until the mid-1830s. Consequently, a more convincing body of evidence collected on an all-India basis was still required, as well as a theoretical basis for adjudging the likely consequences of deforestation. When a widely accepted analysis of the possible dangers of deforestation did finally emerge in the 1830s, it was based on the coincidence of several scientific and political factors. The most potent was the linkage of the concept that deforestation would cause serious streamflow and rainfall changes with a political awareness of the

---

[98] N. Wallich, Evidence to Select Committee 1831–1832, British Parliamentary Papers, Colonies, East India, vol. 10 (1831), Col. 735.

[99] R. Heber, *Narrative of a journey through the upper provinces of India from Calcutta to Bombay, 1824–5* (London, 1828), p. 274.

[100] In that year the Court of Directors had warned the island Council that 'we are of the opinion that encouraging the growth of wood is of utmost consequence to this Island not only from the advantages to be derived from it as a fuel, but because it *is well known that trees have an attractive power on the clouds,* especially when they pass over hills so high as those on your island and we are inclined to believe that the misfortunes the island has been subject to from drought may in some measure have been averted had the growth of wood been properly attended to'. [My emphasis.]

occurrence of famine in the late 1830s throughout India. But there were other contributory developments. By the mid-1830s, the medical service became increasingly concerned about the rise in the frequency of episodes of serious disease taking place in the rapidly expanding cities, especially in Calcutta, the political capital, in part because of an increasing medical interest in epidemiology and the connections between water supply and disease transmission, an interest articulated rather earlier in India than Britain.

Anxieties about the state's responsibility in this field were increasingly raised in moral and practical terms. In 1836 Surgeon Ranald Martin produced a pioneering report (which considerably preceded the comparable efforts of Edwin Chadwick in Britain) on the need for public health measures and the universal provision of clean water in Calcutta.[101] He further proposed the production of a whole series of medico-topographical reports on India by the medical service.[102]

In this way the ambit of urban public health concern became much more widespread to embrace the whole rural topography of India, extending concerns about the provision of water in cities to include villages in regions known to be subject to drought. In this way Surgeon Donald Butter, in his *Topography of Awadh,* drew attention to the connections between the growing aridity of India and that which had taken place historically elsewhere.[103] Significantly, Butter relied heavily for his insights on Joseph Boussingault's translation of Alexander von Humboldt's work.[104] These translations had recently appeared in scientific journals read widely by Scottish surgeons in India. After 1839

---

[101] R. Martin, *The sanitary condition of Calcutta* (Calcutta, 1836).

[102] See discussion of Martin's campaigns in D.G. Crawford, *A history of the Indian Medical Service* (London, 1914), vol. 2, ch. 2. Further medico-topographical reports were compiled for Dacca (1840), Kumaon (1840), Jessore (1837), Assam (1837), and Sora (1839).

[103] D. Butter, *Outlines of the topography and statistics of the southern districts of Oudh and the Cantonment of Sultanpur, Oudh* (Benares, 1839).

[104] See especially J.B. Boussingault, 'Memoir concerning the effect which the clearing of land has in diminishing the quantity of water in the streams of a district', *Edinburgh New Philosophical Journal* 24 (1838), pp. 88–106; and passages in Humboldt's *Personal narrative of travels to the equinoctial regions of the New Continent 1799–1804,* trans. H.M. Williams (London, 1838), vol. 4, pp. 134–139.

Humboldt's arguments linking deforestation, increasing aridity, and temperature change on a global scale were widely quoted by the medical service in India in its increasingly determined efforts to elicit government controls on deforestation and as part of a wider campaign for public health reforms. Furthermore, the publication of the medico-topographical reports sponsored by Martin and the Calcutta authorities coincided with the appearance of another set of lay reports which were, by 1839, causing anxiety to the Presidency governments, particularly to the Bombay government.[105]

These reports, which were received from Collectors throughout Southern India, indicated very rapid rates of deforestation since the early 1820s. Initially the Presidency governments, heeding the advice of the Revenue services, which stood to gain from agricultural clearance more than forest conservation, had ignored such warnings, particularly those of the early 1830s which had originated principally with the Rajah of Nilumbur in Malabar. The famines of 1838–39 finally put paid to this attitude, and government officials began to worry about the social instability which might result from famines exacerbated by deforestation. This fear was only distantly related to much less pervasive concerns about possible timber shortages.[106] During the 1840s, such concerns were considerably sharpened by a spreading awareness of the severity of Ireland's famine. Faced by this situation, the governments of the Bombay and Madras Presidencies began quite deliberately to seek relevant technical expertise, giving Company surgeons the opportunity to put themselves forward as expert technical arbiters, a role that some surgeons readily accepted.

In the Bombay Presidency, Dr. Alexander Gibson had already lobbied the government extensively on the subject of deforestation. In Madras, Assistant Surgeon Edward Balfour had also started, by 1839, to try to persuade the authorities, on his own initiative, of the need for

---

[105] E.P. Stebbing, *The forests of India* (Edinburgh, 1922), vol. 1, pp. 72–81.

[106] See, for example, J.E. Thomas, 'Notes on ryotwar or permanent money rents in S. India, and on the duty of Government in periods of famine', *Madras Journal of Literature and Science,* (1838), pp. 53–78, 200–221; and Grove, *Green imperialism, ch. 8.* The remainder of this chapter is based heavily on the latter pages, which should be referred to for more detailed primary sources.

conservation.[107] However, Gibson's thinking initially carried the most weight, principally because he had already acquired a high reputation while a Vaccinator in Khandeish during the 1830s[108] Furthermore, he had even received gold medals from the Company in recognition of his achievements in pharmacological and epidemiological research. In 1838 Gibson was appointed Superintendent of the Botanic Garden at Dapoorie, near Poona, a position carrying an equivalent weight to the post of Superintendent of the Calcutta Botanic Garden. This appointment meant that he became the obvious source of expertise for the Bombay government in 1839 on forest matters. During a series of subsequent government-sponsored tours through the Presidency, Gibson grew increasingly disturbed by the full extent of deforestation, particularly on the slopes of the Western Ghats. In March 1841, for example, he wrote to Joseph Hooker that

> the Deccan is more bare than Guzerat and the clefts of the Ghat mountains are the only situation where trees are to be found in any quantity and even they are disappearing fast under the increased demand for land for spade husbandry . . . they are too steep for the plough. It is a matter of regret for the naturalist [sic], perhaps also for the economist, that the woods are in such rapid progress of destruction.[109]

Together with two other surgeons, Hugh Cleghorn (stationed at Shimoga in Mysore) and Edward Balfour (stationed at Madras), Gibson was able to systematically propagandise a forest conservation programme with the government. He backed it up consistently with the threat of

---

[107] E.G. Balfour, 'Notes on the influence exercised by trees in inducing rain and preserving moisture', *Madras Journal of Literature and Science*, 25 (1849), pp. 402–408. See also IOL V/27/560/107 for details of the correspondence between Balfour and Gibson.

[108] See Anon., 'Obituary of Alexander Gibson', *Proceedings of the Linnaean Society*, (1867), p. 33. See also entry on Gibson in Crawford, *Roll of the Indian Medical Service*.

[109] Letter, Alexander Gibson to J.D. Hooker, dt 1 March 1841, Letter no. 21, India letters, Kew Archives, Richmond, Surrey. This correspondence records the first direct involvement of Hooker in the tropical deforestation issue, a role subsequently reinforced by his visits to Ascension Island and St. Helena in 1843, and India in 1847–50. Hooker's simultaneous involvement in early conservation in the Cape Colony is outlined in Grove, 'Early Themes in African Conservation', pp. 22–34.

famine and constantly inferred that the responsibility for future famines would be laid directly at the door of government, were it not to implement the conservationist prescriptions put forward by the medical service. The political dynamics of the transition in the relations between scientists and colonial government which took place in India between about 1838 and 1847 (the latter being the date of the formal establishment of the Bombay Forest Department under the Conservatorship of Gibson) were complex. In practical terms and underlying the scenario of cataclysmic climatic change which the surgeons put forward, a fundamental debate opened up. In essence, this debate concerned the proper role of the state in environmental control and the extent of the legal right of government to assert control over forest tracts and the cutting of teak forest. The fact that state controls might pose a potentially decisive barrier to the activities of venture capital in the timber market, for which the state itself was the largest customer, was only admitted at a later date.

In 1824 the state had definitively abnegated pre-colonial state forest controls on the basis of a private rights and laissez-faire orthodoxy favoured by Thomas Munro as Governor of Bombay.[110] After 1837 the Company authorities changed course and sought instead to legitimate an increased degree of government intervention in forest control, arguing repeatedly that this new policy was supported by the powers supposedly exercised by pre-colonial Indian states over the forests of the Presidency. Alexander Gibson seemingly was largely responsible for the form of this initiative. He certainly foresaw the opposition to government controls from the new generation of largely indigenous forest landowners and from the European interests benefiting from the lack of regulation of the timber trade between 1824 and 1838. The whole question of the status of forests as a common property resource also became a matter of discussion and legal debate. Consideration of this problem was stimulated by the developing conflict between the new environmental anxieties of the Company and the forest claims of the private landowners. The Bombay government, now increasingly reliant on the advice of the medical service and on that of Gibson in particular, moved steadily towards a solution involving the formal alienation of forests to Company

---

[110] 'Timber Monopoly in Malabar and Canara', entry dt 26 November 1822, in *Minutes of Sir Thomas Munro,* (Bombay: Government Printer, 1881), pp. 178–187.

reserves and the progressive exclusion of private capital and shifting cultivation from the whole forest sector. This course of action soon brought Bombay into direct conflict with the wishes of the Supreme Government in Calcutta, which still favoured the protection of the rights of private landowners at all costs. Both sides tended to ignore the critically important needs of peasant users of the forest. They became a political football between government and commercial timber interests, especially in the neighbourhood of Bombay and later formed a core of popular resistance to British rule.[111] Although Gibson himself was well aware of the danger of alienating customary rights, his advocacy of peasant needs (specifically involving the setting aside of village forests) did not outlast his own personal influence with government or the imposition of the notoriously unjust Forest Act of 1878. Indeed the new Conservator's own fears about the likely social consequences of restricting customary access to forests were vividly fulfilled in 1851 when he narrowly escaped death at the hands of a crowd of angry forest residents in Thana protesting the imposition of new forest regulations.[112]

Between 1840 and 1846 the authorities in Calcutta continued to be most reluctant about funding the establishment of a formalised forest conservancy. They foresaw, quite correctly from hindsight, that such an establishment would imply a severe reduction in large short-term revenue income in favour of high expenditure on long-term and unquantifiable conservationist benefits. Gibson set himself the task of breaking this bureaucratic procrastination at the highest level of government by demonstrating that the penalty for further neglect of the forests could not be afforded politically or economically. Initially he attempted to do this by emphasising the difficulties that deforestation was causing in supplying firewood for residents in urban areas. At one stage Gibson reported that in the city of Mangalore, 'firewood, formerly so abundant, is now one of the chief items of expense to the poorer classes of people and is a deprivation severely felt by them'.[113] He had previously argued,

---

[111] Richard Tucker, 'Forest management and Imperial politics, Thana District, Bombay', *Indian Economic and Social History Review,* 16 (1979), p. 27.

[112] This incident was recounted by Gibson in the *Bombay Forest Report,* 1856 (Bombay: Government Printer), p. 13, par. 78.

[113] Stebbing, *Forests of India,* p. 120.

in 1843, that 'a careful examination of forests would disclose other productions of value ... from a scientific point of view.'[114] Although the Bombay government was very ready to accept these ideas and was especially concerned about the firewood problem, none of the arguments were found convincing in Calcutta, where the Supreme Government continued to refuse to consider the cost of running a formal Conservancy.[115] Significantly, arguments for conservation based either on local needs or long-term biological potential still proved to be politically ineffective in India itself in 1846.

At this juncture Gibson decided, as a last resort, to use the 'climatic threat' as an argument, not with the apparently hopelessly intractable Calcutta authorities but with the EIC Court of Directors itself. He was encouraged in this by a series of letters from Indian correspondents, including one in February 1846 from Mahabaleshwar, which stated the 'common belief that with the removal of wood, the small streams . . . had dried up'.[116] Gibson was inclined to take the environmental knowledge of the indigenous population of the Western Ghats far more seriously than most non-medical officials. Thus the Mahabaleshwar letter of February 1846 made up his mind. By March 6, 1846, only a few days after receiving the letter, Gibson finished compiling a manuscript report on the destruction of forests in the Konkan in which he specifically mentioned the climatic and economic consequences of deforestation. 'A change of climate,' he wrote, 'is by no means limited to the mere district in which clearing has taken place, but its influence extends far inland.' Deforestation in the Ghats, in the headwards of rivers watering the fertile western coastal lowlands of the Presidency, would, Gibson felt, be clearly affected by such changes. Significantly, the Company attached a great importance to these regions at the time because of their extensive cotton growing projects. The potentially formidable indirect disadvantages of deforestation were therefore unmistakable. Gibson sent the finished report, dated 6 March 1846, directly to the Court of Directors in London in the form of a letter, thus bypassing the Bombay and Calcutta authorities altogether. He then used material

---

[114] Ibid., 111.

[115] Ibid., 118.

[116] MS Letter, written to Gibson from Mahabaleshwar (IOL V/27/560/107).

contained within the report as the basis for a short but prominent paper published in the *Transactions of the Bombay Medical and Physical Society*, a journal with a considerable professional readership among officials in the medical service and in civil positions throughout India.[117]

The political significance of these unilateral actions cannot have been lost among officials in government circles in Calcutta. Gibson had appealed over the heads of both the Bombay authorities, more particularly the Government of India, directly to the Court of Directors on the one hand and the Indian scientific community on the other. This was an indicator, if one were needed, of the political weight which Gibson now felt that his professional scientific status conferred on him. Even so, the action was a gamble. However, it quickly paid off by forcing the decisive intervention of the Court, which compelled the Supreme Government in Calcutta to take serious heed of the advice of this new scientific service. Moreover, Gibson had backed the gamble by documenting his findings in detail among his own medical peers, in the specifically scientific forum of a medical journal. The Company was compelled before long to capitulate to the power of the medical lobby. Thus on 17 December 1846, the Government of India authorised 'the employment of an establishment for the management of the forests under the Bombay Presidency, at a monthly charge of 295 Rupees.' This enabled the Bombay Government, on 22 March 1847, to appoint Gibson as Conservator of Forests, in addition to his duties as Superintendent of the Dapoorie Botanic Garden, and authorised him to 'entertain the establishment which had been sanctioned by the Government of Bombay,' for which he had long campaigned. However, the conversion of the East India Company authorities to the utility of the conservationist case actually went much further. A few months later. in July 1847, the Court of Directors issued a remarkable Despatch indicating an unprecedented official awareness of the global threat apparently posed by artificially induced climatic change. 'The subject', the Despatch argued,

> is one having a strong practical bearing on the welfare of mankind and we are anxious to obtain extensive and accurate information in regard to

---

[117] A. Gibson, 'Report on Deforestation in South Conkan', *Transactions of the Bombay Medical and Physical Society*, 37 (1846), pp. 11–22.

it. We desire, therefore, that you will furnish us with any you may possess, and that you will institute inquiries in such quarters as may be likely to lead to the acquisition of particular facts bearing upon the question. It has been suggested that the circumstances of the district of Azimghur afford some illustration of the subject and we shall be glad to receive a correct report of any facts relating either to that district or others which may be calculated to throw light upon the subject of our enquiry.[118]

By 1847, then, the supremacy of the medical service in its hold over government environmental policy had become well-established and was further institutionalised in Gibson's Superintendency of the Bombay Forest Department. This department was formed with the prime aim, not of securing a steady supply of timber (though this was still a pressing concern), but of inhibiting the whole range of environmental and social consequences which deforestation might cause.[119] The fear of these consequences, especially the fear of widespread climatic change, forced the colonial state to comply with a conservationist prescription. Although these environmental considerations were soon supplemented by other political and commercial claims, especially after the end of Company rule in 1857, the Hippocratic and Humboldtian basis to the conservationism of the surgeons remained a decisive factor in the evolution of colonial forest policy in India and elsewhere. If one seeks a particular historical turning point in the policies of the Company in this respect, the period from 1847 to 1850 is the most critical.

The decisive turning point was probably reached when the Court of Directors, as we have seen, followed up Gibson's report on the Konkan by circularising a Despatch intended to try to establish direct evidence of deforestation and rainfall change. The process culminated in January 1850 with a remarkable statement by Lord Dalhousie, made to the Agri-

---

[118] Despatch no. 21, Coun of Directors, EIC, to Government of India, dt 7 July, 1847, quoted in Balfour papers, V/27/560/107. Azimghur was a district mentioned specifically by Donald Butter in his *Topography of Awadh*. The Court had clearly referred to the work.

[119] For a fuller outline of the philosophy involved, see A. Gibson, 'A description of the system adopted for the forest conservancy of the Bombay Presidency', in A. Gibson, ed., *A handbook to the forests of the Bombay Presidency* (Byculla: Government Printer, 1863), pp. 53–114.

Horticultural Society of India at Lahore. 'During the last season', he wrote,

> I have traversed the plains of the Punjab.... There is one characteristic of the wide tract which could not fail to strike the least observant traveller.... I refer to the almost total absence of forest trees and of even fruit trees and of bushes leaving the whole territory unadorned by the foliage which is its natural cover, nor stocked with timber requisite for a thousand purposes in the everyday life of the people who dwell in it... This is a manifest and will shortly be felt to be an increasing evil unless some measures are taken to provide at present a remedy for the future... the Government should provide some means to that end and should bring them into operation without delay.... I feel strongly the urgent duty of endeavouring to give this country the clothing of forest trees from my knowledge of the well ascertained and beneficial effect which trees produce on the health and fertility of the tracts in which they are found. No power has been more clearly established than this salubrious and fertilising effect of foliage in an Indian climate. It has been the subject of much enquiry and demonstrated in every report submitted from different parts of India, many of which have passed through my hands, and one of which I forwarded to the local government in Punjab some time ago.... None of us can live to see the complete result of that which we now propose to commence. Few of us will gather the fruit where now we plant. But if we succeed in framing this design and advance it in some degree towards completion, we may at least enjoy the satisfaction of the feeling that we shall leave behind us an heritage for which posterity will be grateful.[120]

This statement, an especially revealing one for Dalhousie to make, highlighted the revolution in official perceptions that had occurred as a consequence of the medical service's determined lobbying. Indeed the Lahore memorandum represented, effectively, an unprecedented manifesto for forest protection and sustainable development. The notion of a monolithic state forest sector was clearly one that appealed to Dalhousie's undoubted interventionist and utilitarian ambitions. However, neither this nor the desire for a sustainable timber supply can account for the

---

[120] 'Minute by the most noble the Lord Dalhousie', read to the Agri-Horticultural Society of the Punjab on 20 February 1851, reproduced in G. Henderson, ed., *Select papers of the AgroHorticultural Society of the Punjab* (Lahore: Lahore United Press, 1868).

fundamental change in Company forest policy continued under
Dalhousie. Indeed, the roots of the Governor-General's own interest in
the forest question lie in his own very personal relationship with the
increasingly powerful scientific, especially botanical, lobby.

As early as 1847 Dalhousie had come firmly under the influence
of Joseph D. Hooker, who both accompanied him in his entourage on
arriving in India in 1847 and constantly plied the Governor-General
with letters on the subject of forest conservation.[121] Hooker's main
concern in India was to conduct a series of botanical surveys in the
Himalayas. Forest conservation was an important secondary interest. He
had, however, been firmly convinced since 1842 of a direct relationship
between forest cover and rainfall incidence, mainly through his field
observations on St Helena and through his studies of the beneficial effect
of Governor Alexander Beatson's plantations on the island hydrology.
Hooker firmly believed, therefore, that afforestation and increased
rainfall were closely linked. By 1850 Dalhousie had also become demon-
strably convinced of the same phenomena, both through Hooker's
influence and by reading reports submitted by Edward Balfour and his
colleagues in the Madras government. Both in this respect, as well as in
his voluminous correspondence with members of the medical service in
India, Hooker had performed a decisive and persuasive part.

Despite the significance of the interaction between Dalhousie and
Joseph Hooker, a distinctive model of colonial forest conservancy had,
in fact, already been developed in Sind. This model was based firmly on
an indigenous system, from which the installed colonial forestry system
differed little in detail. Indeed the annexation of Sind by Sir Charles
Napier had first provided an opportunity to set up an embryonic forest
administration based directly upon the infrastructure of *shikargarhs*
(forest and game reserves), which had been steadily built up along the
Indus Valley by the Amirs of Sind since the 1750s. The shikargarhs were
very extensive and served a multiplicity of state needs, including the
widespread provision of a supply of firewood, for which the peasant
population were required to pay heavily. The indigenous development

---

[121] For detailed references to the correspondence on forest conservation carried on
between Dalhousie and Hooker, see L. Huxley, *The life and letters of Sir Joseph Dalton
Hooke* (London: John Murray, 1918), vol. I.

of the shikargarhs in Sind and their influence on later colonial policy indicate that conventional historical interpretations of the primacy of European colonial rule in environmental control and conservation need to be carefully re-examined, particularly in the context of contemporary thinking about the erosion of forests as pre-colonial common property. Thus the precolonial Sind forest system, like many others in India by the mid-eighteenth century, was by no means amenable to traditions of community or village use. Forestry was a subject which much interested Napier, and he had recommended the immediate assignment of an officer 'with some knowledge of forestry' to gain as much information as possible about the system developed by the Amirs.[122] The Amirs had, in fact, frequently carried out widespread village removals to make space for their forest reserves and to curtail access for grazing and fuel collection. After the annexation of Sind, these measures were deliberately relaxed by Napier to elicit a degree of popular support for the new government.[123]

Alongside these examples of both indigenous and scientifically reasoned strategies for forest protection, Dalhousie was soon provided with the expert advice of another member of the medical service, Surgeon John McClelland, an ardent enthusiast of natural history and an advocate of rare plant preservation, in a survey of forests in Burma. This survey served as a further stimulus for action by the Governor-General, since McClelland specifically advised a rigorous system of state control to save the rapidly disintegrating forests of Pegu from private timber merchants.[124]

Although the formal structure of an all-India Forest Department was organised in 1865 specifically to exclude the activities of private capital from the forests, the colonial environmental debate, in which state forestry originated had already been going on in Southern India for

---

[122] Sind File, (Political 201), Napier to Lord Ellenborough, 29 May 1843, Ellenborough Papers, Public Record Office, Kew. For details of the pre-colonial forest system of Sind and its later adaptation, see W. Scott, *Report on the management of canals and forests in Seinde* (Bombay: Government Printer, 1853).

[123] Accounts of pre-colonial evictions and fuelwood fees are in E.B. Eastwick, *Dry leaves from young Egypt* (London, 1849), p. 24; and in J. Outram, *The Conquest of Scinde: a commentary* (Edinburgh: Blackwood, 1846).

[124] I. Burkill, *Chapters in the history of botany in India*, p. 155.

three decades, was dominated by the conservationist thinking of the surgeons appointed to superintend the first two Presidency Conservancies in Bombay and Madras. The Madras Forest Department, established in 1856, was headed by Surgeon Hugh Cleghorn, who had earlier agitated with Alexander Gibson for conservation measures to be taken during the 1840s.[125]

Cleghorn, later made first Inspector-General of Forests in India,[126] was, like Gibson, primarily a botanist and even an early environmental historian.[127] Openly hostile to the kinds of development which promoted forest destruction, he campaigned against many of the contemporary plans for railway development in Southern India. In 1866 he also spoke out directly against the uncontrolled entry of plantation capital into the Nilgiris and Coorg, consistently claiming that the activities of European planters were far more destructive than the long-established shifting *koomri* cultivators.[128] These kinds of opinions, not uncommon with some of the Scottish surgeons of the time, are marked by their anti-English flavour. Indeed, there are strong reasons for understanding the Scottish medical enthusiasm for protecting forests not only as a consequence of their enthusiasm for scientific natural history but as a surrogate for a far more direct kind of critique of English attitudes to India and even of English attitudes towards the Scots at home. The public basis of Cleghorn's environmentalism, however, was based primarily on a fear of the climatic and physical effects of tropical deforestation as part of a wider global problem. These fears are articulated both in his

---

[125] Both of the new Presidency's Forestry Departments were run according to management methods based on the Sindhi, French, and Scottish models with which their medical founders were familiar. Additionally, Hugh Cleghorn was particularly interested in the history of Venetian attempts to control deforestation and soil erosion. In contrast the introduction of German forestry concepts constituted a much later development, and it was not until after 1878 that they were widely applied in India.

[126] The appointment was made jointly with Dietrich Brandis, a German botanist.

[127] An account of Cleghorn's activities in the early years of the Madras Forest Department is in H. Cleghorn's *The forests and gardens of South India* (Edinburgh, 1861).

[128] Cleghorn, in 'Discussion', following on the presentation of a paper by George Bidie, 'On the effects of forest destruction in Coorg', *Proceedings of the Royal Geographical Society*, 1869, pp. 74–75.

Hugh Francis Cleghorn
(Published by permission of the Cleghorn-Sprott family)

report to the British Association for the Advancement of Science in 1851, which was probably the first report in a scientific forum to warn of environmental degradation on a global scale, and in his later books and articles on the development of tropical forest protection[129]

Conclusion

An examination of the motivations underlying the emergence of environmentalism and conservation policies in the colonial context points to a heterodox legacy of Utopian, Physiocratic, and Hippocratic philosophical elements represented in the discourses of an influential minority of scientists. These men were distinctively empowered by virtue of the high status assigned to science by the colonial state, and their environmental preoccupations were closely connected to a variety of agendas of social reform. In surveying the whole colonial context of conservation one needs to ask exactly why the colonial state was prepared to accept the highly unorthodox prescriptions of the early conservation lobbyists and, in particular, to accept their view of the need to subjugate short-term economic benefits to nebulous long-term interests. To date, most accounts of the early history of colonial forestry have explained colonial conservationism as a rationalisation for intensifying the direct exploitation of erstwhile 'common property resources' to serve the needs of the colonial state and the metropole. As we have seen, such explanations can now be perceived as insufficient. Much of the early colonial conservationism was, in fact, directly related to a growing awareness that western processes for economic development were inherently destructive to the environment. It also becomes appropriate to re-emphasise the political significance of the basic insecurity of the early colonial state faced with the risks of a little-understood tropical environment. The ecological

---

[129] H. Cleghorn, F. Royle, R. Baird-Smith and R. Strachey, 'Report of the committee appointed by the British Association to investigate the probable effects in an economic and physical point of view of the destruction of tropical forests', *Report of the British Association for the Advancement of Science, 1852*, pp. 78–102. See also H. Cleghorn, 'On the distribution of the principal timber trees of India, and the progress of forest conservancy', *Report of the British Association for the Advancement of Science, 1868*, pp. 91–94.

changes brought about by the forces of western capitalist development apparently threatened the very existence of the state itself. Faced by the threat of famine and social unrest, the state became quite willing to accept those radical environmental prescriptions for survival proffered by the pioneering generation of scientific experts whom it had already learned to respect in specifically medical circumstances. This may help us to explain how conservation as a state response to ecological crisis emerged first at an economic periphery rather than at the metropolitan centre. It was, in fact, precisely the insecurity of the state at the colonial periphery which allowed a sensitivity to the dangers of ecological change to develop so precociously. In writing environmental history and in reconstructing the history of environmentalism we will need, perhaps, to pay more attention in the future to the fundamentally innovative role of the colonial periphery in terms of its relations with the metropolitan centre. Such a priority, largely dismissed by historians hitherto, would require a radical re-assessment both of the history of conservation and of the state's role in the development of western environmental concern.

3

Scottish Missionaries, Evangelical Discourses and the Origins of Conservation Thinking in Southern Africa, 1820–1900

Current research is beginning to show that the origins of state conservationism in the southern African region date back to the late seventeenth century and that early conservation laws were directed, in the main, towards controlling the effects of settler agriculture. It is also becoming clear that the reasoning behind such policies derived from an emerging belief in the existence of dynamic links between deforestation and rainfall decline. Active promotion of state conservation in the colonial setting emerged initially on small island colonies where the finite limitations of exploitable resources was particularly easy to observe. By the mid-eighteenth century the promotion of conservation practices by the British and French colonial states was well developed, on St Helena and Mauritius in particular.[1] It was not until about the second decade of the nineteenth century, however, that environmental theories nurtured in island contexts started to have an impact in continental situations. This chapter sets out to examine the conditions under which colonial states in southern Africa evolved an interest in conservation and to probe the respective motivations of scientists and the state in adopting conservationist ideas.[2]

In essence, it is argued here, conservationism in the Cape arose out

---

[1] See R.H. Grove, *Green imperialism: colonial expansion, tropical island Edens and the origins of environmentalism, 1600–1800* (Cambridge, 1995).

[2] For an earlier survey see R.H. Grove, 'Early themes in African conservation; the Cape in the nineteenth century', in D. Anderson and R. Grove, eds, *Conservation in Africa: people, policies and practice* (Cambridge, 1987), pp. 22–39.

of a coincidence between changing precepts in western science and a colonial crisis, triggered initially by drought. These ideas developed against the background of a pre-existing and precocious awareness of the speed of environmental change in the Cape Colony in the works of travellers and missionaries in the late eighteenth and early nineteenth centuries. The relative sophistication of the ideology of state conservationism as it developed after 1843 in the Cape was related to the spread of a new idea, that the environment and man were threatened by climatic change operating on a continental scale. Environmental risk, the argument of the experts ran, was being exacerbated by the activities of man. Such a threat had not been put forward in a 'scientific' form before. Thus the threat of a climatic *denouement*, more familiar today, explains at least part of the enthusiasm with which the state took on conservation ideas. To understand this development it is necessary to appreciate both the manner in which the threat of climatic change made itself felt in the scientific mind and, secondly, the way in which the priorities of the colonial state became connected to the prescriptions of science.

A critical factor promoting the development of ideas about conservation in Southern Africa during the nineteenth century was the work of Dr John Croumbie Brown, initially a missionary and subsequently a university teacher, botanist, state scientist and propagandist of conservation.[3] It is the coincidence in time between his personal intellectual crisis and the crisis in which the state found itself which is of concern here. The broad-based conservationist message which Brown espoused was rapidly appropriated to suit the priorities of the colonial state, partly in order to justify the blaming of Africans for the environmental ills of southern Africa, partly to legitimate powerful new instruments of discriminatory land use control. The adaptation for state purposes of the environmental evangelism of Brown and his missionary predecessor, Robert Moffat, far outlasted their own lifetimes. For example, many of the struggles over the management of the first national park in Southern Rhodesia, in the Matopo Hills, can be attributed directly to the influence exercised by Brown's scientific disciples. As experts brought in as consultants from the Cape their ideology of forest reserve administration

---

[3] See R.H. Grove, 'Scotland and South Africa: John Croumbie Brown and the origins of settler environmentalism', in L. Robin and T. Griffiths, eds, *Ecology and Empire* (Edinburgh University Press, 1997). A useful short biography of Brown is P.J Venter, 'An early botanist and conservationist at the Cape, the Rev. J.C. Brown. LlD, FRGS, FLS', *Archives Yearbook of South African History*, 1951.

owed its central legitimation to the writings of Brown and was easily
adapted to the priorities of more modern conservationist ideologies that
had originated outside Africa. Through his very wide network of
scientific contacts and through his prolific output of publications Brown
stimulated the emergence of conservationist movements and state policies in colonies as far apart as Nyasaland and Victoria, Australia, as well
as bringing about the first moves towards a centralised imperial interest
in environmental problems.

In 1821–3, 1845–7 and 1862–3 serious droughts affected the
whole of Southern Africa. They devastated the economies of both
indigenous African and colonial societies and brought about long-lasting
social changes, which remain to be investigated in detail.[4] The droughts
also stimulated the emergence of significant new ways in which colonial
scientists and intellectuals began to interpret relationships between
environmental change and human activity. They assigned blame for
ecological degradation and sought, for the first time, to introduce
conservation measures intended to inhibit artificially induced climatic
change. The most important feature of the European scientific response
to drought episodes in Southern Africa after 1820 was the emergence of
a 'desiccationist' theory linking the removal of vegetations to rainfall
decline and then to regional or global climatic desiccation.

Before the droughts of 1820–3, the inherent vulnerability of the
Cape region to the effects of colonial agriculture in comparison with
more resilient tropical or temperate environments had become well-
known. Under Dutch rule the Cape Colony itself had already become
subject to highly restrictive land-use regulations and early forms of

---

[4] For details of Southern African drought chronologies see S.E. Nicholson. 'A climatic
chronology for Africa: a synthesis of geological. historical and meteorological data'
(Ph.D. thesis, University of Wisconsin, 1976), pp. 282–288. For a discussion of the
impact of drought see C. Ballard, 'Drought and economic distress: South Africa in the
1800s', *Journal of Interdisciplinary History*, XVII. (1986), pp. 359–378; also S E
Nicholson, 'The historical climatology of Africa', in T.M. Wigley et al., eds, *Climate and
history: studies in past climates and their impact on man* (London, 1981), pp. 257–259. The
1820–1823 drought in the Eastern Cape and Transkei is well documented in C. Butler,
ed., *The 1820 Settlers: an illustrated commentary* (Cape Town, 1983), pp. 81–84; see also
J. Guy, 'Ecological factors in the rise of Shaka and the Zulu kingdom', in S. Marks and
A. Atmore (eds), *Economy and society in pre-industrial South Africa* (London, 1980), p.
102.

conservation and forest laws, while the details of environmental degradation had been extensively commented upon.[5] It had been recognised that European agricultural methods were specifically responsible for deterioration in soils and pastures and the destruction of forests. Particularly in late eighteenth century literature European land-use methods had been criticised quite specifically and pejoratively as being far less suitable than indigenous practices for the conditions of the semi-arid Cape.[6] No systematic attempts appear to have been made, however, to link rainfall decline with patterns of human activity or with deforestation, even though such linkages had been made in English and French island colonies as early as the 1670s and had had important consequences for innovations in colonial land-use control.[7]

The droughts of 1820–1823, however, stimulated a new kind of environmental commentary which sought both to relate man-induced vegetation change to rainfall change and to assign blame for these changes to Africans. The most significant commentator in this respect was the missionary Robert Moffat, whose opinions are important not least because they affected the later thinking of John Croumbie Brown.[8] A major philosophical break had developed between earlier scientific writers on the Cape environment some of whom, such as Thunberg and Sparrman, were apt to be critical of the activities of Europeans and the later accounts of evangelical missionaries such as Robert Moffat who, in general, tended to deride indigenous systems of knowledge and land-use practice. There were two aspects of this evangelical mentality which are relevant here; the dismissal (at one level) of indigenous explanations of environmental processes and a transferral of moral conceptions of right and wrong, good and evil, black and white to the state of the environment.

[5] T.R. Sim, *The forests and forest flora of the Cape Colony* (Cape Town, 1907), pp. 76–79.

[6] The early environmental critiques of European land-use methods by C.P. Thunberg, Andrew Sparrman and H. Lichtenstein are reported in T.D. Hall, 'South African pastures: retrospective and perspective', *South African Journal of Science*, XXXI (1934), pp. 59–97.

[7] Grove, *Green imperialism*, ch. 3.

[8] In, especially, J.C. Brown, *Report of the colonial botanist for 1863* (Cape Town, 1864), and J.C. Brown, *Hydrology of South Africa* (London, 1875), p. 104.

Moffat arrived in the area to the north of the Colony among the Tswana at Latakoo (Kuruman) in 1820.[9] This was also the period that the English settlers of 1820 were moving into farms in the Albany district of the Cape as part of Lord Charles Somerset's plan to build up a white population on the eastern frontiers of the colony.[10] Much of this project ended in disaster, partly for ecological and climatic reasons; and Moffat's accounts and his disappointment at the desiccated state of the lands he encountered can be seen in the light of the ecological failure of the 'English' settlements further south.[11]

Moffat 'was no ethnographer or social observer, zealous to relate what he saw and heard'. As his biographer observed, 'his business was to move about with disapproval of nakedness, theft, feasting and witchcraft, to convince people of their state as sinners and "to preach the unsearchable riches of Christ among the heathen"'.[12] The missionary encountered the Tswana at a time when the ravages of drought had already begun to take effect. It was not long before he conceived their sinful state as integral to the 'evil' he saw taking place in an environmental sense. In fact, the evidence suggests that Moffat was pre-disposed to designate the inhabitants of all the dry lands north of the Orange River as responsible for a situation of moral and environmental disorder.

> As an inhabited country it is scarcely possible to conceive of one more destitute and miserable; and it is impossible to traverse its extensive plains, its rugged, undulating surface. and to descend to the beds of its waterless rivers, without viewing it as emphatically 'a land of droughts', bearing the heavy curse of

---

[9] C. Northcott, *Robert Moffat, pioneer in Africa, 1817–1879* (London, 1961), p. 69.

[10] Somerset was responsible for initiating two pieces of ostensibly conservationist legislation as early as 1822, one attempting to legislate to protect large game species, (which were becoming increasingly rare in the western Cape) and another designed to protect plant species. Both were unenforced, but give an indication of the early emergence of state awareness of the speed of ecological destruction at the time; earlier attempts (in 1811) by W.J. Burchell to elicit state action to control soil erosion near Cape Town had been ignored. See Grove, 'Early themes in African conservation'.

[11] For details of this failure see N.C. Pollock and S. Agnew, *An historical geography of South Africa* (London, 1963), pp. 80–83.

[12] Northcott, *Robert Moffat*, p. 75.

'Mans first disobedience, and the fruit
Of that forbidden tree, whose mortal taste
Brought death into the world, and all our woe' [13]

This quotation from Milton's *Paradise Lost* was an important statement since it gives a clue to the manner in which Moffat was already equating the presence of drought with a state of original sin and with the expulsion of Adam and Eve from the Garden of Eden. It was the guiding metaphor to the rest of Moffat's discourse, and underlay the perceptions of other observers at the time. Above all it set the scene, in the missionary's own writing, for a debate about drought framed in terms of a moral economy.

The prolonged absence of rain led, inevitably, to a series of confrontations between Moffat and a Tswana rainmaker. These began in October 1821. Moffat records:

> I found him with his companion making rain, as was his habit. I enquired if it was by means of the boola, (four small pieces of horn, sometimes of ivory, of different sizes, resembling dice, but their prognostications are drawn more from their position than the small holes when thrown down.) He replies "Yes". I told him that I believed that he could not make rain, or he would have made it long ago. He flatly contradicted this and assured me that when he had hitherto exercised his power, abundance of rains had fallen. [14]

Moffat retorted with the assertion that the rain fell amongst the Griquas to the south and also in the desert:

> He said that I asked enough questions. I remarked that I wished to prove from his knowledge whether he was indeed a rainmaker, for I had seen no marks of it as yet. He said that my God dwelt in the South, that their God dwelt in the north ... he looked rather stupid when I informed him that my God ruled over all the earth. I asked him from whence the rain came and where God dwelt. [15]

The rainmaker confessed ignorance of the last question and Moffat insisted:

---

[13] R. Moffat, *Missionary labours and scenes in southern Africa* (London, 1842), p. 66.

[14] Northcott, *Robert Moffat*, p. 77.

[15] Ibid., p. 77.

I asked him how he could pretend to make what he knew nothing about.
I quoted and explained several passages from scripture bearing on that
point. I pointed out to him the different periods in which he had been
guilty of telling lies, that he took that honour on him which belongs to
God alone. The old man seemed to wish to close the controversy, and
remarked that I had surely been long in the world. I replied that age did
not always increase wisdom and referred him to the Book of Inspiration.[16]

This was not the end of the matter. Shortly after this exchange of views
Moffat and his companions were asked to leave the area and informed
that 'measures of a violent kind would be resorted to ... in case of our
disobeying the order'.[17] This attempt at ejection seems to have been
partly based on a fundamental clash between two environmental reli-
gions. Eventually the missionaries were allowed to stay. Buoyed up by his
success in persuading the Tswana to back down Moffat took the
opportunity to develop his own Credo further:

> The charge brought against us by the rainmaker was by every passing
> cloud and blast from the torrid zone brought fresh to our minds ... and
> they thought that having teachers of strange doctrines among them such
> as their forefathers never knew, the country would be burnt up.[18]

For the Tswana, drought had been brought on by the incursion of the
Europeans and their alien religion;[19] while for Moffat it had been caused
by a sinful transgression or a condition of sin. For both, however,
judgements about the social causes of droughts, it transpired, relied on
similar notions of a tradition of a previous pluvial Golden Age; one
transmitted orally, the other more systematised and book-learned.

In truth, Moffat was himself consciously looking out for evidence
of a pluvial, a Golden Age or a Flood, that might back up his notion of
an earlier Eden or a biblical flood. To his surprise and embarrassment,
it seems, he found it in Tswana oral tradition, and in his own writings the

[16] Ibid.
[17] Moffat, *Missionary labours*, p. 327.
[18] Ibid., p. 329.
[19] Robert Moffat to Alexander Moffat, Inverkeithing 25 February 1822. National
Archives of Zimbabwe, M/9/1/5 Doc.5/1822.

indigenous tradition was co-opted to an evangelical notion of a pre-sin environment. To bolster his own position, however, Moffat found he had to question the Tswana interpretation of their very own tradition. The most convenient way of doing this was to accuse the Tswana of having a mistaken pluvial chronology; that is, to imply that their sense of time was wrong.

There was a considerable irony in this for, as one can now confidently state from hindsight and the benefit of more recent geological research, the Tswana climatic chronology was more scientifically correct, and Moffat's far less so.[20]

'They were wont to tell us', Moffat recounted,

> of the floods of ancient times, the incessant showers which clothed the very rocks with verdure, and the giant trees and forests which once studded the Hamhana hills and neighbouring plains. They boasted of the Kuruman and other rivers with their impassable torrents, in which the hippopotami played, while the lowing herds walking to their necks in grass, filling their *makukas* with milk, making every heart to sing for joy.[21]

Moffat's attitude towards this particular piece of oral history was highly ambivalent. While attracted by the notion of a climatic optimum in the past it became essential for the purpose of his own climatic tale to attribute the cessation of the pluvial to the destructive activities of the Tswana and not to the arrival of Europeans and the arrival of Christianity. The way out of the problem, he found, was to debate the issue in terms of the actual physical dynamics of rainfall decline causation. This required an excursion not into the superiority of a European God but into the superiority of European empirical science. As later became clear, this apparent willingness to shift the terms of the debate from religion to science in fact concealed an attempt by Moffat to reconcile his own conflicts between what was at the time becoming known about geological time-scales, especially in the works of Alexander von Humboldt, and

---

[20] See Nicholson, 'Climatic chronology for Africa', pp. 285–287.

[21] Moffat, *Missionary labours*, p. 329. The language used here by Moffat is startlingly reminiscent of Isaiah, chapter 34. verses 17–21 and chapter 35, verses 1–10. The two accounts of springs and rivers in two dry lands seem to have become confused in Moffat's mind.

the restrictions of the Genesis time-scale, to which Moffat, unsurprisingly, found it hard not to adhere.[22] The situation was, moreover, one in which superiority in the interpretation of environmental processes became a symbol or a test of the superiority or truth of the Christian religion. The sharpness of the debate over the time at which pluvial conditions had ceased simply reflected the fact that a Genesis-based chronology of the earth and indeed a whole belief system, was deeply threatened both by new notions of time and by the abundant evidence present in the Northern Cape Colony of environmental changes that were difficult to explain in a Genesis time-scale. This helps to explain Moffat's persistence in questioning the Tswana time-scale.

> It was in vain that we endeavoured to convince them that the dry seasons had commenced at a period anterior to the arrival of the missionaries. Independent of this fact being handed down by their forefathers they had before their eyes the fragments of more fruitful years in the immense number of stumps and roots of enormous trunks of *Acacia giraffea* when now scarcely one is to be seen raising its stately head above the shrubs; while the sloping sides of the hills, and the ancient beds of rivers, plainly evinced that they were denuded of the herbage which once clothed their surface. Indeed the whole country north of the Orange river lying east of the Kalagare desert presented to the eye of the European something like an old neglected garden or field.[23]

It is striking how the terminology of the 'garden' was quite openly developed.[24] The evidence of past higher rainfall was plain and was

---

[22] Alexander von Humboldt's *Personal Narrative of travels to equinoctial regions of the New Continent 1799–1804* was published in six volumes in London in 1819, and Moffat appears to have read them. The relevant passages on the desiccating effects of deforestation appear on pp. 134–139 of vol. 4. Previous to the publication of the Narrative the currency of desiccation theory was far more limited. The government of The Ile de France (Mauritius), The East India Company directors, and the St Helena government were all apprised of the theory as early as 1787. W.J. Burchell, erstwhile Government Botanist of St Helena, 1807–11, was present in the Cape in 1811–1822 so that Moffat may have encountered desiccation ideas by that intellectual route.

[23] Moffat, *Missionary labours*, pp. 329–330.

[24] Moffat had actually received a formal training as a tropical hot-house gardener before undergoing his evangelical tutelage with Dr William Roby, which may help to account for the ease with which he used such images; Northcott, *Robert Moffat*, pp. 18–20.

undisputed, except in its timing, by Moffat. It remained to explain the need of the pluvial in terms of human causation, and in a pejorative way:

> As, however, the natives never philosophised on atmospheric changes [this was a loaded untruth!] and the probable causes of the failure of plenteous years, they were not likely to be concerned such could depend on anything done by man, even though they were credulous enough to believe that their own rainmakers could charm or frighten the clouds into showers or that our faces or prayers could prevent their descending…[25]

Moffat thus put forward the innate superiority of his 'scientific' philosophising (based chiefly on Humboldt) against the much less deterministic and cautious explanations of the rainmaker. While he carefully described elaborate Tswana systems of vegetational prohibitions against tree-cutting he schizophrenically ignored them when 'trying to convince the more intelligent [sic] that they themselves were the active agents of bringing about an entire change in atmosphere'.[26] In the debate between the missionary and the Tswana over who was to blame for drought, it is clear that one environmental theory was being tested against another environmental theory. Both were anthropocentric in their assumptions, although Moffat's theory was far more deterministic in its attribution of power to man as an environmental agent. For him, the very proof of his power lay in a description of the destructive power of the Tswana.

> the Bechuana, especially the Batlapis and neighbouring tribes, are a nation of levellers – not reducing hills to comparative plains for the sake of building their towns, but cutting down every species of timber [here he contradicted his own observations of prohibitions], without regard to scenery or economy … houses are chiefly composed of small timber, and their fences are of branches or shrubs. Thus when they fix on a site for a town, their first consideration is to be as near a thicket as possible. The whole is presently levelled, leaving only a few trees, one in each great man's field, to afford shelter from the heat and under which the men walk and recline. The ground to be occupied for cultivation is the next object of attention; the large trees being too hard for iron axes they burn

---

[25] Moffat, *Missionary labours*, p. 332.

[26] Ibid., p. 330.

them down by keeping a fire at the root. This supplies them with
branches for fences, as well as those in towns, which require constant
repairs, and indeed the fences must be renewed every year, and by this
means the country for many miles around becomes entirely cleared of
timber, while in more sequestered spots, where they have their outposts,
the same work of destruction goes on. Thus, of whole forests where the
giraffe and the elephant were wont to seek their refuge during floods
nothing remains.[27]

From one point of view this is an interesting and convincing description
of the impact of proto-urban settlements on fuelwood supplies but the
full significance of this picture of an alleged intrinsic environmental
destructiveness on the part of the Tswana begins to emerge when Moffat
comes to discuss the disappearance of one particular tree species, the
Acacia giraffea. The underlying concern, again, is with the precise
chronology of the life of the tree, the significance of its age and the timing
of its destruction:

> When the natives remove from that district, which may be only after a
> few years, the minor species of the acacia soon grows but the *Acacia
> giraffea* requires an age to become a tree, and many ages must pass before
> they attain the dimensions of their predecessors. The wood, when old,
> is dark red, rough-grained and exceedingly hard and heavy; after being
> dried for years, when thrown into water it sinks like lead . In the course
> of my journeys I have met with trunks of enormous size which, if the time
> were calculated necessary for their growth, as well as for their decay, *we
> might be led to conclude that they sprung up immediately after the flood,* if
> not before then.[28]

It is the last line of this passage which is most revealing of Moffat's
inflexible and pre-conceived environmental religion. Not only were the
Tswana destructive, he considered, but they had caused permanent
damage to a tree dating back to the time of the biblical flood, and
conceivably before it. The theme, then, concerns the destroyers of the
trees in the 'neglected Garden', possibly the Garden of Eden. The
destructiveness of the Tswana is thus directly equated with the transgres-

[27] Ibid., p. 331
[28] Ibid., p. 331 [my emphasis].

sion which led to the Flood and not only that, but with the continuing transgression which has brought about the drought and the arid landscape of divine retribution. The implication was that those who were responsible for such transgression could not be trusted with the 'garden', as its continued despoliation served to prove. Particular opprobrium was attached by Moffat to the device of veld-burning to stimulate new grass growth.[29]

It is important to observe that, while settling for traditional Old Testament chronology, Moffat was ready to call on a relatively sophisticated set of 'scientific' precedents to define the dynamics of process, essentially, it would seem, because they were not definitively time-bound and thus did not threaten Genesis. While one may be confident that in 1821, at the time his diary was written, Moffat was familiar with Humboldt's account of the hydrological effects of deforestation (and the dialogue with the rainmaker makes this clear) his *post hoc* discussion of the subject, as it was published in 1841, indicates that he still felt the need to seek out the support of authorities published after the date of Humboldt's *Narrative* and after the date of the debate with the rainmaker. The foremost of these authorities was Charles Lyell's *Principles of Geology* published in 1831.[30] The most outstanding feature of this work, (upon which Darwin was extremely reliant for the groundwork of much of his thinking),[31] consisted in its outlining of a vast new geological timescale, completely irreconcilable with Genesis. Nevertheless Moffat, significantly, ignored this critical aspect of Lyell's work and instead utilised him as an authority on the mechanisms of desiccation subsequent to deforestation:

> The felling of forests has been attended in many countries by a diminution of rain, as in Barbadoes and Jamaica. For in tropical countries, where the quantity of aqueous vapour in the atmosphere is great, but where, on the other hand, the direct rays of the sun are most

---

[29] Ibid., pp. 331–332.

[30] C Lyell, *Principles of geology, being an attempt to explain the former changes of the earth's surface, by reference to changes now in operation* (3 vols, London, 1834). Revised editions, any of which may have been used by Moffat, were published in 1837, 1838 and 1840.

[31] See F. Burckhardt and S. Smith, eds, *The correspondence of Charles Darwin* (Cambridge, 1987), vol. 4, pp. xiv, xv, 44.

powerful, any impediment to free circulation of air, or any screen which shades the earth from the solar rays, becomes a source of humidity; and whenever dampness or cold have begun to be generated by such causes, the condensation of vapour continues. The leaves, moreover, of all plants are alembics, and some of those in the torrid zone have the remarkable property of distilling water, thus contributing to prevent the earth from being parched up.[32]

Moffat comments in this connection that 'this was a philosophy which the more acute thinkers among the people could partially comprehend, but which they could not believe'.[33] This was a surprising comment, since at the period Moffat was describing, in 1821, he cannot himself have read Lyell, so that his account of the disbelieving of 'this philosophy' by the 'acute thinkers' of the Tswana is somewhat disingenuous. Moreover, Moffat felt it necessary to bolster his reliance on desiccationism (essential to the depiction of the Tswana as environmental destroyers) by referring to further authorities, that is, to Lyell, and to Lyell's authorities in turn, carefully footnoting all of them in his 1841 autobiography.

It would be easy to pass off Moffat's desiccationist interpretation of drought as being merely an intellectual weapon with which to belabour the Tswana and their land-use methods, thereby, conceivably, to justify their need for European Christian tutelage. There would some reason for such a view, but it would be an over-simplification. Moffat was also undoubtedly faced with the possibility that the facts of climatic change, reinforced by Lyell's thesis of a new geological timescale, (which he would not, in fact, admit to) might not be attributable at all to the actions of man, notwithstanding the local evidence for tree-cutting in the neighbourhood of Kuruman. Admitting this possibility would in turn facilitate the spectre of a world uncontrollable by man and subject to unpredictable and devastating drought or climate change. Time and process were inextricably tied up, and the accepting of a new geological timescale would have meant that ecological damage and (possibly)

---

[32] Moffat, *Missionary labours*, p 332. In a rare footnote, Moffat references this text to Lyell, *Principles of geology*, and 'Phil. Trans, vol ii, p. 294'. The latter (an incorrect transcription) appears to refer to observations made in Sir Hans Sloan's estates in Jamaica.

[33] Moffat, *Missionary labours*, p. 332.

ensuing drought could no longer be tied exclusively to the actions of the Tswana. Above all, the test for religious superiority could no longer be relevant. Moffat was thus hamstrung between the intellectual claims of time, religion, and science and he might truly be said to have, in his own terms, 'eaten of the fruit of the tree of knowledge'! This was a predicament which he was not able to resolve in his own lifetime. In a more practical sense, however, Moffat's intellectual dilemma with regard to the assigning of blame for ecological destruction and drought may enable one to understand his pioneering excursions into the field of artificial irrigation and agricultural development at Kuruman.[34] It is tempting to interpret the missionary enthusiasm for irrigation, (which was shared and developed much further by John Croumbie Brown)[35] as an attempt to re-water a ruined garden, or to restore the rivers of Eden. In a practical sense it certainly represented an attempt to re-assert a human potency in the face of evidence of the inability of man to affect environmental processes; and to assert the ability of the European to control the environment and even reverse the impact of the forces of nature. Irrigation development may be seen, too, as an attempt to forestall extinction, fear of which undoubtedly underlaid much of the later advocacy of desiccation ideas. Ultimately drought threatened human life in a very basic way. Irrigation in the context of colonial settlement offered two further merits: it justified the paternalistic intervention of the European in indigenous land-use and governance and encouraged the permanent settlement of nomadic people. Other comparable kinds of prescriptive interventionism to restore European control over the environment were foreshadowed in another of Moffat's dictums.

---

[34] See letter from Moffat to Rev. G. Burder, London dt 20 January, 1824 (London Missionary Society Archives) quoted in L. Schapera, *Apprenticeship at Kuruman* (London, 1951), pp 112–113; 'I realise when the proposal [to move a settlement down to where Moffat could organise irrigation for BaTswana gardens] was first made it was rejected ... but a variety of examples relating to valley ground and irrigation and the late indubitable and overpowering testimonies of our regard for their welfare here operated powerfully on their minds, influencing them to listen to our counsel.'

[35] For details of Brown's irrigation proposals for South Africa see *Reports of the Colonial Botanists* for 1863, 1865, 1866; and J.C. Brown, *Water supply of South Africa, and facilities for storing it* (Edinburgh, 1877), pp. 196–647.

I do not however, despair of eventually seeing the whole of the population, some of whom are now commencing the building of stone fences
and brick houses, so fully satisfied on this point that they will find it in
their own interest, as well as contributing to the beauty of a country, [sic]
to encourage the growth of timber, particularly as it is only such species
as are indigenous which can grow to any extent.[36]

Moffat did not, in fact, carry through his environmental analysis
or his interventionist prescriptions beyond some minor attempts at
irrigation development. However, his environmental analysis and his
early signposting of a major conflict between science and religion
(stimulated both by empirical observation and a reading of new science)
are useful in outlining the ideological backdrop against which John
Croumbie Brown worked. Almost certainly Moffat's relatively minor
and impractical excursion into the project of assigning blame for
environmental original sin and proposing its expiation would have been
known to Brown when he arrived at the Cape as a missionary with the
London Missionary Society in 1844, even though he did not quote
directly from Moffat until the publication of his first report as Colonial
Botanist in 1863.[37]

It is unclear to what extent Brown shared Moffat's notions of the
Cape and Africa as being the site of an Eden, Garden or Promised Land
requiring spiritual and environmental redemption and intervention.
Considering his career as a whole, Brown's opinions passed through a
series of transitions and he was far more receptive, at one level, to new
scientific ideas than Moffat had been. This was in large part due to the
experience of being employed as a university teacher of Botany at the
University of Aberdeen between 1853 and 1862.[38] This was precisely the
period at which botany as a discipline began to encounter the full force
of the revolution in conceptions of species mutability. However, earlier
on, at the time of his arrival in the Cape (at the age of 36), Brown's

---

[36] Moffat, *Missionary labours*, p 332.

[37] J.C. Brown, *Report of the Colonial Botanist* (Cape Town, 1863); J.C. Brown, *Hydrology of South Africa* (London, 1875), p. 168.

[38] Details of Brown's employment, University Register, Diary, University of Aberdeen
Archives, Kings College, Aberdeen. For other details of his academic employment see
Venter, 'An early botanist', p. 282.

perceptions probably conformed more closely to an evangelical stereotype. In 1844 rainfall levels had been high for a considerable period so that the Cape landscape he would first have encountered was far less stressed and drought-ridden than that encountered by Moffat. Brown was also extremely interested in accounts of the journeys of naturalists and missionaries into the 'interior' and one of the first tasks he set himself was to carry out the first translation into English of the diaries of T. Arbousset and F. Daumas, missionaries of the Paris Evangelical Society.[39]

These accounts covered journeys made in 1836–7 into and through the north of Basutoland. In many respects the diaries were a vividly described epic journey in the French Romantic tradition ending, symbolically enough, with a series of ecstatic descriptions of the mountain which they named 'Mont-aux-Sources'. The imaginative landscape of the narrative, together with the very specific religious and geographical agenda it set, undoubtedly made a great impression on Brown and passages from it are quoted approvingly throughout his works on forestry, hydrology and conservation until the late 1880s.[40]

In terms of an idyllic representation of the landscape of the interior the most important passage in Arbousset's *Narrative* is that which describes his response to the spectacle of Mont-aux-Sources.

> We never tired of looking at the scene; everything around us was grand, magnificent and life-like, contrasting strongly with many a gloomy monotonous scene which had wearied the eye on other journeys we had taken ... that little wood, whose refreshing green does everything possible to soften whatever may be too harsh in the outline of the landscape, everything, in short, concurs to excite in the soul emotions of inexpressible delight. Never had we experienced a sweeter, more ecstatic joy than we did when, with the bible in our hands and our prayers on our lips we turned towards the outlet from that mountain ... to gaze on the work of God and the magnificent vestment with which he had clothed creation. Never before had the contemplation of his works excited such

---

[39] T. Arbousset and F. Daumas, *Narrative of an exploratory tour to the north-east of the colony of the Cape of Good Hope*, original MS of 1836 translated and privately circulated in Cape Town, 1846. Second edition published London, 1852.

[40] See, for example, Brown, *Water supply of South Africa*, pp. 600–605.

transports of grateful feeling. or such deep-tried devotion; not that the Lord had at any time, or in any circumstances, left us without an assurance of his presence. but we have found that those scenes which elevate the soul. like those which soften the heart, deepen the feeling that the Lord is near, and render magnificent to the eye, as it were, the wonders of his goodness and his power...[41]

The mountains of Basutoland were described here in terms quite adequate for the symbolic formulation of a 'holy mountain', with the added virtue of being associated with running water and green woodlands of the kind that Moffat had found so sadly lacking. This Edenic vision, very close in some respects to the descriptions of unspoilt oceanic islands characteristic of French Huguenot refugee literature,[42] was supplemented in Arbousset's account by a moral counterpart in missionary intervention, as one might have expected. In fact, it seems, the vision of the 'green mountain' was set up, in narrative terms, as a counterpoint to a morbid description of the dismal human scene which Arbousset and Daumas conspired to find in the villages north of the massif, at Kuening near Thaba-bosiu. In this neighbourhood, they recorded,

> there are a number of deserted kraals and everywhere around the ground is covered in human bones and skulls and broken pots and such like remains. 'Look at the work of the Matabeles' said Monaile, [Arbousset's guide] 'they kill the Bechuanas as we would kill dogs ... it is well that you men of peace have arrived in our country; but for you we would all have been dead men ... this is what was being done with the black nation ... Kuening both from its fertility and its agreeable situation, is admirably suited for a missionary station ... it is very secure, but this is of little consequence here. The former inhabitants will return with joy to cultivate these fertile valleys from which war has driven them for a time. They will return with eagerness to localities which they have given names expressive of the abundance in which they lived ... one of the rivers they

---

[41] Arbousset and Daumas, *Narrative*, pp. 22–23.

[42] The earliest writing in this colonial genre is to be found in the late seventeenth century writings of Francois le Guat; see S. Pasfield-Oliver, *The voyage of Francois Le Guat of Bresse to Rodriguez, Java and the Cape of Good Hope* (London, 1891). The Huguenot outlook on the natural world, in common with that of the later French evangelists, was characterised by a willingness to locate previously mythical Edens in the reality of the newly-'discovered' natural world.

have named Atan (where the cattle multiply) and another Khomokuan (where the lions are in peace)...[43]

Here once again, as in Moffat, the construction consists in a lost Eden and one which may be regained with the help of the white man, although, on this occasion, it is largely a social idyll which is being discussed. The project then consists in the idea that European missionary intervention is vital to restore the Tswana to their rightful land of milk and honey, by stepping in to end internecine conflict. Essentially the project of the restoration of a social and environmental Eden legitimated, quite clearly for Arbousset and Daumas, the introduction of a European presence and a European intervention. The climatic conditions for the Arbousset journey, as Brown must have absorbed it in the act of translation, were temporarily drought-free, so that the awkward question of assigning blame for drought did not become a conspicuous issue; instead the agenda of social intervention and reform is more explicit.

Nevertheless the two Frenchmen did introduce a highly optimistic environmental test for the success of the missionary endeavour, and one which must have made an impression on Brown.

> It is of importance to geographical science, but still more so to the cause of religion that the state of the heathen countries at the time of the introduction of Christianity should be ascertained with precision, for in every country in which the gospel has been proclaimed it has, without fail, altered the aspect of both land and its inhabitants.[44]

Not only did this passage constitute an explicit piece of cultural determinism, it also amounted to a risky hostage to fortune. It reflected precisely the situation into which Arbousset and Daumas had walked; one blessed by several seasons of good rainfall but with a warring population still crippled by the social disruption caused by the Difaqane and drought. Even in the very year in which Brown first published his translation of the Arbousset-Daumas *Narrative,* in Cape Town in 1846, a drought even more severe than that of the early 1820s began to make itself felt. For Brown this drought seems firmly to have buried any of the facile environmental optimism found in the Arbousset *Narrative.* By his

---

[43] Arbousset and Daumas, quoted in Brown, *Water supply of South Africa*, p. 600.

[44] Arbousset and Daumas, *Narrative*, p. 62.

own account, when Brown left the colony in 1848 at the end of his first visit his mind was filled with images of desiccation and death.[45] Moreover the very starkness of the contrast between a drought landscape and the idyllic landscape conjured up in the *Narrative* served to reinforce Arbousset's 'promised land' as a symbol of environmental salvation in the mind of Brown. The strength of this image, coupled with the ferocity of the drought, which awoke associations of the worst Old Testament disasters in his mind, ensured that Brown's religious mission would become primarily an environmental one. The vigour of this new mission cannot be underestimated. As a self-appointed messenger of the environmental 'word' the erstwhile Congregationalist missionary was later to publish a whole set of environmental gospels; over sixteen books on water, climate and forest conservation.

The drought of 1845–7 ushered in and coincided with major changes in the political and strategic pressures upon the expanding colonial state.[46] It also coincided with important departures in the valuation of the Cape environment by natural scientists. Added together, the new pressures on the colonial state and on scientific perceptions had significant implications for the development of patterns of intervention in the natural environment. Some of the new pressures on the colonial state were attributable directly to the conditions of the drought. Lack of rain throughout the Cape increased the incidence of severe veld and forest fires and encouraged the state for the first time to take a much more active interest in controlling the forests which had been, in name alone, under government control since the onset of British rule (and in some cases since the early 1790s).[47] During 1846 and 1847 the first fruits of

---

[45] 'I took occasion in 1847 to make the tour of the colony. While passing through the Karroo, I witnessed those privations to which the inhabitants were subjected by the aridity of the climate ... my recollections of the journey call up vividly even now oft-recurring visions of bones of oxen at varying distances along the road – the bones of oxen which had succumbed by the way, travelling in a land where no water is', Brown, *Hydrology of South Africa*, p. 8.

[46] Pollock and Agnew, *Historical geography*, pp. 72–98; For the dynamics of the frontier zone see, A E. du Toit, 'The Cape frontier; a study of native policy with special reference to the years 1847–66', *Archives Yearbook for South African history*, 1951, vol. 1.

[47] Sim, *Forests and forest flora of the Cape Colony*, pp. 78–79; Grove. 'Early themes in African conservation', p. 23.

this interest showed itself in a series of practical and legislative attempts that were made to stop soil erosion in the vicinity of Cape Town and to prevent veld burning on the 'Cape Downs'.[48] At the same time a debate on ways of preventing excessive incursions into the governments forests by itinerant bands of woodcutters and cultivators developed. As a result, during the years 1846–1848, the possibility of using the state forests for the purpose of regulating marginal elements of the society (initially Dutch, Coloured and Hottentot itinerants and woodcutters) started to develop in the official mind.[49]

Within a few years this had important consequences for the way in which the concept of land control through state forest regulation was used to counter the much greater scale of threat posed by Xhosa incursions from the East. After an initial war between 1846 and 1848 an attempt had been made to establish military strongpoints and protected European settlements along the Amatola escarpment between Grahamstown and Fort Beaufort.[50,51] In a second Xhosa incursion in 1850 these strongpoints were overrun. When 'peace' was finally established in 1853 the settlement involved a new and experimental solution in land-control. A 'Royal Forest Reserve' was established in old Nggika-Xhosa lands in the Tyumie, Keiskama and Buffalo river headwaters.[51] The aim of this forest reserve was manifold. It aimed to discourage land-hungry European farmers moving east and prevent Nggika re-infiltration to the west. From 1854 'loyal' Mfengu were allowed into the vacant lands of the Royal Reserve. The occupants of the reserve, part of a line from Auckland to the coast at Peddie were 'to act as a sponge, absorbing civilisation from the white man and transmitting it back to the barbarous tribes'.[52] The scheme was later developed to include groups of 'protected' settlements, to which immigration was strictly controlled.[53] The concept of a 'forest reserve' had thus, in the context of the pressures of drought, war and an expanding colonial state, come to acquire a new meaning;

---

[48] Sim, *Forests and forest flora*, p 79.

[49] Ibid., p. 79.

[50] Du Toit, 'The Cape frontier', p. 53.

[51] Ibid., p. 75..

[52] Pollock and Agnew, *Historical geography*, p. 89.

[53] Ibid., p. 92.

essentially as a 'native reserve' and as a highly convenient means of removing unwanted people. It was a useful innovation for the state and one that was not quickly forgotten when more scientific reasons for forest reservation were produced.[54]

The droughts after 1846 also focused attention on agricultural failure *per se* and thus on the possibilities which a more systematic exploitation of the botanical resources of the Cape might offer to an ailing colonial agriculture. After about 1844 pressure had already been building up, largely through contacts between botanists resident at the Cape botanic garden as a regulated and funded scientific institution for the promotion of botanical science and 'economic botany'.[55] In 1846 this resulted in the formal re-opening of the Cape Botanic Garden as a scientific institution under state patronage. It also resulted, far more significantly for the future development of a conservation ideology, in the appointment of Dr Ludwig Pappe as Cape Botanist, thereby providing a platform for relatively autonomous scientific expertise which had been lacking before, and without which J.C. Brown could not have flourished and developed his ideas.[56] The only comparable positions in the imperial world were those posts occupied by the Superintendents of Botanic Gardens in India, where a similar advocacy of desiccationism was starting to take shape, although ultimately of a conceptually far less philosophically grandiose kind than that which emerged at the Cape.[57]

The growing relationship between Cape scientific expertise and the botanical establishment in Britain reflected the increasing interest among the international scientific community, German even more than British in determining the mechanisms behind evolutionary processes in plants, and a realisation of the possibility of the mutability of species. The new relationship also reflected an emerging realisation of the critical part that knowledge of the highly specialised flora of the Cape might play in evolutionary studies.

---

[54] Government Notice of 8 March 1853.

[55] Grove, 'Early themes in African conservation', p. 24.

[56] Pappe to W. Hooker, 28 June 1857, Cape Letters, Kew Archives sheds light on Pappe's view of the expert's role.

[57] Grove, *Green imperialism*, ch. 7.

Growing evidence of the extinction of both plant and animal species in the Cape Colony served only to sharpen the focus on the Cape biota. The introduction of innovatory conservation legislation, including the first formally designated game reserves in the Cape in 1856[58] and the comprehensive Forest and Herbage Protection Act in 1859 can largely be attributed to an anxiety about the effects of veld and forest fire, (which had persisted since the onset of the drought in 1846) coupled with a growing awareness of the rate at which species were disappearing in the colony through hunting, burning and forest clearance.

It was against this background that Brown arrived back in the Colony in 1862. He was a much changed man from the departing missionary of 1848. As an academic botanist he had become well acquainted with the shifting debates about species derivation which had come to a crisis with the publication of *The Origin of Species* in 1859, the same year as the passing of the Forest and Herbage Preservation Act.[59] By the time Brown arrived back to his appointment as Colonial Botanist in 1862 the worst drought of the century in Southern Africa was already underway, the third in a series of progressively severe droughts.[60] As a result the bulk of his writings, in his capacity as a state expert and subsequently as an independent commentator, reflected two developments; the increasingly severe progression of drought and, secondly, the natural-philosophical revolution that surround the publication of *The Origin of Species*. His response to both developments was directly influenced by perceptions formed during his earlier residence at the Cape and by the evangelical thinking of men like Moffat. But now it was also affected in quite a different way by the work of three non-British

---

[58] Government notice no. 263 regulated the 'Preservation of Elephants and Buffaloes in Crown forests'. Contrary to the model put forward in J. Mackenzie, *The empire of nature* (Manchester, 1988), these early game reserves were motivated primarily by a interest in species protection rather than by a wish to arrogate hunting rights to a colonial elite. In general the timing of species protection legislation. (and early game reserves) whether in the Cape, Tasmania. Victoria, Britain, Mauritius or the USA can be located to the decade 1863–1873 as a direct response to Darwinian theory.

[59] C. Darwin, *The origin of species* (London, 1859).

[60] Nicholson, 'Climatic chronology of Africa', pp. 282–288.

scientists, J.M. Schleiden,[61] (a German), E.M. Fries[62] (a Swede trained by Linnaeus) and Ludwig Pappe, (an Austrian and his innovative predecessor as Colonial Botanist at the Cape). Confronted by evidence of the economic and environmental devastation wrought by the 1862 drought and the floods which took place in its aftermath, Brown became increasingly reliant on the work of the three scientists. There was no accident in this. All three men were close to, or actually involved in debates about the mutability of species, and all three were convinced of some kind of evolutionary process involving extinction. Though his legacy in writing was less than the other two, Pappe had been before his untimely death, a frequent correspondent and collector for Joseph Hooker, the scientist most closely involved with and cognisant of the direction of Darwin's thinking.[63] Principally because of this, Pappe had been highly sensitive to the implications of the process of extinction as it could easily be observed in the Cape. Linked to his, the growing appreciation of the necessary interdependence between species and (in an evolutionary sense) between species and their physical environment which was shared by Brown's mentors meant that these scientists had all developed a sensitivity to the impact of 'European civilisation' on environments at a continental or even global scale. Brown quoted parts of the work of all three, along with the work of Moffat, in his official

[61] Jacob Mathias Schleiden, 1804–1881. A polymath, after 1833 Schleiden came into contact with A. von Humboldt. Having acquired a doctorate in law, he taught botany at Jena and then studied anthropology. A pioneer of cell theory, Schleiden's Humboldtian essays were published in *Pflanze und ihre Leben* in 1848 and would have been read by Brown in the translation by A. Hentrey in 1853. L. Errera wrote, 'As a populariser he was a model; as a scientist an initiator'.

[62] Elias Magnus Fries, (1794–1878), was convinced from the 1820s of the importance of evolutionary processes in the natural world; see *Systema mycologia* (New York, 1952 ed.). However, he found it hard to accept mechanisms of natural selection in evolution, while accepting the general theory of it after his own reading of Darwin in 1859; T.O. Krok, *Bibliotheca botanica* (Uppsala, 1925), pp. 199–215.

[63] For details of correspondence between J.D. Hooker and Charles Darwin on the critical importance of the floras of the Cape and St. Helena and their affinities see Burckhardt and Smith, eds, *Correspondence of Charles Darwin*, vol. 4, pp. 69, 311, 312, 400. Apart from the Galapagos material it was these areas, along with the Falkland islands, that were of most importance to Darwin in his theorising.

Report of the Colonial Botanist, published in late 1863.[64] This was a document which served, effectively, as a manifesto for the whole body of his later conservationist writing and indeed for much of the programme of state environmental policy into the twentieth century in the Cape Colony, Natal and Southern Rhodesia.

Schleiden and Fries both effectively destroyed any notions Brown may have had of any essential beneficence being involved in European interactions with the Cape environment.[65] Nevertheless he coupled the work of Schleiden and Fries with that of Moffat believing them all to be important texts with the apology that,

> it may be unusual to insert in a professional report lengthened quotations from published works. An intense desire to carry home conviction must plead my excuse for the case I have favoured ... I have thus shown that I do not stand alone in any opinion that increased heat and drought follow all such destruction of vegetation and may thus secure more careful attention to my remarks on the conservation and extension of forests as a means of counteracting the evil referred to.[66]

This, then was Brown's project. The care he took in detailing his sources, one may suggest, arose quite simply from the fact that he rightly guessed that his diagnosis of the environmental problems facing the Cape might prove deeply unpopular and difficult for both the state and the settler community to accept. After all, the core of his argument and of his official report of 1863 was that drought and the long term desiccation of Southern Africa as a whole, as well as floods, soil erosion and pasture deterioration were all caused as much by the nature of settler farming

---

[64] Also quoted in Brown, *Crown forests of the Cape of Good Hope* (Edinburgh, 1887), pp. 94–98.

[65] Three other works served, between 1850 and 1865 to confirm Brown's adherence to Schleiden and Fries. Pappe, in his *Silva Capensis* (Cape Town 1854), and his *Reports* of 1859 and 1860 alluded to desiccation arguments from an unknown source. Brown may also have read J.S. Wilson, 'On the general and gradual desiccation of the earth and atmosphere', in *Report of the Proceedings of the British Association for the Advancement of Science*, 1858 ,pp. 157–158; and in *The hydrology of South Africa* he refers to J.F. Wilson, 'On the increasing desiccation of inner South Africa', *Report of the proceedings of the British Association for the Advancement of Science*, 1865, pp. 160–161.

[66] Brown, *Crown Forests*, p. 97.

practices as by indigenous land-use methods. Thus, while quoting
Moffat in his 1873 report, Brown qualified his partisan condemnation
of the Tswana by noting,

> that the heathen in their ignorance have acted as described need not
> surprise us; but what better has been the course pursued by the more
> civilized? Is it not the case that the history of civilized man in his
> colonisation of new countries has been in every age substantially this –
> he has found the country a wilderness; he has cut down trees, and he has
> left it a desert?[67]

Brown's new critique on the impact of European 'civilisation' on the
'wilderness' was derived in part from the historical perspective learnt by
his reading of Schleiden.[68]

However it was Elias Fries who proved the more important source
for Brown as the inspiration for his own conception of the leading role
of the scientist or the 'truly cultivated man' in mending the ecological
damage caused by European colonial expansion. Fries' narrative was one
which saw the European creating what amounted to an expanding
system or engine of destruction which developed from a central point
and left a devastated interior. In this model, colonial territories such as
the Cape Colony now stood on the threatened periphery.

> A broad band of waste land follows gradually in the steps of cultivation.
> If it expands, its centre and cradle dies, and on the outer borders only do
> we find green shoots. But it is not impossible, it is only difficult, for man
> without renouncing the advantage of culture itself one day to make
> reparation for the injury which he has inflicted.... True it is that thorns
> and thistles, ill-favoured and poisonous plants, well named by botanists
> 'rubbish-plants', mark the track which man has proudly traversed across
> the earth. Before him lay original nature in her wild and sublime beauty.

---

[67] Ibid., p. 96.

[68] 'Almost everywhere in the great characters in which nature writes her chronicles, in
fossilised woods, layers of peat, and the like, or even in the little notes of men, for instance,
in the records of the Old Testament, occur proof, or at least indications that those
countries which are now treeless and arid deserts, part of Egypt, Syria, Persia, and so forth,
were formerly thickly wooded, traversed by streams now dried up and shrunk within
narrow bounds; while now the burning glow of the sun, and particularly. the want of
water, allow but a sparse population.' Schleiden, *The plant: a biography*, pp. 305–306.

Behind him he leaves a desert, a deformed and ruined land; for childish desire of destruction, or thoughtless squandering of vegetable treasures, have destroyed the character of nature; and man himself flies terrified from the arena of his actions, leaving the impoverished earth to barbarous races or animals, so long as yet another spot in virgin beauty smiles before him. Here again, in selfish pursuit of profit, consciously or unconsciously he begins anew the work of destruction. Thus did cultivation, driven out, leave the East, and the deserts perhaps previously robbed of their covering; like the wild hordes of old over beautiful Greece thus rolls this conquest with fearful rapidity from east to west through America, and the planter often now leaves the already exhausted land, the eastern climate becoming infertile through the demolition of the forests, to introduce a similar revolution into the far west.[69]

From this millenial vision of devastation, Fries believed, the world could still be salved by the intervention of 'nobler races of truly cultivated men' who 'even now raise their warning voices'.

It was this programme for the restoration of nature and the cultivating of natural science which Brown saw as his duty to advocate as Colonial Botanist. By aligning himself with Schleiden and Fries, Brown identified himself with a whole school of protoevolutionists for whom the growing debate about the mutability or otherwise of species, with its emphasis on the process of extinction, highlighted notions of interdependence between species and their environment. In this context, empirical evidence of species extinction or of substantial or irreversible desiccation acquired peculiar significance, serving also as a reminder of the vulnerability of man to natural processes. Evidence of extinctions also fuelled feelings of social insecurity engendered by the erosion of a traditional Christian mental world by the emerging evolutionary schemas of contemporary natural science.

In managing to attribute a human causation to processes of climatic change Schleiden, Fries and Pappe had, in fact, found an effective psychological way of coping with the central implications of the revolution which evolutionary thinking implied, particularly in the sense that it had newly defined man, a well as other species, as dependent on the vagaries of environmental processes. Above all the necessary process

[69] Brown, *Crown Forests*, pp. 96–97.

of extinction threatened the place of man himself in creation. In this context we can see species protection and forest conservation concerns, which had both developed extremely early at the Cape, as two distinct ways of coming to terms with an existential problem, essentially by attempting to re-assert control over the new terms of disorder which evolutionary thinking dictated. It was to become an obvious temptation to solve problems of political disorder among a colonised people by similar means.

Even the struggle between colonial settler and indigenous pastoralist (with his allegedly incendiarist tendencies, as they were frequently portrayed) acquired new meaning in terms of the Darwinian debate. Although in the language of *The Origin of Species* successful colonisation might infer evolutionary success, environmental failure as a corollary could be construed as symbolising an evolutionary failure. In this sense one can distinguish at least two underlying motives on the conservationist agenda at the time that Brown became Colonial Botanist. Both were comparatively new fears, far more developed than the vague apprehensions that one can detect in Moffat as he tried to come to terms, not with species extinctions, but simply with the implications of new geological time-scales. However, while Brown may have incorporated the underlying agendas of his Germanic and Swedish mentors, it is clear that he still retained, at one level, a significant remnant of the evangelical environmental moral economy which Moffat had espoused, albeit with some important modifications. While this ambivalence is not so apparent in the cold official dictums of his 1863 report, it is quite manifest in the pages of his first book, *Hydrology of South Africa,* first published in 1875. Here, his accounts and survey of the effects of the 1862 drought alternated wildly between rigidly empirical and methodical description and short excursions into the realms of Old Testament allegory and analogy.[70]

---

[70] Although in fact Brown states emphatically: 'it is the truth alone which I desire should be discovered. But in view of the importance which I attach to the discovery of truth, whatever the truth may be, I would fain secure for my statements an attentive perusal and calm consideration.' It seems apparent that Brown did not actually believe he would get a fair hearing of his opinions in some official circles in the Cape, a conviction which was borne out eventually by the manner in which his post was terminated.

As distinct from Moffat's biblical allusions, which offered a straightforward moral lesson and conceived of drought as the wages of environmental sin or sins of moral disorder, Brown's use of the Old Testament is far more circumspect, and without clear moral lessons. He refers to descriptions of drought and famine in the Bible more as historical data concerning natural events whose causation was open to debate.[71] Indeed, he appeared to believe that the sufferers of Biblical droughts were more vulnerable simply because they did not have the wherewithal to understand the reasons for drought. Instead, then, any conventional moral lesson was converted to a conviction that if contemporary science could assign causation, then the societal implications of that science must be religiously followed through. Thus here, too, there is an important distinction to be made between the environmental moral economies of Moffat and Brown, in that Brown saw the 'truth' of scientific analysis as the major plank in his programme of response to environmental crisis.

In spite of this there remained a permanent element of doubt in Brown's mind. On the one hand his religious antecedents encouraged him to see drought as a form of moral retribution holding out the possibility of a millenial climatic disaster for which conservation might be expiatory. But in the majority of his writings he is far more speculative about the causes of climatic variability. It may be that his resorting to Biblical precedent, (that is, to accounts of climatic fluctuation in a semi-arid land) represents a recognition of the inherently fluctuating nature of the Cape climate, and an antidote to the idyllic unreality of Arbousset. Ultimately though, the evangelical aspects of Brown's thinking undoubtedly underpinned his conservationist enthusiasms. In this sense his obsessive interest in compiling information and experimental evidence about the dynamics of the relationship between forests, moisture and climate can be interpreted as a search for a moral or religious truth

---

[71] Brown, *Hydrology of South Africa*, pp. 11–12. Brown quotes instances of drought from Jeremiah XIV, 2–16, I Kings XVII, 10–12, and I Kings XVIII, 5–6. He found the cycles of drought and flood pre-figured in I Kings, XIII, 41–45 and it is tempting to suggest he saw himself as a modern climatic Elijah.

pursued through scientific discipline.[72] In this respect he was by no means unique among Victorian naturalists. Brown's elevation of the role of the expert and his determined advocacy of the expansion of scientific expertise by the colonial state can be seen in the same light; problems in nature (and the colonial state was manifestly faced by many of them) could be solved by technology. In 1865 he wrote that he considered it expedient 'that there should be some official of whom it might be required to report upon all communications made to the government on subjects connected with irrigation, forest economy, arboriculture, horticulture. agriculture and botany ... in other lands similar duties have been discharged by officers under other designations.'[73] Brown developed the theme further in his 1865 Report, advocating the popularisation of science and its institutions among settler farmers:

> There is a prejudice against science. Science is simply systematised knowledge and all systematised knowledge is science. Impart science as thus defined to the practical man, and you increase his powers for good to himself, his family, to his country and to his race.... I should require to see or hear of the colony being studded with such institutions [experimental farms]; supported by funds raised in the different districts in which they are situated; but in order to do this is seems to be necessary that one should first be tried at the expense of the whole community.[74]

There is no doubt that in the aftermath of drought Brown found himself in a powerful position vis-a-vis the colonial government, and in a position to promote his own social prescriptions. To borrow the terminology of Mary Douglas, the Colonial Botanist was able, with the authority of science behind him, to threaten the state with God, death, time and money; the experience of drought as well as the future threat of it imposed pressures on government and white farmers in all these ways,

---

[72] In 1863 Brown sent out circulars to 'Civil Commissioners, District Magistrates, Conservators and wardens of Crown Forests' and scientists in many other colonies including St Helena, Victoria (Australia) and India, requesting reactions and responses to his desiccation/climate theories.

[73] Brown, *Report of the Colonial Botanist for 1865*, p. 21. This was a thoroughgoing Baconian programme for which, at the time, there were no contemporary precedents in British colonies.

[74] Ibid., p. 21.

playing on economic and moral fears.[75] Despite this, in his relations with the state in the longer term, Brown had developed a major weakness; his analysis of the environmental deterioration of the Cape was too even-handed with respect to assigning blame to settlers and Africans. His projections for the role of the expert, in promoting irrigation, setting up experimental farms, and educating farmers in ways of preventing soil erosion, veld-burning and flooding were almost entirely directed at white settler farmers. Brown was, in fact, (especially in his 1865 and 1866 reports) setting out a embryonic rural development programme, the principal plank for which (and one is reminded here of Moffat's Kuruman scheme) was government-funded irrigation. His plans were rejected almost in their entirety, once the spectre of economic collapse in the immediate wake of drought had died away.

This rejection was indicated in a practical sense by the retrench-ment of funding for the post of Colonial Botanist in 1866 and Brown returned to Scotland in that year. Nevertheless the central message of his official reports and of his later books, that deforestation and veld-burning were linked to the threat of climatic change, continued to be used to legitimate a programme of forest land control. This was a political course upon which the Cape government had already embarked for reasons that had little to do with conservation and far more to do with an interest in selectively controlling the settlement pattern of African pastoralists and farmers. After his return to Scotland Brown continued to propagandise his model of conservation for Southern Africa in a series of books and articles, the most influential of which were *Hydrology of South Africa*, *Water Supply of South Africa*, *Forests and Moisture* and *Reboisement in France*.[76]

In all these books Brown continued to press the themes that he had advocated in his official reports as Colonial Botanist, in particular the need to prevent forest and veld-burning, conserve and extend forests,

---

[75] M. Douglas, 'Environments at risk', in *Implicit meanings; essays in the sociology of perception* (London, 1979).

[76] J.C. Brown, *Hydrology of South Africa; Forests and Moisture, or effects of forests on humidity of climate* (Edinburgh, 1877); *Reboisement in France; or records of the replanting of the Alps, the Cevennes and the Pyrenees in trees, herbage and bush* (London, 1876). For a full list of Brown's works see Venter, 'An early botanist'.

plan irrigation and provide adequate training for a body of experts specialising in forestry and conservation.[77] While at first Brown's official reports and later books were substantially ignored by the Cape government they quickly came to the attention of the British botanical establishment. Ludwig Pappe's academic collaborator, Joseph Hooker, (now director of Kew) first gave Brown's warnings publicity in Britain in an article in the *Journal of Applied Sciences*.[78] Hooker was already distressed, as a botanist, at the accelerating rate of forest loss throughout the tropics and saw Brown as a useful anchor for his lobbying for imperial forest protection, which had already borne some fruit in India, but not elsewhere. It was only after Hooker had praised Brown that the Cape Government felt compelled to respond; and in 1875 J. Storr Lister of the Indian Forest Service was appointed 'Superintendent of Plantations at Cape Town'. In 1880 funds were voted for a 'Superintendent of Woods and Forests' and the office conferred on Count Vasselot de Regne, a French forest officer, directly as a consequence of Brown's advocacy of French expertise.[79] In Britain Brown became a persistent lobbyist on his account for the cause of colonial conservationism. This became more effective after the publication of *Hydrology of South Africa*. As a result, for the first time, between 1875 and 1879, colonial governments started to be questioned by Whitehall about their plans for and spending on afforestation and conservation. The convening of the Natal Forest Commission was an early result of this development.[80] Attempts had been made by individual experts as early as 1841 to alert the imperial

---

[77] In all these matters contemporary French practices were put forward as worthy of imitation. Brown believed that the superiority of French forest conservation dated back to the 1669 Forest Ordinance promoted by Colbert. This brought all French forests under the absolutist purview of the state, and was thus, one might suppose, a model easily adapted to the absolutist conditions of colonial rule.

[78] J.D. Hooker, 'Forests', *Journal of Applied Science*, (August, 1872), pp. 221–223. In the same issue, an article appeared by Baron von Mueller, the Government Botanist of Victoria laying out a programme for forest conservation in Australia entitled 'Forestry and its relation to industrial pursuits'. It drew heavily on Brown, to whose work Mueller had been alerted by the Cape circular of 1863.

[79] See Grove, 'Early conservation themes in Africa', p. 33.

[80] See Governor Bulwer's preamble to the *Report of the Natal Commission on the extent and condition of forest lands in the Colony* (Pietermaritzburg, 1880), pp. 1–4.

centre to the problems of environmental degradation.[81] However, none of these pleas had been framed, as Brown's was, in terms of a global climatic threat, and in terms of a process which might threaten colonial economics in the tropics as a whole. Even then, Brown's conservation gospel was only taken up by the Southern African governments very selectively and was used, particularly in the Cape, simply to justify the alienation of land previously unused by Europeans for the purpose of forest reservation. As most state timber needs already had to be satisfied by the import of timber from outside South Africa, Brown's desiccation arguments proved especially useful.[82] Almost without exception, however, adverse commentaries on destructive land-use methods were confined after Brown's departure to situations in which the activities of African farmers were the main concern. In this way a language of moral disapprobation, derived originally from Moffat and Brown, was used to condemn the activities of Africans and used to justify the forest reserve as a tool for their expulsion from forest land. Veld-burning, on the other hand, still widely carried out by European farmers, received much less attention.

The chief exponent of this language of conservationist exclusion was D.E. Hutchins, previously an officer in the Indian Forest Service, who was appointed to the Eastern Cape Conservancy in 1881.[83] He shared with Brown an academic interest in the causation of drought, even writing a book entitled *Cycles of Drought and Good Seasons in South Africa*.[84] However it is his reports on the forests of the eastern Cape and the Transkei that are of most interest.[85] Rejecting the relatively non-

---

[81] In June 1841, a series of letters were exchanged between 10 Downing Street and Sir George Gipps, Governor of New South Wales, on the advisability of soil conservation legislation in Australia. [Mitchell Library, Sydney NSW, ref/ A1288, no.21389. Lord Russell to Gipps, 21 June 1841.] This followed the publication of P. Strzelecki's *Physical description of New South Wales* which had exposed evidence of very widespread erosion. No action was taken but Strzelecki's warnings re-surfaced in the Report of the Natal Forest Commission in 1880, p. 4.

[82] Sim, *Forests and forest flora*, pp. 84–92.

[83] Ibid., p. 34.

[84] Nicholson, 'Climatic chronology of Africa', p. 317.

[85] See Sim, *Forests and forest flora*, p. 46, for a discussion of these reports.

partisan approach of Brown, Hutchins chose to revivify Moffat' s vocabulary of moral environmental economy, directly equating veld-burning and tree-felling carried out by Africans with moral degeneration and criminality. The end result, much as it was in the Indian Forest Service in which Hutchins had been trained, was to justify, through a selectively applied desiccation theory, the widespread criminalisation of those individuals forced to work lands in or adjacent to forests by the expansionist activities of European planters and settler farmers.[86] In brief, the indigenous farmer or fuelwood gatherer was transformed into a poacher.

The slow diffusion of the themes of social Darwinism after about 1870 served to reinforce the terms of the new discriminatory environ-mentalism. The first indications of this had emerged in 1865 when John Croumbie Brown was cross-examined by the Cape Assembly Select Committee appointed to assess his 1865 *Report*. Justifying his recom-mendations for the widespread afforestation of the Cape with exotic Australian tree species (ostensibly to reduce desiccation) Brown ex-plained that 'it is alleged by Darwin' that 'Widely ranging species … which have already triumphed over many competitors in their own widely extended homes, will have the best chance of seizing on new places, when they spread into new countries … thus they will become still further victorious, and will produce groups of modified descendants'.[87] In this fashion, the language of early Darwinian ecology was easily converted into a surrogate code for anxieties about colonial success. Consequently, success in forest protection or in afforestation with exotic species became a matter loaded with symbolism.

This was reflected in official forest conservancy reports. Remark-ing on the failure of the Forest and Herbage Act of 1859, as it had been drafted by Ludwig Pappe, Hutchins opined that 'forest property is similar to game, it is widely dispersed and difficult of protection. It is as easy for a Kalfir to slip into the forest, cut a sapling, and sell it as a pole at the nearest canteen, as for a poacher to knock over a pheasant' .

---

[86] Quoted in J.C. Brown, *Management of Crown forests at the Cape of Good Hope under the old regime and under the new* (Edinburgh, 1887), p. 293.

[87] Brown, *Crown forests*, p. 121.

Without stringent new laws, Hutchins believed, 'the attempt to preserve the forests of the Cape Colony ... must inevitably end in failure'.[88] At the time this was written Hutchins was engaged in lobbying for the criminal provisions of the 1882 Madras Forest Act to be applied in the Cape Colony. His strictures on the Transkeian forests in the same report reflected a second line of approach. Forest reserves served to protect not only economic wealth but scenic beauty. 'It is the opinion of a large number of people' he stated, that,

> the destruction of the forests means the deterioration of the most fertile, and the disfigurement of the only beautiful parts of the country ... whatever view may be taken as regards the future of the country, it is as much the moral duty of a civilized government to set its face against forest destruction in these latitudes, as it is to discountenance any other social evil, such as slavery or witchcraft. No-one would propose that slavery or witchcraft should be encouraged in the Transkei, for the sake of a few hundred pounds revenue, yet there are countries where events have shown that the temporary evil of slavery is as nothing compared to the irremediable evil of forest destruction.[89]

Here once again it is clear that evangelical critiques of the evils of despoiling an Eden, whether 'beautiful' or 'fertile,' had re-surfaced, in terms as vivid as those used by Moffat and Arbousset. Hutchins was not, however, content with such arguments, pragmatically aware, as he would have been, that the state had actually sanctioned deforestation in the Transkei for its own purposes.[90] In such straits Hutchins was forced back on to the reasoning preferred by Brown, coupling moral with climatic arguments.

> In independent native states, such as the Pondos ... the policy should be pursued of setting our faces against forest destruction as firmly as other

---

[88] Ibid., p. 303.

[89] Ibid., p. 303.

[90] Contrary to Hutchins statements, and in the opinion of another of the Cape Conservators (significantly, a German), most of the destruction in Transkei was not initiated by Africans at all. Indeed much of it had actually started after Hutchins opened up the forests to timber-working on the Indian pattern His colleague, conservator C.C Henkel, was well aware of this *Report of the Conservator of Forests* (Cape Town, 1889), p. 94.

moral evils are faced. Cruisers are maintained on the West Coast of
Africa from purely sentimental and philanthropic motives. But when
our neighbours propose to destroy their forests, not only are they ruining
their own country, but they are decreasing our rain supply ... Should we
permit our neighbours to cut off our scanty water supply which nature
has given us in this dry country?... I make these remarks with the object
of urging that the timber trade from native states should be looked on
as immoral, for exactly the same reasons that the liquor traffic is looked
on as immoral, and laws passed for its suppression in native areas.[91]

Hutchins quite clearly makes the connection here between the protection of forests and the desire to secure and legitimate the possession of
land for Europeans to live in; moreover, he used John Croumbie Brown's
desiccation theories to clinch the argument. The use of Brown's writings
in promoting the alienation of land for forest reserves, coupled with
notions of forests as scenic Edens from which 'evil' deforestation
activities must be excluded, did not end in the Transkei, however. When
Rhodes started his development of the Shona and Ndebele lands for
European settlement it was quite logical that Cape forestry experts
should have been summoned to act as consultants in the management of
the forests of the new colony.[92] Cape forest conservators such as C.C.
Henkel and T.S. Sim. as well as Hutchins, were all involved in the
planning of the first forest reserves, consistently offering desiccation
arguments and referring to Brown's works as the basis for their recom-
mendations. The Cape Colony Forest and Herbage Act of 1859/1888
was even introduced unchanged as Rhodesian legislation. However, it
was as little applied as it had been in the Cape Colony, and largely for the
same reasons: that its strictures applied to settler farmers as well as
Africans. Instead, the new colonial state focussed its attention on the
founding of forest reserves and, a new departure, on the foundation of a

---

[91] Ibid., p. 303.

[92] T R. Sim was commissioned to report on the Rhodesian forests in 1902. Referring to
Brown's work on the dangers of global desiccation he wrote 'to counteract such an
enormous evil even to some little extent and to delay as far as possible the advent of what
lies beyond man's power, is a pressing duty alike to Government and the individual; and
in the maintenance and extension of forests Government is taking an active step in that
direction.' *Forests and forest flora*, p. 49.

National Park in the Matopos at the behest of Rhodes and by the terms of his will. Even here, the ruling conservation ethos of Cape forest policy, with its emphasis on the exclusion of African peasants from forest reserve Edens, continued to exercise a strong influence.[93]

The Salisbury authorities had initially been much puzzled by the vague terms of Rhodes' will which had stipulated that 'a part of my said property near Bulawayo be planted with every possible tree, and be made and preserved and maintained as a Park for the people of Bulawayo'.[94] Part of the solution they adopted represented a reversion to an old pattern; Conservator D.E. Hutchins was appointed in 1903 to compile a report on the future management of the Matopos park. He entitled the first chapter 'An Arboretum in the Matopos'. The agenda of the Hutchins report was, in fact, a re-enactment of the ecological Darwinism first espoused by Brown in his responses to the Cape Select Committee of 1865. The Park was to be extensively planted with exotic tree species brought in from every corner of the Empire. These exotics would, he stipulated, need to be carefully protected, particularly from grazing animals and shifting cultivators; in short, Africans were to be excluded from the Matopos. One might argue that J.C. Brown, from whom the rationale of this mode of management derived, would not have been happy with the way in which his ideas were finally applied. It is, then, a considerable irony that Hutchin's vision of the Matopos park, shared by later Rhodesian Forest Department officials, was vigorously opposed by Dr Eric Nobbs, the Director of Agriculture and grandson of J.C. Brown. Instead, his vision of a National Park consisted in a wilderness (without exotic trees) which would permit the residence of Africans living in 'traditional' ways. This object, in essence, was to recreate the idyllic, Edenic, landscape of Arbousset and Daumas. Two entirely different visions of conservation had thus emerged out of the writing of Brown by

---

[93] See T. Ranger, 'Whose heritage? The case of the Matobo National Park', *Journal of Southern African Studies*, 15 (1989). The National Park was first suggested (as an extension of Rhodes' more limited urban/forest park concept) by Dr Eric Nobbs, grandson and archival executor of John Croumbie Brown, when Director of Agriculture in Southern Rhodesia.

[94] Quoted in D.E. Hutchins, *Report on the Matopos Park and trees suitable for planting there and in Southern Rhodesia; also a note on forest policy in Rhodesia* (Cape Town, 1903).

the early twentieth century, one Darwinian and racist, the other evangelical and atavistic. As the century progressed later struggles between
peasant and settler state, both in Rhodesia[95] and in Nyasaland[96] (in
forests and National Parks) tended to show that the more humanistic and
evangelical part of the early Cape conservationist gospel could not
survive alongside the ideologies of the colonial settler states.[97]

Far from being simply 'scientific', the ostensibly rational accounts of
early environmentalists in Southern Africa concealed a whole collection
of discourses and tales. Many of these evolved as part of the attempt made
by botanists, and by missionaries above all, to come to terms with a
rapidly changing semi-arid environment and with indigenous societies
under pressure from climatic turmoil brought about by a revolution in
natural science. The narratives of Moffat and Brown were confused and
often contradictory, and they were the product of an unprecedented
philosophical dilemma in the context of an arduous and rapidly changing natural environment. Conservation ideas emerged as part of a
complex mental and physical programme to re-assert control amid the
shifting sands of a debate about and a crisis in belief, God, descent,
origins, time and desiccation. Attempts to protect or to recreate previous
Golden Ages can be seen, perhaps, as a way of resolving personal and
scientific crises. The project of controlling an intellectual as well as
environmental disorder, in which previously accepted parameters of
belief and natural process could all be questioned, led almost inexorably
to a displacement of the social priorities of the 'scientists' and to the co-
option of their conservationist ideas by the state. This process was

---

[95] For a recent study of the use made by colonial officials of conservationist arguments,
to rationalise the expulsion of African farmers from unforested Forest Department land
in Eastern Rhodesia see J.F. Mtisi, 'Population control and management; a case study of
Nyamukwara Valley tenants at Stapleford Forest Reserve, 1929–1971', paper presented
to session on 'Conservation and rural people' of African Studies Association of the UK
conference, Cambridge, September 1988.

[96] The early development of forest protection in Nyasaland was also based on Cape
experience. Forest reserves were instituted mainly for 'watershed protection'. When the
Dzalanyama reserve, near Lilongwe, was declared several entire villages were forcibly
'removed' [Malawi National Archives; Forest Department records; Central Region files].

[97] This theme is developed more fully in Chapter 6.

sustained, especially after the publication of *The Origin of Species,* by a continuing promotion, especially by John Croumbie Brown, of conservation propaganda which both threatened further climatic change and preached the virtues of environmental intervention by the state. Progressively, in the late years of the nineteenth century, the much-trumpeted universality of conservation was legitimated by reference to an international scientific community. It was this, in particular, that allowed the colonial state to use the righteous language of conservation and to confine and regulate the activities of peasant farmers in the marginal lands to which they were becoming increasingly restricted.

4

The East India Company, the Australians and the El Niño: Colonial Scientists and Ideas about Global Climatic Change and Teleconnections between 1770 and 1930

Research by historical climatologists and oceanographers over the last few years has served to emphasise the very remarkable correlations and connections between the strength of the El Niño current and Southern Oscillation (ENSO) and the characteristics of global climate, especially in terms of the variation in strength of annual meteorological events, the occurrence of droughts, monsoons, hurricanes and the occurrence of extreme weather events. A close knowledge of the archival record over many centuries has been vital to uncovering the nature of the relations between ENSO and global climate, but in many instances historical knowledge has been inadequate in drawing firm conclusions about the nature of global climatic teleconnections. From existing historical data on the strength of the El Niño since approx. 1500 AD we already know that particular years stand out as having experienced very severe El Niño conditions. For most of these limited number of years, until recently, it has been very difficult to piece together the global impact of a very severe ENSO. In the course of this chapter some new evidence for the global impact of the ENSO of 1791 is examined. This evidence makes it clear that the event gave rise to well-documented drought conditions in Australia, Southern Africa, South Asia, the Atlantic, the Caribbean and Mexico. These droughts gave rise to severe famine conditions in some regions. The very distinctive evidence for the marked global impact of the 1791 ENSO is of intrinsic climatological interest in demonstrating the closeness of the connections between ENSO and globally occurring extreme climatic events, and more particularly in the connections between ENSO and the Indian monsoon. However a study of the 1791 events is also of wider interest and implication for the environmental historian and the historian of South Asia. This is because 1791 stands out as the first occasion on which weather and agrarian observations made by scientific observers and others in the tropics were sufficiently elaborate and sufficiently coordinated in new intellectual networks for some of the first speculations to be firmly made about global rather than regional climatic events. By 1816, for example, the 1791 events were identified by a number of authorities as having some collective or connective significance. It was principally the institutional reach and complexity of the East India Company, with its newly founded botanical and medical services, that allowed a relatively sophisticated analysis of the 1791 events to be made, not least through the prior existence of long runs of consistent meteorological observations and the systems of regular correspondence that had built up to service the new imperial botanic gardens and to regulate the relationship between the East India Company in London, its colonial scientists and the Royal Botanic Gardens at Kew. Similarly rigorous observations of weather and agrarian stress were also being made by this time in the Caribbean, not least in Montserrat and on St Vincent, the latter of which was the site for the first botanic garden in the Western hemisphere. In India, St Helena and St Vincent the drought experiences of 1791 led to an unprecedented interest in the possibilities of forest protection as a means of forestalling further declines in rainfall that were widely feared at the time. While a widespread and reasoned belief in a relationship between rainfall and forest cover was by no means new the 1791 global drought certainly encouraged fears of regional and even global desiccation and even heightened apprehensions that man himself might ultimately be responsible for damaging change in climate. In East India Company territories at St Helena and in Bengal, Bihar and Orissa such anxieties even led, under the leadership of William Roxburgh, to widespread programmes of tree-planting for the express purpose of encouraging above-average rainfall, or of conserving existing rainfall patterns. Furthermore fears about revolutionary climatic change may have mirrored very palpable fears among the British that revolutionary political change might engulf the smaller colonial possessions or even India itself, or that the two phenomena might be linked.

Two other general points might be made that relate to current debates in the history of imperialism and in the history of colonial science. There have been some suggestions that in considering the 'empire of development' as one might term it, there were two major phases. The first took place during what Vincent Harlow called 'Britain's second empire' between about 1763 (The Peace of Paris) and about 1815. This was at a time when Britain inherited the revolutionary physiocratic thinking that had originated with the French but which died in France and in most French colonies with the Revolution. The second phase, arguably, lasted from about 1880 (the end of the great Indian drought of 1877–1879) until 1914 and saw a wide range of 'development' policies and institution building take place in the British (and French) colonial empires. It also saw effective federation and nation building in Australia and South Africa (which in turn spawned a range of institution building, especially in science and land-management). This chapter serves, I think, to provide material to examine the validity of this two stage thesis. Secondly it may shed some critical light on the theories about colonial science originating in the work of Louis Pyenson. Pyenson, essentially, sees science in the colonies as having been derivative, the handmaiden of imperial capital, and scientifically imitative and unoriginal.[1] This is a notion sharply disputed in this chapter. On the contrary I seek to show that science at the periphery, especially in India and Australia, lay at the cutting edge of new knowledge and theorisation.

Colonial Science and the Indian Climate

The ENSO phenomenon links climate anomalies across the globe.[2] During an ENSO (or warm event) a specific spatial pattern of climate fluctuations develops (e.g. droughts in Australia, Indonesia, India, Southern and North East Africa, heavy rains and floods on the Pacific

---

[1] See Lewis Pyenson, *Cultural imperialism and exact sciences: German expansion overseas 1900–1930* (New York, 1985); and Pyenson, *Empire of reason; exact sciences in Indonesia, 1840–1940* (Leiden, 1989).

[2] N. Nicholls, 'Historical El Niño/Southern Oscillation variability in the Australasian region', in H. F. Diaz and V. Markgraf, *El Niño: historical and paleoclimatic aspects of the southern oscillation* (Cambridge, 1992).

coast of South America). So, because of the ENSO, climate fluctuations in many localities can appear almost simultaneously. These climate fluctuations can be said to be teleconnected.

Climate fluctuations have the potential to cause suffering. Droughts, floods, storm surges and strong winds from tropical cyclones may directly affect human health or lead to famines or epidemics. Climate-related health problems, including famine, epidemics, death and injury from wildfire, flood or storm surge in areas affected by ENSO may also be teleconnected. As with the climate anomalies themselves, the climate-related health impacts in various ENSO-related areas tend to occur simultaneously. For instance drought-related food shortages can be a potential problem in several counries bordering the Indian Ocean in the same year; that is, the temporal and spatial distributions of drought-related food shortages are not random. Similarly epidemics of mosquito-borne diseases and other diseases associated with widespread flooding, may occur almost simultaneously in several countries.

There are important connections between the incidence of drought in India, institutional responses to it and the beginnings of modern understandings of climatic teleconnections between global scale tropical circulation and the strength of the Asian monsoon.[3] The 1877–79 drought and accompanying famine in India led to a flurry of institutional innovations, a new famine code and a great deal of debate about the connections between deforestation and rainfall change, most of it coordinated by Edward Balfour, Surgeon-General of India.[4] We now know that this 1877–79 event was global in its impact.

What is interesting however is that thinking about global teleconnections and the chronological incidence of extreme climatic events bringing about extreme health and economic consequences had actually begun a whole century before the post mortem of the 1877–79

---

[3] G.N. Kiladis and S.K. Sinha, 'ENSO, monsoons and droughts in India', in M.V. Glantz, R.W. Katz and N. Nicholls, eds., *Teleconnections linking worldwide climate anomalies* (Cambridge, 1991), pp. 431–458. See also G.N. Kiladis and H.F. Diaz, 'Global climatic anomalies associated with extremes of the southern oscillation', *Journal of Climate*, 2, 1069–1090.

[4] See R.H. Grove, *Green Imperialism; colonial expansion, tropical island edens and the origins of environmentalism, 1600–1860* (Cambridge, 1995), ch. 8.

disaster began. The key, of course, to thinking about the mechanisms of climate change and its impact was the collection of meteorological data, and exposure to extremes of climate change and exposure to its consequences. Frequent foreign travel and growing ease of information exchange about diffferent parts of the world were further enabling factors.

During the 1780s there was much speculation, in terms of basic mechanisms, about the connections between air quality, volcanoes and climate. Visiting Paris in 1783 Benjamin Franklin (a good example of a well-travelled scientist) was struck by the very wintery conditions of the French summer, in a year when it snowed in Paris in July. This was followed by a very severe winter in 1783–1784. At this stage Franklin reached the conclusion that a global cooling in the temperate latitudes could safely be attributed to volcanic action. The cooling layers of dust that could be observed in the skies of France and the United States were, he thought, due to the vast quantity of smoke, long continuing to issue during and after the eruption issuing from Mount Hecla in Iceland. Franklin wrote up his speculations, which by current scientific thinking were broadly accurate, in Passy, France in May 1784. They were published in the *Transactions of the Manchester Philosophical Society* under the title 'Meteorological imagination and conjectures'.[5]

Equally important observations were being made at Madras and over a much longer period of time. Meteorological observations had been begun at Madras at a relatively early date, in fact rather earlier that in contemporary Europe, and had been made by German and Danish missionaries. It was against this background that William Roxburgh arrived in Madras as a young surgeon in 1776. From 1778 he was based at Samulcottah, in charge of a Company botanic garden on what had earlier been the site of a Mughal garden. From the time of his arrival in India, however, Roxburgh kept systematic meteorological records, analyses of which he published in 1778 and 1790.[6] These records were commu-

---

[5] *Transactions of the Manchester Philosophical Society*, 1784, pp. 373–377.

[6] 'A meteorological diary kept at Fort St George in the East Indies', *Philosophical Transactions of the Royal Society*, 68 (1778), pp. 180–190, and 80 (1790). While assistant surgeon at Fort St George Roxburgh took measurements three times a day, using a Ramsden barometer and Nairne thermometers.

Photo-etching.   Survey of India Office Calcutta February 1895

William Roxburgh, Superintendent of the Botanic Garden, Calcutta,
1793–1813.

nicated to the society by Sir John Pringle. As such they consititute part
of the meteorological movement stimulated by Joseph Priestley's chapters of 1772. In this sense Roxburgh can be grouped along with
Alexander Anderson, Edward Long and General Melville (all of whom
worked in the West Indies) as enthusiasts of climatic mensuration
working all over the new colonial empire. Moreover Roxburgh's Indian
observations seem to have awoken an interest in Indian meteorology in
Sir Joseph Banks himself, for we know that in 1788 Banks presented a
seven year diary of Bombay weather observations for publication in the
Royal Society's *Transactions*.[7] It may seem puzzling at first that Roxburgh
should embark with such vigour on detailed weather observations so
soon after his arrival in India. But Roxburgh had been trained under John
Hope, the Linnaean experimental plant physiologist and curator of the
Edinburgh botanic garden. Hope was himself an enthusiast for the work
of Stephen Hales and Duhamel du Monceau and had lectured extensively on the climatic theories of these two men while Roxburgh had been
his pupil at Edinburgh in the early 1770s. Hope had also brought
Roxburgh, as his star student, into contact with two important intellectual networks, those of the Royal Society and the Royal Society of Arts.
From the Royal Society Roxburgh took up the contemporary enthusiasm for systematic meteorology, while from Hope and the Society of Arts
he also adopted a related and life-long interest in tree-planting.

As an East India Company surgeon Roxburgh integrated these
meteorological and arboricultural programmes into a more specifically
medical discourse, as part of a programme of interventionist interaction
with the tropical environment which he developed after 1776. Finally he
became a pioneer in the collection of tropical meteorological data, to an
extent unrivalled elsewhere until the 1820s (except among indigenous
Chinese observers). It was this basis of detailed measurement over many
years that facilitated Roxburgh's diagnosis of climate change and famine
incidence as part of his more generalised critique of the colonial impact
on the Indian environment [8]

---

[7] Joseph Banks, 'Diary of the rain at Bombay from 1780 to 1787 and part of the year
1788', *Philosophical Transactions of the Royal Society*, 80 (1790), p. 590.

[8] Note that neither Pierre Poivre on Mauritius nor Alexander Anderson on St Vincent
collected discrete and systematic meteorological data, while Banks and Beatson only
commenced collection of rainfall data on St Helena after 1811.

A major centre of calculation encouraging the collection of meteorological data was the Royal Society itself. The society's connections with systematic meteorology dated back to 1723 and were, in origin, closely connected to the discoveries of Hales and the publication of *Vegetable Staticks*. In 1724 Junius Jurin, a close colleague of Isaac Newton, had published *Invitatio ad observationis meteorologicas communi consilio institituendes*. This appeal for data resulted in the submission of temperature and rainfall records from as far apart as St Petersburg, Massachusetts and, not least, Bengal, where some East India Company servants had been directly involved. While important for the Royal Society as an exercise in initiating a data collection network the wars of the mid-eighteenth century effectively disrupted these pioneering efforts.[9] However, after about 1770 an interest in meteorology and meteorological networks arose again quite abruptly. This time the motivation behind them was more directly connected with a widespread shift in Europe towards the collection of systematic data as a part of wider state policy and it was more medically oriented. In essence, medical and agricultural climatology became institutionalised as European states increasingly intervened in matters of public health and health welfare. In France, for example, a national network of observers was established in 1778 under the auspices of the Societe Royale de Médecine, while contemporaries spoke of meteorology as a 'new science'.

The work of two observers contributed to the revival of meteorology after 1770. These were Jean Deluc's 1772 *Recherches sur les modifications de l'atmosphere*, and Joseph Priestley's 'Observations on different kinds of air', also published in 1772. The dissenting and reformist connotations of Priestley's work meant that from 1772 onwards British meteorology involved a radical set of agendas at least as strong as the climatic moral economy implicit in the ideas of Poivre and his Physiocratic colleagues in Paris. Roxburgh could not have avoided the social messages of this meteorological radicalism, and indeed seems to have embraced them with enthusiasm in a tropical region where meteorological fluctuations were so much more extreme than in Europe

---

[9] T. S. Feldmann, 'Late enlightenment meteorology', in T. Frangsmyr, J.L. Heilbronn and R.E. Rider, eds, *The quantifying spirit in the eighteenth century* (Berkeley, 1990), p. 147.

(and often fatal in their consequences) and where they might be interpreted as signifying more important social lessons. Roxburgh, like his Scottish compatriot on the island of St Vincent, Alexander Anderson, became sharply aware of the new moral significance ascribed by their joint mentor, Sir John Pringle (President of the Royal Society), to the atmospheric function of Priestley's research findings. Pringle placed Priestley's pneumatics in the context of the aerial system of fevers and also linked it with the model of a benevolent economy which Priestley had begun to map. 'From these [Priestley's discoveries] we are assured that......every individual plant is serviceable to mankind if not always distinguished by some private virtue, yet making a part of the whole which cleanses and purifies our atmosphere'. Storms and tempests (i.e. extreme meteorological events) would shake 'the waters and the air together to bury in the deep those putrid and pestilential effluvia which the vegetables upon the face of the earth have been insufficient to consume'.[10] The importance of this line of thinking to the later development of climatic environmentalism can hardly be over-emphasised, as it became an essential part of the link made between the environment and the reformist notions of moral economy among Scottish surgeons in the Indian medical services.

While on St Vincent Alexander Anderson had eventually followed the implications of Pringle's sweeping environmentalist dictums by seeking to protect existing natural forests. Roxburgh, for his part, intended to go one significant stage further in India by cultivating new plantations and, implicitly, thereby serving humanity by purifying the atmosphere and increasing the social virtues represented by the survival or renewal of vegetation. The gradual unfolding of of Roxburgh's Priestleyite environmental programme (of course among many other mainly botanical activities) can be identified almost from the date of his arrival in Madras in 1776. In that year he began a series of meteorological observations for the Coromandel coast (using a Nairne thermometer and a Ramsden barometer) which remained unbroken until his posting to Calcutta in 1793. Logic dictated that Roxburgh should send his obser-

---

[10] Quoted in Douglas McKie, 'Joseph Priestley and the Copley medal', *Ambix*, 9 (1961), pp. 1–22; see also Priestley, 'On the noxious quality of the effluvia of putrid marshes', *Philosophical Transactions of the Royal Society*, 64 (1774), pp. 90–95.

vations back to the Royal Society and he duly sent his records for 1777–1779 to Sir John Pringle, thereby reaffirming the theoretical and ideological basis for the observations and incorporating the Indian environment into the ambit of the dissenting and reformist networks of Priestley and his associates. There were in fact great difficulties of time and space involve in prosecuting this policy and a letter from Roxburgh to Banks in 1782 indicates that many of the records which he sent to Pringle in London were lost en route. However Pringle ensured that Roxburgh's first sets of weather records from the Madras Presidency were prominently published in the *Philosophical Transactions of the Royal Society*, in 1778 and then much later in 1790.

During the first years of his residency in the Madras Presidency Roxburgh spent much of his time as a surgeon at Nagore and in supervising the construction of an acclimatisation and botanic garden at Samulcottah north of Madras. Here he embarked on a long run of plant transfer and tree planting experiments very much on Physiocratic lines. It was while resident at Nagore between 1778 and 1780 that Roxburgh first became interested in the interconnections between drought, famine and food supply. In times of scarcity he noted, the supply of coconuts (a major food item in the region) from Ceylon quickly dried up. He therefore advocated Company sponsorship of food-tree planting along canal banks and village streets to secure supplies of coconuts, sago, dates and palmyra palms, as well as plantain, jackfruit, breadfruit and *opuntia* trees.

Meanwhile Roxburgh's meticulous record keeping meant that he obtained a very detailed empirical view of the local impact of the globally occurring droughts that took place between 1788 and 1793 and which particularly affected semi-arid zones in Australia, South Asia, Africa, the Caribbean and Central and South America. These drought episodes were almost certainly caused by an unusually strong El Niño event in the flow of the ocean currents along the west coast of South America. This current is now believed to be the single most effective variable in controlling fluctuations in the global atmospheric circulation and in particular in the Southern Oscillation of the atmosphere. Through what is now known as ENSO we can trace very distinctive effects on, for example, the timing and strength of the Asian monsoon and the incidence of droughts in many other parts of the world. In 1791 the El Niño experienced one of its strongest known episodes, and possibly the strongest episode known in written history.[11] Already devastated by a famine in 1780 the Circars of the Madras Presidency were again very badly affected by drought in 1789–1792 and many villages in the Godavery delta were entirely depopulated. Alexander Beatson later reported that 'owing to a failure of rain during the above two years, one half of the inhabitants in the Northern Circar had perished in famine and the remainder were so feeble and weak that on report of rice coming up from the Malabar coast five thousand people left Rajahmundry and very few of them reached the seaside, although the distance is only fifty miles'.[12] This information had been culled by Beatson from a letter written by James Anderson, curator of the Nopalry garden in Madras, to Robert Kyd, the curator of the Calcutta botanic garden. There is little doubt that this drought was one of the severest ever to be experienced in India in recorded history.

The resulting famine was much discussed in Europe and Edmund Burke particularly referred to it. Roxburgh made a particular point of praising pre-colonial irrigation methods and, like Burke, believed that the Company was largely responsible for the decline in artificial irrigation and for the increased vulnerability to famine that resulted in periods of drought. While there is no proof that Roxburgh was actually aware of Burke's critique of the Company in this respect there is no question that both men belonged to the same party in this case.[13] In fact, since 1782, according to Buchanan, rainfall levels had deteriorated steadily in southeast India. This decline had been noticed by Roxburgh and had, in fact, led him to speculate on the periodicity of drought events and to compare the severity of the late 1780s rainfall deficit with those of earlier periods in history. The results of these investigations were reported to the Company in 1793.[14] 'There are but few, if any', Roxburgh wrote, 'of the

---

[11] See W.H. Quinn and V.T. Neal, 'El Niño occurrences over the past four and a half centuries', *Journal of Geophysical Research*, 92 (1987), 14449–14461.

[12] See Alexander Beatson, *Tracts on the island of St Helena* (London, 1816), p. 198.

[13] See Edmund Burke, 'Speech on the Nabob of Arcot's debts', 28 February 1785, reprinted in P. Marshall, ed., *The writings and speeches of Edmund Burke* (Oxford, 1981), vol. 5.

[14] William Roxburgh, 'Suggestions on the introduction of such useful trees, shrubs and

lower Maritime Provinces of India that are not subject to (I dare scarce venture to say periodical, because our knowledge of meteorological facts is but as yet very imperfect) visitations of drought, more or less according to unknown circumstances'. 'In recent years', he added, 'we have seen and heard of the dreadful effects of such droughts prevailing over many parts of Asia'. It was sufficient, he carried on, 'for my purposes to take notice of that which has taken place in the Circars for no less than three years successively, to the dreadfull effects of which I have been a constant eye-witness'.

Roxburgh's awareness of the unusual severity of the 1789–93 droughts, a direct consequence of his long-term weather observations, led him in three directions. Firstly, he became interested in locating the 1789–93 droughts in a comparative historical and chronological context. Secondly, he sought to blame the nature of zamindari landlordship as it had been reconstructed by the Company for the seriousness of the famine that resulted from the drought. Thirdly, the famine increased Roxburgh's interest in planting trees both to provide famine foods and to try to increase the incidence of rainfall. This last concern would have been further stimulated as a knowledge of the passing on St Vincent of the Kings Hill Forest Act of 1791 started to permeate among East India Company officials and among the members of the Royal Society of Arts, to which Roxburgh belonged.

By taking an interest in the history of Indian droughts, a logical outcome of his meteorological interests, Roxburgh soon became aware of a comparable drought period one hundred years earlier, in the period 1685–1688. This drought, too, appears to correlate closely with a strong El Niño event or couple of events. Roxburgh actively sought out documentary and oral evidence for these earlier droughts, finding a rich source of material in an informant whom he refers to as 'the Rajah of Pittenpore's family Brahmen'.[15] This informant had found among the 'records of his grandfather an account of a most dreadful famine which prevailed over the northern provinces' during the years 1685 to 1687.

---

other plants as are deemed the most likely to yield sustenance to the poorer classes of natives of these provinces during times of scarcity', report to the President's Council, Tamil Nadu State Archives, Privy Council Volume clxxxl, entry dt 8 February 1793.

[15] 'Note', in Roxburgh, TNSA, PC Vol. clxxxl, 8 February 1793.

During 1687, it was said, 'only one shower fell' and 'very few people survived these three years'. Roxburgh noted, too, the incidence of lesser famines in other years, especially in 1737. But the severity of the 1680s and 1780s seem to have made a deep impression on him, much as the 1770 famine had done on Robert Kyd in Bengal (an event that had led Kyd to found the Calcutta botanic garden, in order to develop famine resistant crops). The scale of mortality involved meant, Roxburgh thought, that the government would have to address the issue by reforming land-ownership and tree-planting. 'I fear,' he commented, 'that no great deal of good can be done while the present system of renting the lands of these provinces prevails, viz., that the Sower scarcely knows whether he will reap or not, and if he mends the bank of a water course or digs a well, he knows not but it may be for the benefit of another'. Government would have to restore permanent title to the ryots, he thought, 'that we may hope soonest to see the resources for the poor, hitherto unknown in these parts, springing up'.[16] In fact, at least on chapter, the Madras government approved these suggestions, resolving to 'procure cocoanuts from Colombo, sago-palms from Travancore and bread-fruit from the Nicobars for sowing and planting'.[17]

Shortly after submitting his famine report to the Madras government Roxburgh was transferred to Calcutta as director of the botanic garden after the death of Robert Kyd. This meant that his policy initiatives for food security, land reform and tree planting were interrupted on the Coromandel coast. Nevertheless there were plenty of opportunities to develop such physiocratic policies in Bengal. In particular Roxburgh set about improving on Kyd's teak-planting experiments and expanding them into a fully developed plantation programme in Bengal, Bihar and Orissa. To aid him in this he brought with him large supplies of teak seeds from Rajahmundry.[18] Between 1793 and 1813 (when Roxburgh died) the plantation programme was steadily expanded and continued to be enlarged by Nathaniel Wallich after Roxburgh's

---

[16] For further details of this see Roxburgh correspondence, British Museum (Natural History), for 1787–1793.

[17] H.D. Love, *Vestiges of old Madras* (London, 1913), vol. 2, p. 410.

[18] Roxburgh, letter to Court of Directors, 7 March 1796, quoted in Love, *Vestiges of old Madras*, p. 230

death. As the first planted trees started to mature after about 1805 Roxburgh began to write chapters dealing with their growth and comparing it with the characteristics of natural teak stands.[19] At least one of these chapters was reprinted in the *Transactions of the Royal Society of Arts*, and is indicative of the close relationship which Roxburgh maintained with this society, its tree-planting campaigns and environmentalist personalities. Roxburgh did not, in fact, drop his meteorological interests during this period, becoming particularly concerned with the provenance of the seasonal drying winds which caused so much agrarian havoc in deforested landscapes. Significantly, he published the results of these researches in medical journals.[20] There is no doubt that Roxburgh's insights into the mechanisms, chronology and scope of droughts in India were far ahead of their time and were profound. The outcome of his insights was more important in terms of tree planting and attitudes to deforestation than in terms of understanding global climate. However the East India Company continued to provide the setting for further progress in understanding global climate interconnections and to stimulate thinking about climatic dynamics in general.

Alexander Beatson and the Climate of St Helena and the West Indies

Alexander Beatson, Governor of the EIC territory of St Helena and later author of *Tracts on the Island of St Helena*, (one of the books that Darwin took with him on the Beagle) took a keen interest in forest-climate dynamics and long-term climate change as a result of his exposure to the deeply degraded and problematic island of St Helena where he was governor from 1808 to 1813. Beatson was extremely widely travelled and read, and thus well prepared to think in global terms. Moreover he was

---

[19] Roxburgh, 'A table of the growth of trees in the botanic garden at Calcutta', *Nicholson's Journal*, XVII (1807) pp. 110–111; 'Letters on various productions of the East Indies', *Nicholson's Journal*, XXVII (1810) pp. 69–76; 'Some account of the teak tree of the East Indies', *Nicholson's Journal*, XXXIII (1812) pp. 358–354 [This paper was reprinted in the *Transactions of the Royal Society of Arts*, vol. 30].

[20] See for example, Roxburgh, 'Remarks on the land winds and their causes', *Transactions of the London Medical Society*, 1 (1810), pp. 189–211.

an enthusiast for the work of Alexander von Humboldt, who was a global thinker and integrator *par excellence*. Beatson's reading of Humboldt made him particularly open to notions of change in the environment over time. Encouraged by Sir Joseph Banks, Beatson, like Roxburgh before him, started a programme of systematic rainfall measurement on St Helena, which was begun in 1811. Initially Beatson was anxious to demonstrate linkages between forest cover and rainfall, which he proposed to address (again, like Roxburgh) by a programme of tree-planting. But it was his wide correspondence and reading that led him to more complex notions of climate change. In his *Tracts* he notes

> The stratum of shells and muds on the hills of Agrigentum, three miles from the harbour, and 1200 feet above the sea, the oyster shells found on the high mountains of Jamaica, the fossil bones of elephants found by Mr Humboldt in the Andes, 3420 yards above the level of the sea, and many other instances that might be adduced, serve only to furnish the most incontestable proof that this globe has undergone many surprising changes since it was first created.[21]

Beatson, then, was already alert to the possibility of climate change on a grand scale and was ready to draw together material from many different locations to back up his theorisations. Thus in 1815, alluding to the 1791–1792 drought in St Helena, he wrote that 'the severe drought felt here in 1791 and 1792 was far more calamitous in India. But those years, he added, were also 'unusually dry in Montserrat'. The sources for Beatson's remarks on the Indian drought are known with confidence, since he quotes letters from John Berry and James Anderson, curators of, respectively, the botanic garden and the Nopalry garden in Madras. Beatson had compiled a secret report in 1794 for the EIC on the state of Mauritius and his information networks were well developed. It is difficult to establish the source of his remarks about Montserrat, although Alexander Anderson and Joseph Banks are possible candidates. An examination of the Montserrat Assembly records, however, demonstrates that the situation there in the El Niño phase was, if anything rather more severe than Beatson implied. Thus on 13 August 1791, in a Petition

---

[21] Beatson, *Tracts*, p. x.

to the King, William McKealy, a prominent Irish planter of Montserrat stated, on behalf of the Board (or Council) of Montserrat the following:

> That this your faithful and loyal island for several years has very much decreased in its crops, as your petitioners conceive, from repeated hurricanes, a succession of dry weather and lately from the ravages of the noxious insect emphatically denominated the borer....that your petitioners sorely feel their inability to pay the high rate of interest of 8 % at which monies are at present lent in this island. That willing to relieve themselves they did lately frame a bill to reduce the said interest of 8% to 6%, but that your Majesty declined giving assent to the said bill.[22]

On 6 August 1792 (a whole year later!) a reply was belatedly received by the much-troubled Council of Montserrat denying their application for help. The letter (dated 6 March 1792) had been sent by the 'Commissioner of Council appointed for the consideration of all matters relating to Trade and Plantations'. The letter declined the substance of the petition and added, quite callously:

> It is not advisable in their Lordship's judgement to reduce the rate of interest by law or to make any regulation for the purpose unless special circumstances could be stated to justify the same....further of opinion that the rate of interest should be regulated by the value of money at the market, and that to attempt to reduce it below that rate is as contrary to the interest of the landowner as of the lender.[23]

This heartless response raises the question of exactly what 'special circumstances' would have been severe enough to allow interest rate reduction. But in fact, in November 1792 the Council tried a more crafty, not to say threatening approach to the imperial centre. They pointed out that 'under the distress occasioned by various calamities which we in common with neighbouring islands have experienced for many years by insects, bad weather and other events we are incapable to bear any additional expense for the pay of troops for the necessary

---

[22] Petition of the Council of Montserrat, laid before the board 13 August 1791; Montserrat Assembly Proceedings, Government Archives, Public Library, Crown Colony of Montserrat.

[23] Letter of 6 March 1792 received from Commissioner of Council to Council, Montserrat Colony, laid before Council 6 August 1792.

protection of the islands'.[24] This was no idle threat. As the Montserrat Assembly Proceedings recorded a month earlier, the progress of the French Revolution had given great cause for alarm throughout British colonies.[25] Thus the Board of Montserrat referred in their proceedings to 'the very precarious and dangerous circumstances of the times occasioned by the enthusiastic spirit of liberty which mistaken and impolitic zeal has raised'[26] and to 'the present situation of the West Indies Islands, made perilous from mistaken and ill-informed ideas of Philanthropy prevalent in Great Britain'.[27] On another occasion the Proceedings even refer to the fear felt by the planters of the 'wild and pernicious doctrines of liberty and equality' that were rampant even in the West Indies.[28]

In this way we can see that the effects of the 1791 El Niño were feared all the more on account of the revolutionary situation, not just in France but , more particularly , in the erstwhile colonies of the West Indies which so nearly neighboured British possessions. It has occasionally been argued (and not without some justification) that the bad harvest of 1789 and in succeeding years in France had some stimulative effect in provoking the popular discontent that characterised the Revolution.[29] But as far as the British were concerned the relationship between climatic and political turmoil was, in the main, only psychological, but no less potent for that. The fear that climatic disasters might bring about social unrest and rebellion was a very real one, however, on St Helena where Beatson, as Governor, was responsible for putting down a major military mutiny in 1811 among a garrison and slave population that were undoubtedly dissatisfied with their living conditions.[30] With the added

---

[24] Montserrat Assembly Proceedings, 3 November 1792, Government Archives, Public Library, Crown Colony of Montserrat.

[25] One of the most important anti-slavery campaigners of the time, Olaudah Equiano, a Yoruba from southern Nigeria, had himself been imported at the age of 11 into Montserrat as a slave and had stayed there until the age of 18; his writings would have been well known by the authorities in Montserrat.

[26] MAP, 6 October 1792.

[27] MAP, 3 November 1792.

[28] MAP, 29 December 1794.

[29] See Simon Schama, *Citizens: a history of the French Revolution* (London, 1989).

[30] It is no coincidence, of course , that 1811 was also the date that Beatson began official obersvation of the islands rainfall.

apprehension of the French military threat, disastrous droughts, or the threat of them, acquired a more than usually worrying connotation. Beatson's observations on the simultaneity and indeed teleconnection between droughts in different parts of the world actually allows us to pinpoint the impact of the 1791 El Niño and look for evidence in a way that would not otherwise be possible. Earlier analyses of severe climatic events in the Caribbean (which have anyway tended to focus on hurricanes rather than droughts) have ignored much significant archive material.[31] Since El Niño events have historically been shown to coincide with low hurricane incidence this is an important problem.[32] Drought incidence has, in general, tended to be at least as disastrous on some West Indies islands (especially in the Leeward islands such as Montserrat) as hurricane incidence but involves a more thorough and in-depth knowledge of archival sources.[33] The important point about the impact of the El Niño in India, St Helena and Montserrat is that a possible interconnection between severe weather in those locations was recognised by at least one relatively contemporary observer, Alexander Beatson. The records of Roxburgh and Beatson give us an insight into the severity of the 1791 event. It is true that since 1987 collated historical evidence has been made available through the work of Quinn and Neal, who have suggested, at least, that the El Niño of 1791 was 'very severe' in their classification; that is to say, that the 1791 ENSO has been equalled in severity in the last three centuries only in 1720, 1728, 1828, 1877–78, 1891, 1925 and 1982–1983.[34]

---

[31] See for example, R. Walsh and A. Reading, 'Historical changes in tropical cyclone frequency within the Caribbean since 1500', *Wurzburger Geographische Arbeiten*, 80 (1991), pp. 199–240.

[32] See W.M. Gray, 'Environmental influences on tropical cyclones', *Australian Meteorological Magazine*, 36 (1988), pp.127–139; and W.M. Gray and J.D. Sheaffer, 'El Niño and QBO influences on tropical activity', in Glantz et al., *Teleconnections*, pp. 257–284.

[33] Unfortunately the archives in Montserrat, Dominica and St Vincent, to name only three islands, are in extremely bad condition. For further information on historical rainfall levels see R.P.D. Walsh, 'The influence of climate, lithology and time on drainage density and relief development in the tropical volcanic terrain of the Windward Islands', in I. Douglas and T. Spencer, eds, *Environmental change and tropical geomorphology* (London, 1985), pp. 93–121.

[34] W.H. Quinn, V.T. Neal and S.E. Antunez de Mayolo, 'El Nino occurrences over the

There is compelling evidence to indicate, certainly in India, and possibly in Australia, that the 1791 El Niño was indeed, the most pronounced of all these events. As such, it is perhaps not surprising that its global consequences came to the notice of contemporaries. There are other historical records of the severe consequences of the 1791 event that were not known to either Roxburgh or Beatson. Thus J.H. Unanue recorded in 1815 that floods (a characteristic of strong El Niño events in Peru) were very serious in coastal Peru in 1791.[35] There is also considerable evidence of widespread and apparently unprecedented drought and famine in Mexico at the same period,[36] while severe droughts were recorded in South Africa in 1791–1792. Nile Flood Records, as recorded since as early as AD 622 on the lower Nile give a sound guide to rainfall levels in the Ethiopian highlands. Quinn shows that a very low flood period lasted from 1790 to 1797 and that this can be verified by three separate sets of data ; (weak Nile floods also occurred in AD 650, 689, 694, 842, 903, 967, 1096, 1144, 1200, 1230, 1450, 1641, 1650, 1694, 1715, 1783, 1877, 1899, 1913 and 1972).[37] Other related records of the severity of the 1791 event can be demonstrated from parts of Northern China and the East Indies.[38] In terms of alarms sounded by colonial scientists, however, the records are much more limited. There is at least one other important set of contemporary colonial records that are relevant, however.

past four and a half centuries', *Journal of Geophysical Research*, 92 (1987), pp. 14449–14461; and W.H. Quinn and V.T. Neal, 'The historical record of El Niño events', in R.S. Bradley and P.D. Jones, eds, *Climate since 1500* (London, 1995), pp. 623–648.

[35] *La clima de Lima* (Madrid, 1815).

[36] Dr Sara O'Hara, Dept.of Geography, University of Sheffield, personal communication.

[37] W.H. Quinn, 'A study of Southern Oscillation-related climatic activity for A.D. 622–1990 incorporating Nile River Flood data', in Diaz and Markgraf, eds, *El Niño*, pp. 119–150.

[38] See J.G. Palmer and I.O. Murphy, 'An extended tree-ring chronology for Java', in *Proceedings of the Koninklyke Nederlands Akademie von Wetenschapen, Series C; Bio. and Med. Series*; 96 (1993), pp. 27–41. This paper analyses a period between 1531 and 1931 and suggests the evidence for 50 year ENSO cycles.

The Australian Connection

The fear of climatic danger and popular rebellion was an issue in another colony severely affected by the 1791 El Niño, that is, the fledgling convict colony at Port Jackson. Although Beatson was not apparently aware of rainfall deficit in Australia we know now that it was substantial and quite prolonged. This is evidenced well by comparing early drawings of the colony, in 1792, 1803 and 1804.[39] In November 1791 Governor Philip reported that what is now known as the 'Tank Stream' had been entirely dried up for some months. As this was one of the main water supplies for the settlement this was a serious matter. In November 1791, therefore, a series of large basins were hewn out of the sandstone, with great labour, in the hope that they would collect and conserve the little remaining spring water. These basins were called tanks, after Indian irrigation practice, with which some of the colonists would have been quite familiar. Henceforth the stream became known as the 'Tank Stream'. The dried-up course of the stream is easily visible in a drawing of 1792; and there are even trees and shrubs shown growing in the bed of the stream itself. In a later drawing of about 1800 (engraved by F. Jukes and published in 1804), the new tanks are clearly visible and are carefully labelled as such. By 1803 a drawing by G.W. Evans of the east side of Sydney cove shows a very considerable flow going down the tank stream. In fact all subsequent illustrations of the locality show a sizeable flow in the tank stream. 1791–1793 was, therefore a quite exceptional period, and ensured that the colonists experienced conditions far more arduous than those which would appear to have been promised by the observations of high rainfall and lush vegetation made on the Cook expedition. In fact throughout the nineteenth century, and ever since, the process of Australian settlement has had to confront the consequences of a series of deceptively lush conditions, punctuated by the arduous years of severe El Niño events. This was, of course precisely the same phenomenon encountered by the East India Company in its schemes of annexation and agricultural development in India, in which years of expansion were punctuated by monstrous famine events. However it was not for some

---

[39] These are drawings and paintings collected together in Timothy McCormick, *First views of Australia, 1788–1825; an early history of Sydney* (Chippendale NSW, 1987).

years that this very important comparison came to be made and, with it, the development of a first true awareness of the the mechanisms of global climate fluctuation. Until the critical comparison was made between India and Australia, serious droughts tended to be blamed solely on geotectonic mechanisms or on the effects of artificially-induced deforestation processes. So how did the link between Indian and Australian climate come to be made and with it an awareness of the potency of the ENSO phenomenon?

In 1877 to 1879 a drought occurred throughout almost all of India that was the worst in living memory and probably the most pronounced since 1791. Up to 50 million people perished during a three-year period from its direct effects. Even before it had ended a panic-stricken colonial government began a flurry of innovative investigations into the causes of the severity of the drought and a number of bureaucratic departures were made.[40] The entire investigation of the drought was written up as the *Report of the Indian Famine Commission* of 1880. The Indian Meteorological Service was one of the resultant institutional innovations, along with a new Department of Agriculture and a new Forest Act (of 1878). Sir Henry Blandford, the first Director of the IMO, noted the very high atmospheric pressures over Asia at the time and, crucially (and in the manner of Beatson), requested pressure information from other meteorologists around the world. Sir Charles Todd, the South Australian Government observer, in response to Blandford's request, included pressure observations from various Australian stations in an annual series of publications recording monthly observations made in South Australia and the Northern Territory. Pressures were high during 1877 over Australia too, and much of the country suffered from drought that year. The coincidence of high pressures and droughts in India and Australia obviously stuck in Todd's mind. In 1888 Australia was again struck by a severe drought. An extensive discussion between the Government observers from South Australia, New South Wales and Victoria, on the cause of the drought, was published in the *Australasian* on 29th December 1888. Todd suggested that Indian and Australian droughts usually coincided; 'comparing our records', he wrote, ' with

---

[40] E.g. see Charles Danvers unpublished appendix to the Famine Commission report of 1880 entitled 'A century of famines', X classification, Top Floor, Edinburgh University Library; see also copy in BM; IOL.

those of India, I find a close correspondence or similarity of seasons with regard to the prevalence of drought, and there can be little or no doubt that severe droughts occur as a rule simultaneously over the two countries'.[41]

By 1896, H.C. Russell, the New South Wales Government Observer, was also convinced that Indian and Australian droughts often coincided.[42] Russell, in a chapter published that year, attempted to

Australian droughts	Indian droughts
1789–1791	1790–1792
1793	
1797	
1798 1800	
1802–1804	1802–1804
1808–1815	1808–1813
1818–1821	
1824	1824–1825
1827–1829	1828
1833	1832–1833
1837–1839	1837–1839
1842–1843	
1846–1847	
1849–1852	
1855	
1857–1859	1856–1858
1861–1862	
1865–1869	1865–1866
1872	
1875–1877	1875–1877
1880–1881	
1884–1886	1884

Table 1. Coincidence of Australian and Indian droughts (after Russell)

---

[41] Sir Charles Todd, *Australasian*, 29 December 1888, quoted in N. Nicholls, 'Historical El Niño/Southern Oscillation variability in the Australasian region', in Diaz and Markgraf, eds, *El Nino*, pp. 151–174.

[42] H.C. Russell, 'Notes upon the history of floods in the river Darling', paper read to the Royal Society of New South Wales, 3 November 1896.

demonstrate the periodicity of droughts but, almost incidentally, indicated the coincidence of droughts in the two countries (Table 1). Not all droughts coincided but many did. This remarkable observation has since been confirmed[43] and forms part of the set of climate teleconnections now known as the Southern Oscillation (SO). Other recent empirical studies have once again demonstrated that Indian and Australian droughts both tend to occur during El Niño episodes. El Niño-associated droughts in both countries usually start around May. The discovery of the first hints of the Southern Oscillation is usually attributed to Hildebrandsson in 1897.[44] Sir Charles Todd deserves some credit however for identifying, a decade earlier, the global scale of these teleconnections.

When Sir Gilbert Walker of the IMO named and documented the SO in the early decades of the 20th century, its close relationship with Australian rainfall quickly became apparent. Walkers's work indicated that north Australian summer rainfall could be predicted with an index of the SO. In 1929 Quayle indicated that spring rainfall farther south could be predicted in the same way.[45] After that, only a trickle of chapters discussed the relationship between SO and Australian climate, until the mid 1970s when the worldwide attention on El Niño led to a resurgence of interest among Australian meteorologists. Subsequently climatologists have become increasingly preoccupied with what they see as the dominating influence of the ENSO on world climate.

The central point remains, however, that the first steps towards recognising such global influences and fluctuations were enabled and founded upon the relatively sophisticated global networking of East India Company scientists and their post-1857 successors and, in particular on the colonial networking between Indian and Australian colonial scientists. Once again, it seems, (and to refute the assertions of Louis Pyenson) the periphery provided both initiative and innovation in extending human knowledge.

---

[43] E.g. by M.A.J. Williams, D.A. Adamson and J.T. Baxter, 1986, 'Late quaternary environments in the Nile and Darling basins', *Australian Geographical Studies*, 24 (1986), pp. 128–144.

[44] H.H. Hildebrandsson, 'Quelques récherches sur les centre d'action de l'atmosphere', *Konglica Svenska Vetenskapsakademiens Handlingar*, (1897), pp. 29–33.

[45] E.T. Quayle, 'Long range rainfall forecasting from tropical (Darwin) air pressures', *Proc. Roy. Soc. of Victoria*, 41 (1929), pp. 140–164.

5

Chiefs, Boundaries and Sacred Woodlands: Early Nationalism and the Defeat of Colonial Conservationism in the Gold Coast and Nigeria, 1870–1916

This chapter aims to assess some of the attempts made by the British colonial states to introduce forest conservation programmes into Anglophone West Africa and to sketch out the nature of some of the more elitist indigenous responses to those attempts. In the course of the chapter I also aim to characterise the changing emphases and fashions of conservationism in West Africa and make some brief comparative remarks about contemporary developments in other parts of the Empire.

The story of colonial conservation in West Africa was inextricably bound up with the developing tension between two entirely different agendas of power, one indigenous and the other governmental, within which the state attempted to assert its own notions of environmental control and land-use planning, reflecting both international changes in conservation thinking as well as an empirical and institutional learning process on the part of the local colonial apparatus. Simultaneously the indigenous populations, or at least their leaders, learnt increasingly to adjust to the weaknesses of the colonial state as specifically manifested in an environmental policy, seeking eventually to manipulate the agendas and mechanisms of colonial conservation to their advantage, often with some success. This chapter then, sets out quite deliberately to question the assumption engendered in some quarters[1] that colonial conservation

---

[1] E.g., R. Guha, *The unquiet woods: ecological change and peasant resistance in the Himalaya* (Delhi: Oxford University Press, 1989); N.L. Peluso, 'Co-ercing conservation? The politics of state resource control', *Global Environmental Change*, June 1993, pp. 21–42.

was, throughout the imperial context, a vigorous and militarised instrument of colonial oppression. Certainly, in British West Africa this was far from the case. On the contrary, the evidence indicates that, in the context of western economic penetration, the general pattern of land use change and forest survival was dictated far less by the colonial state than by indigenous political interest groups in close alliance with the interests of metropolitan capital. This analysis actually corresponds with existing and highly insightful research by economic anthropologists.[2]

To a greater extent than in other parts of the colonial world, conservation in West Africa was affected by the distinctive conditions of indirect rule and local autonomy. Far from succeeding in establishing an environmental hegemony, the conservation propagandists of the colonial state found themselves, from the outset, in an extremely weak position and one in which any 'success' in their programmes was entirely contingent on the support or acquiescence of the indigenous rulers and elites. Indeed, in the Lagos Colony Forest Ordinance of 1902 this principle of acquiescence was actually enshrined in law. As a result, when more broad-based popular resistance developed to the very real commoditisation and sub-division of the landscape by the state and its collaborators, it was manifested less in terms of direct clashes with the colonial state and more in terms of conflicts between indigenous groups, tribes and classes and, not least, between men and women. In other words colonial conservation helped to intensify and internalise economic and political struggles in terms both of gender and class.

The fundamental weakness of the colonial state in West Africa in its conservationist guise was closely associated with the limits of the colonial state in general, particularly with regard to the lack of control over land. This meant that the opportunities for social control and resource control which developed in some other colonies did not develop very far in the Gold Coast and Nigeria. Instead, especially in the Gold Coast, the struggle between rulers and ruled quickly developed into an open arena for the testing of relative political strengths and the creation of political identities. Partly as a consequence of this the economic

---

[2] E.g. P. Hill, *Migrant cocoa farmers in southern Ghana: a study in rural capitalism* (Cambridge, 1963).

ambitions of the colonial state were diverted far more quickly than elsewhere into a discourse about 'development', as ambitions for straightforward control slowly foundered. This discourse had very early origins in the policies of Alfred Moloney, a visionary and conservationist colonial official. In both Ghana and Nigeria these ambivalent tendencies were intensified by the close proximity of the biologically wealthy wet forest zones to the coastal trade routes and towns, the nature of preexisting trade patterns and the rapidly escalating commercial demands for tree and plantation crops. In this setting the fight for indigenous control over land was fired by the desire to retain control over commercial potential and incoming capital. As we shall see, this led to a considerable contradiction, and one in which the colonial state found itself hopelessly enmeshed.

The dynamics of external economic penetration as well as the externally derived antecedents of colonial environmental attitudes dictated the environmental history of the region. In particular the environmental histories of the Gold Coast and Nigeria were closely intertwined. While they often diverged (especially in Nigeria where there were important regional differences in the development of forest policy) the inter-colonial (even international) nature of colonial scientific expertise meant that important cross-connections were retained in the development of colonial environmental policy. More importantly, the political networks of 'ecological resistance' became increasingly closely connected, particularly between the Gold Coast and the Lagos Colony.

The Mankesim Incident

The conflict between colonial European and indigenous African views of nature had deep roots in West Africa. Moreover, as time went by it became a steadily more complex social clash, complicated primarily by the varying incentives offered by capitalist penetration and the lure of profits to trading elites, both African and European. Indeed the identities and motivations of these interest-groups were often deeply intertwined and united in opposition to colonial conservation policy.

To begin with, however, the story was a simpler one, and had more to do with clashes between different religious interpretations of the environment rather than conflicts between different economic groups. A series of incidents that took place at Mankesim, near Cape Coast, helps to illustrate this point.[3] Both the initial cause of the conflict and the nature of the indigenous response to the problem were much constrained by the influence of Christian missionary education. One of the major centres for this activity was at Cape Coast where both Basel missionaries and the Wesleyan church were active.[4] An early Wesleyan school was founded during the 1840s at Asafa, a village near Mankesim, well inland from Cape Coast. The foundation was thus very close to the shrine of the great Brafo fetish at Mankesim. This shrine was, effectively, one of the most sacred religious sites of the Fanti peoples.[5] The Brafo was believed to dwell in a sacred hollow in the forest adjacent to Mankesim, and was consulted both by local people and by pilgrims, some of whom came from a great distance. Any movement of Christians to a point near the shrine would therefore be unwelcome. Local communal politics therefore came to a crisis in late 1849 when Christian converts from Asafa felt the need to abuse and ridicule the Brafo's worshippers. Finally, they even went so far as to clear the bush in the immediate neighbourhood of the sacred grove in order to make their farms and take advantage of the rich unworked soil which was to be found there. This was much more than the priests were prepared to stand for and they called upon the chiefs and people to defend the honour of their god. They did not, however, take more direct action, being convinced that the Brafo would avenge himself without human aid. It was not until they had been disappointed in this and had seen unusually good crops growing in the Christian farms, (and seen one of the invaders actually shoot a deer within the woodland), that it was felt incumbent on the priests to do something more active. A council was then held and it was agreed that the Fanti chiefs should combine to defend the honour of the fetish.

---

[3] W.E.F. Ward, *A history of the Gold Coast* (2 vols, London, 1948).

[4] The Basel missionaries were particularly active in promoting the spread of new varieties of seeds and plantation crops, introducing coffee and cocoa and founding the some of the first botanic gardens in the Gold Coast.

[5] The Brafo is said to have been appointed by the God Bobiwisi of Winneba Hill, as a 'deputy' in local matters, and was brought to Mankesim from Ashanti, where he had been pointed out by local priests. The deity thus had an importance over a very wide area of the Gold Coast at the time.

Adu, King of Mankesim, was appointed the immediate guardian of the shrine, and proceeded to rally the support of neighbouring chiefs. Soon after this arrangement was made one of the fetish priests, of a lesser grade, decided to join the Christians and, with others, entered the sacred grove and cut several poles there for building purposes. Hearing of this the priests went to Adu and called on him to punish the miscreants. Adu then collected his people, invaded the Christian village at night, burnt it to the ground, and carried away ten Christian villagers to Mankesim. Very soon afterwards, the Governor at Cape Coast came to hear of the incident and summoned Adu to Cape Coast.

A neighbouring chief, Amoku, King of Anomabu, was also summoned by the Judicial Assessor at the Castle and asked to intervene and prevail on Adu to comply with the Governor's summons, which he had initially chosen not to do. By now, however, the Fanti chiefs from further afield were gathering and, to the Governor, all the makings of a very troublesome rebellion appeared to be present. Moreover, a massacre of Christians was threatened, while Adu threatened to have the turncoat priest drowned. Suddenly, however, as quickly as the rebellion had threatened, the chaos started to die down. This was because a sufficiently large number of the chiefs summoned by Adu, many of whom had initially supported him, became far more concerned about the interruption to trade and the increasingly disturbed state of the country. They preferred to persuade Adu to come to Cape Coast and, eventually, to reach an amicable settlement with the Governor. The Christians, meanwhile, were discouraged, apparently, from further violations of the sacred woodlands of Brafo.

The Mankesim incident highlighted, in a microcosm, some of the apparently contradictory factors that were to shape and constrain the struggle between the Gold Coast Chiefs and the inroads of Christian culture, more especially when the contest involved European claims over forest land long endowed with indigenous religious and customary meaning. Already though, at Mankesim, the increasingly attractive priorities of trade had already made themselves felt. Two important shifts were to take place in this dynamic. First of all the prosyletisers of Christianity and the products of the Cape Coast Christian establishment were to change sides, ending up as redoubtable defenders of indigenous sacred sites and indigenous control of forests and lands. Anomabu had already, at Mankesim, indicated that an undisturbed hinterland for trade took precedence over the moral economy of sacred woodlands. While apparently contradictory, these two developments, the advocacy of native land rights by the Christian educated elite and the growth of African capitalism, together sowed the seeds for an incipient nationalist movement in the Gold Coast and, within that, the basis for an increasingly strong movement against colonial conservation.

Without doubt, a marriage of convenience took place between the defence of ancestral land rights on the one hand and the advocacy of unrestricted African capitalism on the other. The contemporary strength of the latter should not be under-estimated, as it formed, for example, the formative force behind the dynamic growth of the indigenous cocoa industry in the early twentieth century.[6]

While the seeds of hostility to colonial environmental and land policy were already in existence at the time of the Mankesim incident, the beginnings of a real movement did not appear to take root for a further forty years. By then, the indigenous movement had to face a conflict with a forest conservation ideology that was both complex in its origins and comprehensive in its ambitions for control of land. The multi-faceted roots of colonial conservation ideology are now beginning to be better understood, and had oriental as well as western roots. The motivations behind conservation ideology were far more than simply economic, and, arguably, it was the 'scientific' moral economy behind much of colonial conservation that gave it strength, and made it such a useful ally of colonial control agendas in India and other parts of Africa.[7] In West Africa, however, this ideology encountered an equally complex and resourceful indigenous adversary.

Alfred Moloney and the Elements of British West African Conservation Ideology.

The origins of the kind of forest conservation that colonial governments attempted to apply in West Africa can be found in conservation strategies

[6] Hill, *Migrant cocoa farmers.*
[7] See Chapter 2; also, R.H. Grove, *Green Imperialism; colonial expansion, tropical island Edens and the origins of environmentalism, 1600–1860* (Cambridge, 1995).

first worked out in Mauritius, India, Burma and the Cape Colony.[8] How were these strategies adapted to the purposes of the late-developing colonial state in West Africa? Essential to the early development of conservationism was the involvement of a cadre of professional botanists nurtured in the medical schools of the Scottish Universities and the botanic gardens of Paris and Edinburgh and, more latterly, at the Royal Botanic Gardens, Kew. One of the central figures propagandising state forest conservation in India and South Africa had been Joseph Dalton Hooker, Director of Kew for several decades.[9] In his view the application of the kind of state forestry that had developed in India was far too long delayed in other parts of the colonial empire. In 1868, at the Paris Exhibition, he decried the fact that it was only in France, Germany and India that forest management and training was firmly established. 'Wherever English rule extends', he wrote,

> with the single exception of India, the same apathy, or at least inaction prevails. In South Africa, according to colonial botanists' reports, millions of acres have been made desert, and more are being made desert annually, through the destruction of indigenous forests... [10]

It was this account of the danger of widespread desiccation, with its implied threat to the economic basis of colonial rule, (lent further

---

[8] R.H. Grove, 'Early themes in African conservation: the Cape in the nineteenth century', in D. Anderson, and R. Grove, eds, *Conservation in Africa; people, policies and practice* (Cambridge, 1987); Grove, *Green imperialism.*

[9] M. Allan, *The Hookers of Kew* (London, 1967); Grove, 'Early themes'.

[10] J.D. Hooker, 'Forestry', *Journal of Applied Science,* 1 (1872), pp. 221–223. He continued in this vein: 'In Demerara the useful timber trees have all been removed from accessible regions, and no care and thought given to planting others; from Trinidad we have the same story; in New Zealand there is not now a good Kundi (Kauri) pine to be found near the coast; and I believe that the annals of almost every English colony would repeat the tale of wilful wanton waste and improvidence. On the other hand in France, Prussia, Switzerland and Russia, the forests and waste lands are the subjects of devoted attention on the part of the government, and colleges, provided with a complete staff of accomplished professors, train youths of good birth and education to the duties of state foresters. Nor in the case of France is this law confined to the mother country. The Algerian forests are worked with scrupulous solicitude; and the collections of vegetable produce from the French colonies and New Caledonia etc. contain specimens which, though not falling technically under Class 87, abound in evidence of the forest products being all diligently explored'.

credibility by Hooker's position as Director of Kew), that first encouraged the Colonial office to contemplate some kind of unified environmental policy in the colonies. As we shall see, Hooker and his successor at Kew, Arthur Thistleton-Dyer, continued to act as a *de facto* conservation lobby, continually exhorting the Colonial Office and individual colonial governors to pursue forest protection policies and to develop official biological expertise, generally by founding botanic gardens. Unlike in much of India and Southern Africa the manifestly rich West African coastal forests were, in the 1870s, as yet little affected by deforestation. Desiccation would both forfeit their commercial potential and threaten more drastic climatic consequences. Hooker's Paris warning was reprinted in the *Journal of Applied Science* in 1872, thus reaching a much wider audience.[11]

Within two years the Colonial Office had taken the decision to issue a Circular Despatch (along with a copy of representations made to it, on the basis of Hooker's paper, by the English Commissioner of Woods and Forests), to all the 'Officers Administering the Governments of Her Majesty's Colonies'. A similar endeavour was made in June 1874 by the Foreign Office, 'through Her Majesty's representative abroad, towards the collection of information on the production and consumption of timber in foreign countries'. [12] The Circular required answers to a long list of questions, drawing particular attention to rates of deforestation and the threat of climatic change, as well as the commercial potential of forests. Particularly significant was the question; 'Are the forests.....owned by the Government, or private persons?' [13]

---

[11] Hooker, 'Forestry'.

[12] The result was compiled in Command Paper C. 1161 of 1875.

[13] The full list was:

    1. What are the kinds of timber trees produced in the country, and to what uses are they generally applied?

    2. Are the forests or lands producing trees owned by the government or private persons?

    3. What is the approximate extent of timber-producing forests or lands at the present time?

    4. Is this area increasing or diminishing?

    5. If diminishing, from what cause?

    6. Are any steps being taken for the prevention of waste or for replanting any area which has been cleared?

Fairly rapid responses were made to these circulars by the Cape Colony and Natal, and by the African island colonies, above all St Helena and Mauritius. On the West African mainland, however, the only official response was one received from the Gambia.[14] A fuller response from the rest of West Africa had to await the appearance of a book written by Alfred Moloney, a Roman Catholic colonial official (later Governor of Lagos Colony), and an enthusiastic advocate of forest conservation. His book, first published in 1887 and entitled *Sketch of the Forestry of West Africa,* formed the basis and the main stimulant for official conservation policy in the region, and also seems to have influenced the attitudes of the Colonial Office itself.[15] Its constituent ideology is therefore worthy of some attention.

More than most contemporary colonial administrators Moloney had had the opportunity to travel widely throughout West Africa and he was especially familiar with conditions in the Gambia, Sierra Leone, the Gold Coast and Lagos Colony. Two main influences seem to have moved Moloney to write his conservationist tract, a work which might be compared with earlier, and more widely influential, pieces by Hugh Cleghorn and George Perkins Marsh.[16] Firstly, Moloney had long been

7. What is the quantity of timber which might be fairly cut every year without permanent injury to the forests?
8. What is the quantity actually cut every year?
9. What is the proportion of home consumption and export?
10. What have been the annual exports of each kind of timber during the last ten years; stating the proportions to each country, and the value of such exports?
11. What are the reasons for or causes of the small exportations in comparison with the capability of production?
12. (If it be so), what are the the the causes of the small exportations in comparison with the capability of production?
13. Have any observations been made or conclusions arrived at as to the climatic influence of forests or the effect of their clearance on rainfall, floods etc.?
14. Forward any reports made by departments or societies, or any Acts of Legislature bearing on the subject [These two last points bear a strong resemblance to parts of a questionnaire sent out by the East India Company in 1847].

[14] The responses were compiled by the Colonial Office in a Command Paper (No 2197) in 1878.

[15] A. Moloney, *Sketches of the forestry of West Africa* (London, 1887).

[16] H. Cleghorn, *The forests and gardens of South India* (Edinburgh, 1861); G.P. Marsh, *Man and nature* (New York, 1864).

a keen advocate of the development of the rubber industry in West Africa. Equally, he had become increasingly aware of its destructive effects, particularly in French West Africa and on the coast of Mozambique. 'In Gaboon', he wrote,

> it is well known that there has been almost an extermination of the tree that produced this valuable article of commerce ... which has now caused it, I am told, to be excluded among the exports from that part of West Africa – how different it would have been had there been some system of forest conservancy or re-forestation or even had timely advice been tendered and advantageously followed as to the treatment of the trees and the collection of the rubber. This was a regular case of killing the goose for the golden eggs and adds another instance ... of the result brought about by the reckless destruction of trees ... blind adherence to one industry is not to be advocated, as was proved though somewhat late, to the cost of many, in some of our colonies; but when we have a good thing we should treat it kindly and tenderly.[17]

There was no reason, he thought, why such destruction should take place in 'Her Majesty's possessions on the Gambia, on the Gold Coast, and at Lagos'. 'Let the sad experience here recorded', he added, 'be a lesson both to buyers and collectors in Colonies named, that we may not have ..... to listen to a tale of woe and to the cry of 'spilt milk', in consequence of the destruction of the rubber trees'. Furthermore, he believed that large scale re-afforestation might be advisable and suggested the use of *Casuarina* trees.

　　Moloney was most concerned, however, with the likelihood, as he saw it, that deforestation might cause rapid climatic change. The dry and treeless reaches of the Accra plains were early evidence of this, he believed. During the early 1880s he had actively propagandised this view, writing frequent letters on the subject to the *Lagos Times,* ironically at a time when he was also actively supporting expansion of the rubber-collection industry, one of the chief agents of deforestation in Lagos Colony and the phenomenon that eventually provoked the first forest legislation in the colony. He quoted Alexander von Humboldt on deforestation, (who had said 'by felling trees which are adapted to the soil of the sides and summits of mountains, men, in every climate, prepare for future generations two

---

[17] Moloney, *Sketches,* p. 90

calamities at once, want of firewood and scarcity of water') and also repeated the pessimistic dictum of Schleiden that 'forests precede a population, and deserts follow it'.[18]

With respect to the threat of desiccation and desertification the field evidence which Moloney found most convincing consisted in the formal replies, published in 1878, that had been made to the Colonial and Foreign Office Circulars of 1874. He recorded approvingly that, at the Cape Colony, 'the immunity which British Kaffraria enjoys from the droughts so common in South Africa is believed to be due to the influence of the forests'.[19] At St Helena and Mauritius, despite pioneering attempts at state conservation, early uncontrolled deforestation had brought years of disastrous and alternate floods and droughts. The lessons of this experience, he said, needed to be learnt in West Africa before it was too late. 'Let landlords', he exhorted, 'be influenced by the suggestions briefly given in this chapter, and let them specially conserve, at least, such belts of wooded land as cover for mountains or hills and the flanks of rivers and streams.' He spoke out against 'shortsighted greed for a yard or two more ground for the production of sugar cane or some other plant when the price of sugar....stood temporarily high – sheer selfish greed for immediate gain.' Sugar cane plantations had, of course, nearly destroyed the forests of Mauritius at an earlier period and the crop was not yet important in West Africa. Nevertheless the commoditisation of agricultural output and the penetration of European market demand was, as Moloney hinted he knew, largely responsible for what he admitted was a very recent increase in rates of deforestation, as local farmers and rubber collectors (rather than plantation owners) responded to the growing market, especially, at this stage, in Lagos Colony, and to the financial impositions of the colonial state.[20] The main message of Moloney's book was that uncontrolled deforestation would lead to

---

[18] Moloney, *Sketches*, p.238; A. von Humboldt, *Personal narrative of travels to the equinoctial regions of the New Continent, 1799–1804*, trans. H.M. Williams (6 vols, London, 1819); M.J. Schleiden, *Die Pflanzen und ihr Leben: Populare Vortrage* (Leipzig, 1848).

[19] This would, in fact, have been an opinion expressed in the writings of John Croumbie Brown, the pioneering Colonial Botanist of the Cape Colony (Grove, 'Early themes').

[20] See O. Omosini, 'The rubber exporter trade in Ibadan, 1893–1904', *Journal of the Historical Society of Nigeria*, 10 (1979), pp. 21–42.

uncontrollable declines in rainfall, and he quoted what appeared to be convincing figures from the far more deforested colony of Sierra Leone. Such rainfall declines would lead to famine, he said, and 'it would be well to take warning from our Eastern allies, profiting by their experience, and put a stop to this unlimited practice of shaving the forest of timber.'[21] Moloney remained unspecific as to the methods by which forest conservation might be introduced into West Africa. This was partly because he was clearly aware of the problems of adapting traditional land-holding arrangements to the threat posed by the new economic situation. Selling of concessions by Gold Coast and Yoruba chiefs to timber cutters was already widespread by the 1880s. One solution, he thought, might be to impose conditions of re-planting on the concession holder. Moloney was, perhaps surprisingly, very well informed about the environmentally stabilising impact of the religious importance attached to certain trees and woodlands in Yorubaland, a region which he had already come to know well. 'I may mention', he said,

> that I am aware of the superstitious respect that attaches in the Yoruba country to the *Oroko, Afon, Araba, Ashori*, and other large trees, and to the consequent immunity they enjoy from the axe, as also the understanding that palm trees on allotted sites are preserved and remain the property of the landlord.[22]

But more than this was now necessary, he considered, and it would be to the landholder's commercial advantage to adopt conservation methods, 'notwithstanding he will surely be ready to increase the value of his recognised vested interest by the adoption of my suggestions as they stand, or in some modified, yet advantageous form.'

To sum up, Moloney's conservation message, as outlined in his book, exhibited some unusually sophisticated views about the social realities involved in controlling environmental change, particularly in a book intentionally published in 1887 to celebrate such an obviously 'imperialist' event as Queen Victoria's Golden Jubilee. Much of the book was consciously development-oriented, particularly in its prescriptions for the establishment of Model Farms and Botanic Gardens, and for the

---

[21] By 'our Eastern allies', Moloney presumably meant the Government of India.
[22] Moloney, *Sketches*.

introduction of new crops, specifically for local production on small-holdings. It was also, however, intended to panic colonial administrators, with its constant references to the dangers of climatic change, into declaring new forest laws. There was 'no time to be lost', he cajoled. 'Let us take time by the forelock', he suggested,

> in the older colonies, such as the Cape of Good Hope, Ceylon, Mauritius, Canada, New Zealand, South Australia, laws and regulations now exist for the conservation of their forests. There it was not that 'necessity had no law', but rather law became an absolute necessity, and legal restraints had to be exercised. It was in some instances almost a case of shutting the stable door after the horse had got out.

Traditional land-use practices would have to be overridden, he implied, for the greater good. Furthermore, Moloney recommended the revolutionary idea that African natives should be fully trained for service as technicians and forest conservation experts. He quickly put this into practice and in 1889 Thomas Dawodu and George Leigh proceeded to training at Hope Gardens, Jamaica and the Royal Botanical Gardens at Kew. They later took control of the Ebute Metta horticultural station and in the 1890s toured the whole of Yorubaland promoting agricultural extension policies and providing expertise.[23] In 1897 Dawodu and Leigh wrote a critical joint paper highlighting the serious deforestation in Ijebu and Ibadan close to Lagos.[24] They also made constant pleas, significantly emulating Moloney's colourful imagery, that indigenous rubber tappers should not 'kill the goose that lays the golden eggs'. Their expertise was useful ammunition for the government and was quickly utilised.

As we shall see, once Moloney's notions and his staffing policies were taken up by alarmed (or opportunist) colonial governments, the scene was set for complex conflict.

---

[23] O. Omosini, 'Background to the forestry legislation in Lagos colony and protectorate, 1897–1902', *Journal of the Historical Society of Nigeria,* 9 (1978), pp. 45–69.

[24] F.E.R. Leigh and T.B. Dawodu 'Report on Nigerian Forests', 28 July 1897, PRO CO 879/65, No. 635, quoted in C.W. Newbury, *British policy towards West Africa: select documents 1875–1914* (Oxford, 1971).

The politics of conservation in the Gold Coast 1887–1902

To some extent, the conflict between indigenous landholders and colonial restrictions on land-use had already emerged in the Gold Coast well before Moloney's book was published in 1887.[25] Initial protests were provoked by the conditions of the Public Lands Ordinance enacted in 1876. By 1886, King Tackie, a chief of Usshertown, Accra, objected to new boundaries drawn by the government under the Act for construction purposes on the edge of Accra. His protests were successful and, when the government sought to strengthen the Act, the request was turned down by the Secretary of State for the Colonies in London.[26]

By 1889 Moloney's views had become well known and were clearly reaching official ears in Accra. In that year the Governor, Sir Brandford Griffith, proposed a remedy to all the gathering arguments on state versus chiefly land control, by proposing that the whole colony should be taken over as 'Crown land' and administered to 'greater advantage than the inhabitants could do it for themselves'. This was not, of course, quite what Moloney had in mind. Conservation arguments were, often, in this way, twisted to the advantage of a colonial executive. The Colonial Office itself remained more cautious and asked for more detailed proposals. However, the hidden agenda of the government in Accra was now on open display as far as the chiefs were concerned. Already apparent, too, was the clearly different view taken in London. These differences soon became even more apparent.

During 1891 the Chief Justice of the Gold Coast, J.T. Hutchinson, was asked to consider a proposal for taking over all 'waste lands' as government 'property'. He immediately warned that 'the importance of the chiefs and heads of families would be reduced and a sense of injustice and consequent hostility to government would be created in the minds of the people'. This was a prophetic statement, and made by a lawyer who already realised the very weak legal position of the government. Instead, Hutchinson suggested, the Crown might take control of minerals and 'unused or unoccupied forest land'. Brandford Griffith was not satisfied

---

[25] This section draws heavily on D. Kimble, *A political history of Ghana: the rise of Gold Coast nationalism, 1880–1963* (Oxford, 1963).

[26] Kimble, *Political history of Ghana*.

with this, however, and, at the suggestion of his son (significantly a colonial administrator in Jamaica), proposed the introduction of a land tax which, if not paid, would render lands forfeit to the Crown. In response to this Hutchinson pointed out that there were two very practical obstacles to such a policy. Firstly, the country had never been surveyed (as, by contrast, the whole of India had been by this period) and lacked any fences and boundary marks. Secondly the chiefs, who had never accepted the principle of trusteeship, were already selling land to speculators and to each other, often utilising English property law; such transactions could not, retrospectively, be undone. By late 1893 the Governor was forced to try another tack and announced that 'the rapid expansion of the timber trade would make legislation necessary at no distant date; in order to ensure fair play (sic) to landowners and to prevent the loss of valuable resources'. At this stage the Secretary of State for the Colonies, Lord Ripon, was now seriously worried about the apparently high rate of loss of the timber resource, almost certainly alerted (as Brandford Griffith had been) by Moloney's warnings, as well as by what he was learning about plans for a timber railway, to be constructed between Elmina and Cape Coast.

Pressure from London during 1894 then resulted in the drafting, in Accra, of a Lands Bill designed, contrary to Hutchinson's consistent advice, 'to vest waste lands, forest lands and minerals in the Queen'. By this measure an end would be put to the system whereby rural chiefs could conclude mining or timber rights over vast and ill-defined areas of country. Receiving the draft bill in London the Colonial Office agreed that the government should be able to prevent the lands of the colony falling into the hands of (European) concession mongers for a bottle of rum or a case of gin'. This patronising attitude (in fact large sums of money were involved in concession sales!) foreshadowed a severe under-estimation of the reaction of the population to the 1894 Lands Bill. Almost immediately after the first reading of the Bill in the Legislative Council protests began to coalesce and gather strength, initially around Accra itself. Soon newspapers such as the *Gold Coast Methodist Times* took up the issue, foreshadowing both the later involvement of the Cape Coast Methodist lawyers in the forest issue and the critical part played by African newspapers in popularising it among the educated classes. The first petitions to the Legislative Council argued that the Public Lands Ordinance of 1876 was already quite powerful enough for the government's purposes. The real intention of the Governor, they feared, was to deprive the chiefs of their 'lands, their gold mines, their gum trees, their rubber trees, their kola trees and everything that is worth having and which descended to them from their remote ancestors'. There was, the petitioners argued, no such thing as 'waste land' as all land was 'owned by Kings, chiefs or private individuals'. This assertion was, in fact, far from the truth.

In late 1894 the Attorney-General and Colonial Secretary both returned to the Colony after an absence to find the issue well ablaze. Though having somewhat different views of the matter, both men were highly critical of the concept of the Lands Bill, which had been introduced while they had been on leave. Hodgson, the Colonial Secretary, was especially concerned about casual and illegal annulment of all existing ownerships of vast tracts of so-called 'unoccupied' forest land. He believed, too, that such heavy-handed interventions were quite unnecessary. The government would profit itself far more, he wrote with perspicacity, by safeguarding 'the interests of the inhabitants and the capitalists'.

At this point Brandford Griffith, the originator of the Lands Bill, left the Gold Coast for good. Meanwhile the agitations which he had first provoked continued to grow, having now spread as far away from Accra as Tarkwa and Anomabu, towards the South-West. Europeans sympathetic to the native view, such as James Drew, now pointed out that the 1876 Ordinance had, as the chiefs had realised, already securely confirmed and legitimised their land rights. The Gold Coast, Drew asserted, was in quite a different position from other colonial protectorates, since it had not been acquired by conquest, cession or treaty. John Maxwell, the Governor succeeding Brandford Griffith, does not appear to have accepted this critical difference. Instead, in the first of many appeals to 'legal' precedents established in other colonies, he argued for the adoption in the Gold Coast of the system applied on the Malay States, whereby land sales concessions by chiefs would only be valid if countersigned by British authorities. This too proved unworkable under the terms of the 1876 Ordinance.

By 1895 there was an additional factor in the situation, in the form of a new Colonial Secretary, Joseph Chamberlain, an arch-advocate of non-intervention and of business interests. It was this latter preference, as well as his desire to maintain good relations with the chiefs of the Gold Coast and Yorubaland, that set the scene for the subsequent episodes of resistance against forest policy in both regions. The issues in the two areas continued to be seen as interconnected, particularly as far as Chamberlain was concerned. He felt, however, that some legislation was necessary in order to prevent indiscriminate felling, but refused to be hurried into a decision that could prove politically damaging, in direct contrast to the local governments in Accra and Lagos. In October, 1895, therefore, Governor Maxwell decided to drop the Lands Bill and focus on a newer and narrower Bill. The chiefs, with the effective aid of Chamberlain, had therefore achieved an extraordinary initial victory.

The protesters' complaint was not only about the disruption of traditional land-use claims and family identity. It also concerned a more basic racial theme. The implication of the Governor's Bill was, essentially, that African claims were not as valid as imposed European legal principles. The English-language newspapers recognised this as an unacceptably racial matter. One Journal, *Truth*, commented with heavy irony that 'the native's untutored mind does not grasp the idea that the colour of his skin justifies the confiscation of his property'. This was the issue in a nutshell. On the other hand, the efficacy of opposition to the Lands Bill was related, above all, to the close involvement of African lawyers from both Accra, and, more particularly, from Cape Coast, where the early institution of secondary schooling by Wesleyan missionaries had produced, by the mid-1890s, a considerable crop of London-trained lawyers and potential campaigners, many of whom were thinking in increasingly nationalist terms. Indeed, in 1895 an exasperated Maxwell was led to complain that opposition to the Lands Bill was 'fostered and fed on every conceivable occasion by African lawyers'. The lively Gold Coast newspapers added their literate voice, with sometimes increasingly Shakespearean hyperbole. The *Gold Coast Methodist Times* commented, for instance, that the Lands Bill was 'pregnant with fell and butcherly stratagems....by an erroneous, mutinous and unnatural hypothesis, land of economic importance' was being 'diplomatically enveloped in the term "waste" so that it could be wrested from its owners', a procedure which the newspapers termed 'unusual robbery and British Brigandism!'

The more restricted Lands Bill of 1897 sought only to 'administer waste and forest lands and not to vest them in the Queen'. However it met with equally determined resistance, as the mechanisms it proposed for concessions threatened the wholesale conversion of traditional rights to rights sanctioned by European law. The arrival back in the Gold Coast of J.E. Casely-Hayford, later a prolific writer and nationalist, also served to encourage the protesters, who had, to some extent, already tasted success. Resistance to the 1897 Bill, after it had been put to the Legislative Council, now gave rise to a new movement. This was based on the Fanti association known as Mfantsi Amanbuhu Fekuw, an established grouping at Cape Coast. In April 1897 this was now re-named The Gold Coast Aborigines' Rights Protection Society (or ARPS).[27] The ARPS was, of course, led by an elite group closely allied, especially at Cape Coast and Axim, with more militant members of the Wesleyan Church. However the relations with the church could be quickly used as a network to convene meetings and 'educate' the Chiefs of many districts as to the state of play on the forest issue. From hindsight it can be argued, quite correctly, that the ARPS was supporting the interests of incipient indigenous land speculators and capitalists, many of them in league with European capitalists and traders. However, this does not detract from the sincerity of the movement, which was quickly finding that it had powerful and perhaps unexpected allies abroad. Already, the Liverpool

---

[27] The society's opening public statement ran: 'Whereas in former times , all measures intended by the government for the whole Protectorate were brought before a meeting of the various Kings and Chiefs of the Protectorate convened for the purpose, and who in turn communicated them to the people of their respective districts by gong-gong. And Whereas this time-honoured and effective custom has for some time been set aside and superseded by the Gazette And Whereas a very large majority of the population of the Gold Coast Protectorate are still unable to read And Whereas even the greater part of those able to read cannot well comprehend the meaning of the Bills passed from time to time by the government, the above society of which natives and residents alike can be members has been formed to discuss various Bills intended to be passed by the Government from time to time with a view to fully understanding the meaning purport object and effect thereof that every person may have the opportunity of understanding the same.

and Manchester Chambers of Commerce had expressed their dislike of the Gold Coast land bills and other proposals to restrict forest use.

Joseph Chamberlain, himself a highly successful Birmingham businessman, as well as radical politician, clearly took the same kind of view. A decisive moment came in June 1897 when a Dispatch was drafted to the Governor in Accra, warning him that 'alarm and uncertainty amongst capitalists in Britain might discourage enterprise in the Gold Coast'. The ARPS was also finding useful ammunition from other official sources. In 1895 Governor Maxwell had commissioned a study of Gold Coast land tenure systems.[28] He had hoped that this would strengthen the hand of government (as similar studies had done in India). However the report was inconclusive and unhelpful as far as the government was concerned. The ARPS, however, found that it could be used to support their case. The report confirmed that 'every piece of land in the Gold Coast' had an owner. Only on the failure of successors, it pointed out, did it fall back into the common land of the village, subject to control of chiefs and elders. 'Not only are the bonds of society to be snapped, but family ties are to be broken and family relationships destroyed', wrote Mensah Sarbah, a lawyer of the ARPS. The report, he said, showed that the Bill 'refers to the whole land of this country, depriving the aborigines of their right in the soil of their native land'.[29]

Chamberlain's June 1898 draft Despatch to the Governor indicated how the tide had turned in favour of the ARPS. Thus although Casely-Hayford, in 1898, led a deputation of lawyers and chiefs to London to protest against the 1897 Bill, the Colonial Office had already itself conceded to the opposition and determined to have the Accra government drop the Bill. Instead a 'Concessions Ordinance' was brought forward and passed through the Legislature in 1900. To avoid unnecessary argument this Bill was actually drawn up in consultation with the solicitors of the ARPS in London. It merely restricted the size of concessions and made no claims to public lands or interference in African ownership. Finally, all clauses relating to forest protection had been removed.

---

[28] *Report upon the customs relating to the tenure of land on the Gold Coast,* London, 1895.
[29] *The Gold Coast Methodist Times,* 30 June 1897.

Ultimately, then, the colonial government, pursuing an agenda which combined conservation aims with a desire for greater control over land (as well as political control over chiefs, one may surmise), was defeated by what was eventually a very multi-faceted alliance of chiefs, lawyers, British business interests and radical politicians, personified by Joseph Chamberlain, Casely-Hayford and Mensah Sarbah. A somewhat concealed element in the story relates to the political instability on the borders of Yorubaland, caused by apprehension about French territorial ambitions. This was a matter that was actually uppermost in Chamberlain's mind in 1897, and from which the Gold Coast anti-Land Bill movement clearly benefited. Chamberlain was in fact now even more determined not to upset the political economy of Yorubaland and the Lagos Colony.

Opposition to Forest Conservation Proposals in the Lagos Colony

The progress and success of the opposition to the 1897 Lands Bill in the Gold Coast had an immediate impact in the Lagos Colony where, in November 1897, a Bill had been introduced that was aimed primarily at controlling the wave of forest destruction being caused by the kind of uncontrolled rubber-tapping which Moloney had previously warned against.[30] This bill, intended to become law on 1 January 1898, would have made it unlawful for any person to cut or remove trees or timber (except for firewood or building) or to collect fibre, gum or rubber, without a licence from a District Commissioner, Travelling Commissioner or Chief Magistrate. Although the bill aimed, on the basis of the Gold Coast experience, to avoid land tenure matters, it still evoked an immediate tide of opposition, encouraged by local newspapers which were, as in the Gold Coast, very prominent in raising issues and binding opposition forces together. 'The forests of Yoruba', the *Lagos Standard* trumpeted, 'are not government property, nor are they subject to any alienation to any foreign power [sic]. It is to be presumed, therefore, that considering local considerations and feeling, the proposed Ordinance

---

[30] Omosini, 'Background to the forestry legislation', 'The rubber exporter trade'; E.O. Egboh, 'Background to the forestry legislation in Lagos Colony and Protectorate, 1897–1902', *Journal of the Historical Society of Nigeria*, 9 (1978), pp. 45–69.

will be withdrawn and nullified'.[31] The *Lagos Weekly Record* was more geographically ambitious and added:

> forest lands in Africa compose lands allowed to be fallowed and every forest has its owner. To demand that an owner should first obtain a licence and pay a royalty before he can collect the products of his own land is arbitrary to say the least; while it will be more arbitrary still to declare that no ownership attached to such forest lands and thereby deprive the native of his legitimate rights. Nor would it be less arbitrary and objectionable for the governor to be vested with power to determine by proclamation when a man could collect the produce of his own land, and when he could not.....the bill overshoots the mark and is calculated to cause trouble and vexation rather than to confer benefits. [32]

The Bill had, in fact, been framed on the basis of an Indian forest conservation model, after Sir Ralph Moor, the High Commissioner, had proposed to the Colonial Office that the Indian forest system was ideal for the Lagos Colony. This marked one of the first of many attempts to impose Indian land-use models on the region, a concept finally discredited only as late as 1938, with the publication of the Leverhulme Commission on West African Agriculture.

By November 1897 the campaign against the 1897 Lands Bill in the Gold Coast was reaching a climax, and this caused Sir Henry McCallum, the Lagos Governor, to withdraw the Lagos Forest Bill from the legislature in 1898 with unusual speed, almost before local opposition had got off the ground. The Colonial Office acted with even more haste, demanding that the Bill should be withdrawn completely. Not only had the extent of the Gold Coast opposition become apparent in the critical six months between March 1897 (the date of the Gold Coast Lands Bill) and November 1897, but the threat from the French had also grown greater.

---

[31] 'The Forest ordinance', *Lagos Standard,* 10 November 1897, quoted in Egboh, 'Background to the forestry legislation'.

[32] ' The proposed Forest Ordinance', *Lagos Times,* 17 November 1897.

The Trouble at Ijebu-Ode

The apparent willingness on the part of government to placate opposition by the Lagos Colony chiefs to the bill was further supplemented in early 1898 by the explosive political impact of a clash between guardians of a traditional religious site and Christian converts, very much on the lines of the Mankesim incident in the Gold Coast of fifty years previously. Considerable local unrest had been caused at Ijebu-Ode, (north of Lagos), when Christians had violated a sacred *Oro* woodland and carried away a pig. The matter came to a head when the Police Inspector-General, Mitchell, arrived at Ijebu-Ode to investigate the matter, and ordered the Awujale, the local king, to be sent for. When the Awujale did not respond, Hausa soldiers were sent in the fetch him. Fighting broke out, and some chiefs were wounded.

The matter was only finally resolved when the Governor appointed a Commissioner to deal with the situation. The Commissioner appreciated the harm that was done and the Awujale received an official apology. George Denton, the Acting Governor, also authorised the King to collect a heavy duty on all rubber collected in the area. This effectively drove a coach and horses through the provisions of the 1897 Bill. Denton minuted that:

> At the present juncture I am desirous that the great unrest which has just been tided over, should not again be resuscitated at a time when foreign politics are so much more important than domestic politics, especially as the government is in such matters dependent upon the active assistance of the natives....

Chamberlain reinforced this argument, writing that, 'the bill should be dropped notwithstanding the fact that the destruction of rubber trees is so serious as to call for prompt measures to stop it.' [33]

One immediate result of these political concessions to the Yoruba chiefs was that deforestation continued unabated. A copy of a report on the level of destruction eventually reached Thistleton-Dyer, Joseph Hooker's sucessor as Director of Kew. It was, of course, Thistleton-Dyer who had encouraged Moloney's enthusiasm for the rubber trade. Now

---

[33] Colonial Office Minute, 8 Feb., 1898, CO147/121/314

he was seriously alarmed at the consequences of the trade and put the Lagos government in an embarrassing position by calling for immediate action to stop timber-cutting. Chamberlain reluctantly agreed to support some measures and, in January 1899, draft Forest Rules were circulated. On this occasion the Director of Kew made the innovative suggestion that the chiefs and local authorities should be made responsible for forest management.

This suggestion was immediately taken up by Chamberlain as a way out of his dilemma. MacGregor, the new Governor, was vehemently opposed to this notion, and horror-struck at the degree of power that would thereby be conferred on the chiefs. Nevertheless eventually even he agreed that there was no alternative way out of the problem. Essentially, by July 1899, the onus of responsibility had been handed over to the chiefs, leaving the government with only an advisory capacity. Although this situation did not persist without alteration for long an important principle had been conceded, largely at the behest of Thistleton-Dyer and Joseph Chamberlain. It amounted to the beginnings of a far more conciliatory policy than that which was to prevail in the Gold Coast where the power of the chiefs in terms of forest management was retained largely through (albeit successful) prolonged resistance and confrontation. In Lagos Colony the principle of local management was to develop into the formalised system of Native Administration Forest Reserves, a device designed by Sir Frederick Lugard to recognise the *de facto* submission of the colonial government to the ecological, land tenure and religious claims of the Yoruba chiefs.

The concessions to the Lagos chiefs in 1899 did not mean, of course, that the majority of the rural population were happy with the arrangement. On the contrary, they now had to pay fees to the chiefs for produce that had, until now, been freely available. The compromise was thus one that benefited the (senior) chiefs and benefited the colonial government, which could remove itself from unnecessary confrontation. On the other hand this policy now displaced serious conflicts about changing mechanisms of resource allocation into a series of disputes between those privileged by the colonial state and those who had been, effectively, restricted or impoverished as a result. In fact, in this context, and for the next sixty years, disputes over forest use in Nigeria often involved, (through this process of social distortion), the making of appeals to officers of the colonial state against the chiefs. Such appeals were, characteristically, made by shifting cultivators, migrants, and, not least, deputations of women, the latter protesting against agreements made between the indigenous patriarchy and the Forest Department. In the Gold Coast, where land was generally passed down through the female line, such disuputes were less common. It was only in the late 1920s and 1930s that the government again found itself in conflict with the higher echelon of chiefs, as a direct consequence of changes in conservation policy.

In 1899 a report written by Dr Cyril Punch for Thistleton-Dyer on the forests of Lagos Colony had indicated that the rubber industry was continuing to cause serious damage. On receiving his copy of the report in May 1899 Chamberlain expressed a further apparently unorthodox view; he thought that it 'might be practicable to educate the indigenous population to act more wisely in future' with respect to forest resources. This was a logical further step to supplement the principle of control being handed over to the chiefs. Unfortunately the development of such interesting notions was disrupted by Denton, the Governor, who declared an arbitary ban on rubber collection, thereby destroying any obvious economic incentive the chiefs might have for preventing defor-estation, through fee income. In fact Denton's measure actually served to re-awaken opposition and, moreover, to bring in the Liverpool and Manchester Chambers of Commerce on the side of the chiefs, just as had happened in the Gold Coast.

Once more, under pressure from Kew, a new Forest Ordinance was brought forward by Governor Denton in October 1900. He found himself supported by Kew. Thistleton-Dyer had by this time changed his mind and decided to opt for a system of direct government control.[34] The

---

[34] Thus he wrote in Febuary 1900; 'At first I was under the impression that these forests were so considerable that the risk of exhaustion was of little moment compared with the direct benefit from the export trade. But it is now evident that this is not so and that an important natural asset is being rapidly used up....the ultimate result will be for the land to become naked and dispossessed of its natural resources. It scarcely requires argument to show that such a state of affairs is eminently undesirable and would not be creditable to the British administration'; Kew Gardens to CO, dt 21 Feb 1900 PRO: CO879/65/635/146.

new Bill led to mass meetings in Lagos on September 19th 1901 and to unrest in Egbaland a week later. The Alake and his chiefs then visited Sir Gilbert Carter, the new governor. At the meeting the Egbas pointed out that the bill transgressed all the premises of the 1893 Egba treaty with the British. Once more, as with the 1876 Gold Coast Ordinance, the British were hoist by their own legal petard. Subsequently, opposition developed among a whole variety of elite groups. Moreover, the level of opposition to the Forest Bill in the Lagos colony was faithfully reported in the *Gold Coast Globe and Ashanti Argus* and in *West Africa*.

Eventually, Chamberlain was once again forced to intervene to accept the local protesters' view that the proposed legislation transgressed traditional land rights. The Colonial Office therefore forced an amendment to the Forest Bill by stipulating that the Governor might apply forest regulations subject only to the consent of any African rulers in the districts affected. This was, of course, a major concession, and marked the effectiveness of the popular and business pressures that had been exerted against the Lagos government. Furthermore, by requiring chiefly consent to forest regulations, the Colonial Office effectively defused opposition to the Forest Bill, which was passed in an amended form on March 11th 1902. It also ended most organised opposition to state forest conservation, at least in South-West Nigeria, and laid the basis for Lugard's special treatment of the Yoruba chiefs, formally notified in the context of the Nigerian Forest Ordinance of 1916.

The Native Administration Forest Reserves, a concept designed by Lugard, (and at first unique to Nigeria) were a belated recognition of the extent to which real power over forests had been conceded to the Yoruba chiefs. However, the success of the resistance movement affected a much wider area than Yorubaland and even ensured that in some areas, particularly in the Delta and Calabar regions of Southern Nigeria, no government forest reserves were declared at all, for fear of arousing uncontrollable political turmoil.

By 1916 the extent of structural adaptation of a colonial forest conservation system to the realities of Lugardian indirect rule, to the religious and political significance of the Southern Nigerian forests, and to successful pressure-group tactics, was being tacitly admitted by government. This became especially apparent in Lugard's own *Memos on*

Forestry in Nigeria, published as part of a more general treatise on colonial government in 1918:

> The conditions which prevail in the Oyo and Abeokuta provinces are to some extent different from those obtaining elsewhere in Nigeria. These progressive Yoruba-speaking Provinces formerly asserted a quasi-independence by treaty. They are exceedingly tenacious of the tribal or family ownership of the land (including forests), and their proximity to the Colony of Lagos, and the influence of native lawyers who have become imbued with European ideas of land tenure, have combined to introduce among them the beginnings of a conception of individual ownership – though this conception is fiercely combatted by the conservative chiefs. For the reasons given in Para. 4, I favour the creation of forest reserves owned by the state, which (while providing for all the requirements of the local communities, which participate in their control, and share their profits) will add to the General Revenue, and thus decrease taxation.... in view of the special circumstances in the two provinces to which I refer, and to their great forest wealth, I am not averse to the creation in them of one or two 'Native Administration Forest Reserves' as an experimental measure....the Native Administration will undertake not merely their protection, but also their management.....it may be found necessary to apply some of these principles to some of the Reserves in the the Northern Provinces.[35]

Further Resistance in the Gold Coast, 1911–1916

Meanwhile, in the Gold Coast, the government had been faced with the almost entire collapse of their forest conservation plans. Between 1900 (the date of the Concessions Ordinance) and 1916 the Accra administration made a series of attempts to resurrect forest control legislation and to found a forest department. All of these failed ignominiously, so that, by 1916, the chiefs and their European timber-trading collaborators were left in effective control of the forest estate. The fact that, after 1916, the cocoa industry, with its associated agricultural migration and forest clearance, was becoming increasingly potent, only set the seal on what was described in the Gold Coast Blue Book of 1923 as an 'utterly useless'

[35] F. Lugard, *Political memoranda*, ed. A.H.M. Kirk-Greene (London, 1970), pp. 430–455.

situation, as far as forest conservation was concerned.[36] Perhaps the single most humiliating decision forced on the government during this period was that which brought about the closure in 1917 of the Forest Department, which had been set up by Indian Forest Service staff in 1909. What were the historical roots of this fiasco, unrecorded in any other colony?

The ARPS had continued to oppose all legislation affecting forests, often assuming, wrongly and naively, that the economic interests of the chiefs were identical with those of the rural population as a whole. The forest issue had, in fact, become the political core, if not *raison d'etre,* of emergent Gold Coast nationalism, in a way in which it had never done in Nigeria. The rise to prominence of the ARPS and the forest movement as joint vehicles of nationalism was due, in part, to the abilities of Casely-Hayford as a charismatic leader, writer and lawyer. It was also due to the extraordinary 'Magna Charta' statement made by Chamberlain, under some pressure, on the occasion of the ARPS deputation to London in 1898.[37] As it turned out, the forest issue lay largely dormant for a few years, until raised again by the introduction of a new Forest Ordinance in 1907. On paper, this measure prohibited the cutting of immature trees, but it was entirely ineffective. Then, in 1908, the Chief Conservator of Southern Nigeria, H. N. Thompson (earlier of the Indian Forest Service and previously, in 1880, a consultant to the Mauritius Government) visited the Gold Coast and recommended the introduction of the Southern Nigerian system. This gave rise to the introduction of yet another Forestry Bill. The ARPS was quickly goaded into action, one of its first actions being to telegraph the Colonial Office in protest, thus bypassing the local authorities. Suddenly appreciating the nature of the gathering political storm, the Conservator of Forests (in charge of a Department that was less than two years old) arrived in Cape Coast to try to convince the ARPS of his case. He was effectively ignored, while

[36] Hill, *Migrant cocoa farmers*; Gold Coast Government, 'Blue Book' for 1923.

[37] Chamberlain had stated; 'I think I can give you the assurance you wish.... I am willing that, in all cases where natives are concerned, the native law shall remain and prevail....with regard to the devolution of land. And I am also willing that the Court which is to decide upon these questions should be a judicial court' *Report of the proceedings of the deputation*, Accra 1898.

Casely-Hayford set about writing a major propaganda piece on the new Bill, entitled *Gold Coast Land Tenure and the Forest Bill*.[38]

Although the Forest Bill was passed in the Legislative Council in January 1911 it continued to run into opposition from the ARPS and the Head Chiefs of Accra and Osu. Casely-Hayford, meanwhile, prepared to lead another delegation to London. It was this plan which finally provoked the Colonial Office into despatching a Special Commissioner, H.C. Belfield, to report on the controversy. Belfield spent three months dutifully gathering evidence and holding enquiries at different centres, to which Casely-Hayford, the chiefs and the ARPS all made copious contributions. In the course of so doing, even the 'Lagos' option (that is, as in the 1902 Lagos Colony Ordinance), in which regulations would remain subject to a total chiefly veto, was rejected. Going even further for the opposition, Casely-Hayford and his colleagues specifically rejected the whole concept of 'scientific forestry'. Moreover they asserted, possibly in an attempt to avoid being seen as specifically anti-conservationist, that,

> the principle of conserving forests is not unknown to the people of this country. The chiefs now and again set apart certain parts of the forest for the preservation of game, the collection of forest produce and as sacred groves. This has been done from time immemorial to the present day, so that, apart from the taking by the timber industry and the mining industry of timber for fuel, the forests would be in a state of good preservation.[39]

Belfield's own studies actually bore out the truth of this statement. It was only when the spread of the cocoa-farming industry was well under way that blame for substantial deforestation could really be attached to indigenous rather than European activity.[40] Incidentally, it could be argued that the situation before about 1916 in the Gold Coast differed considerably from that found in Lagos Colony, where deforestation was undoubtedly severe as well as largely indigenous in its dynamic. Furthermore the evidence produced for the Belfield Commission was politically

---

[38] J.E. Casey-Hayford, *Gold Coast land tenure and the Forest Bill* (London, 1912).

[39] Ibid.

[40] Hill, *Migrant cocoa farmers*.

decisive. While the government in Accra still pressed for the 1911 Forest Bill to be implemented on the basis that 'injury that is irreparable within any reasonable period is being done to the Gold Coast forests', the Colonial Office itself took the quite different view that, 'because land tenure questions are now under detailed consideration' the chiefs should simply be told 'to stop felling trees indiscriminately'.[41] In other words, the Colonial Office did not wish to pursue the matter further. The Accra government had thus, for the moment, entirely lost the support of Whitehall.

Between 1912 and 1917, when the Office of Conservator of Forests of the Gold Coast actually had to be abolished, no forest reserves were created at all in the colony, as the government did not possess the necessary statutory powers. To this extent Casely-Hayford, the chiefs and the ARPS had achieved their professed objective. Significantly, though, some prominent chiefs still expressed the need to protect forests, especially in the face of the rapid clearance which the cocoa industry was stimulating.[42] In 1915 Chief Ofori Ata of Akim Abuakwa, for instance, was the first ruler to publish bye-laws controlling deforestation in his district. Such bye-laws, all passed at the initiative of the chiefs, prohibited cultivation of cocoa or food crops on all the outstanding hills in the district (thus, ironically, closely following the dictums of Moloney and the 1908 Thompson Report), and included a list of the forest trees that could not be felled without permission. The pattern established by 1915 never substantially altered in the Gold Coast itself and the colonial authorities remained embarrassed until independence at their failure to carry out the kind of forest conservation objectives that were considered normal in India or Burma, for example. This position was neatly summed up by Major F.M. Oliphant in a report made to the Gold Coast government in 1934. The situation, Oliphant complained bitterly,

> appeared to be largely governed by the fact that the domestic and export trade is in the hands of Africans, the lack of organisation being such that the whole month might well have been spent in examining that position

---

[41] Dispatch No. 747 of 30 November 1912 from Harcourt to Bryan, Ghana National Archives.

[42] Hill, *Migrant cocoa farmers.*

alone. On the question of supplies, I found that the measure of Government control over the forests was so small, destruction was proceeding so rapidly, and, for reasons given later in this report, both the present and future situation were so uncertain that no reliable opinion could be formed without a very searching enquiry and detailed inspection of forest areas.[43]

In Nigeria, by contrast, the colonial government was briefly able, during the period between 1919 and 1939, to establish a more draconian forest conservation policy, thus incurring considerable localised resistance, particularly from women opposing reserve policies jointly concluded by male chiefs and colonial administrators.[44] After 1945, however, the situation was transformed by the influence of returning West African troops, many of them thirsty for political change. Thus, Nigerian Geological Survey staff during the early 1950s well knew that their researches and plans for conservation would only be tolerated in some districts; and they were forced to curtail their survey plans accordingly.[45]

Conclusion

By 1916, both in Nigeria and the Gold Coast, the conservation debate had come full circle. At least temporarily, indigenous interest-groups, with the aid of some unusual allies, had been successful in re-asserting control over forest landscapes which, still imbued with social and religious meaning, were now increasingly significant in an economic sense. This did not mean, of course, that the tension between new economic development pressures and traditional management methods were resolved. They had simply been displaced into a new dispensation of power, but one in which European conservation models had had to suffer a severe adaptation.

To a marked degree, I think, the environmental debate and struggles of the 1890–1916 period in West African history foreshadowed

---

[43] F.M. Oliphant, *Report on the commercial possibilities and development of the forests of the Gold Coast* (Accra, 1934).

[44] I deal with this in an essay currently under preparation.

[45] A.T. Grove, *Land use and soil conservation in parts of Onitsha and Owerri provinces* (Zaria, 1951), and personal communication, 1994.

current concerns much more sharply than is generally appreciated. Specifically, then, in this paper we can highlight the extent to which the practitioners of forest conservation, both African *and* European, chose to reject or were compelled to reject the colonial land management models which they had institutionally inherited or had thrust upon them, and which had earlier found favour in the Indian and Southern African colonial context. We can also trace the way in which colonial rulers were forced to select regionally adapted models of conservation that more truly reflected the weakness of the colonial state in West Africa, particularly as regards the relatively successful retainment of power by local chiefs and rulers vis-à-vis the state, amidst a context in which European settlement always remained a low priority. This pattern of adaptation was probably not limited to the Gold Coast and Nigeria, but we would need further detailed local research in the African context to come to such conclusions. In particular I believe that we need to seriously question the notion of a homogeneous kind of 'colonial state' as far as the history of environmental policy was concerned. In fact it seems that the differences between colonial state policies were very much greater and more significant than the similarities. Even in India, where the forest department had long been considered by its harshest critics[46] as a formidable oppressor of the people, it is now being established that there were enormous regional disparities in the way in which policies were actually adapted to real social conditions on the ground.[47] In colonial British and Francophone Africa the disparities were almost certainly far greater. The way ahead, therefore, will be to construct much more detailed local environmental histories, both at government and village level, taking care to discard most preconceptions about colonial environmental policy along the way. At first this task will not be easy since, arguably, environmental history

---

[46] E.g., M. Gadgil and R. Guha, *This fisured land: towards an ecological history of India* (Delhi, 1993).

[47] M. Rangarajan, 'Production, desiccation and forest management in the Central provinces 1850–1930'; A. Skaria, 'Timber conservancy, desiccationism and scientific forestry; the Dangs region, 1840–1920s', in R. Grove, V. Damodaran, and S. Sangwan, eds, *Nature and the Orient: essays on the environmental history of South and Southeast Asia* (Delhi: Oxford University Press, 1997).

in Sub-Saharan Africa outside Nigeria[48] and the bounds of the white settler states of South Africa, Southern Rhodesia, Tanganyika and Kenya is still very much in its infancy.

In much of South Asia and southern and eastern Africa it is probably true that the failure of the colonial state to heed indigenous valuations and uses of the environment, as well as the failure of the colonised population to effectively resist colonial land-use ambitions, meant that social pressures were stored up for what were eventually far more explosive political outcomes, of the kind that finally provoked the Mau-Mau rebellion in Kenya or the Naxalite revolts in post-independence India[49]. In the course of such a storing-up of structural disadvantage the possibility of the widespread application of indigenous knowledge and the chances of a conservationist local response to the impact of capital penetration were often largely obliterated. By contrast the substantially different pattern which prevailed in some parts of southern Gold Coast and Nigeria set the scene, one might argue, for a more creative context for the development of indigenous land-use methods and tenures in the contemporary period.

---

[48] See O. Omosini, 'Alfred Moloney and his strategies for economic development in Lagos colony and hinterland, 1886–1891', *Journal of the Historical Society of Nigeria*, 7 (1975), pp. 657–677;.Omosini, 'Background to the forestry legislation', 'The rubber exporter trade'; Egboh, 'Background to the forestry legislation'.

[49] See Chapter 6.

6

Colonial Conservation, Ecological Hegemony and Popular Resistance: Towards a Global Synthesis

---

In most historical analyses of the colonial impact on indigenous rural societies there has been until recently an almost exclusive preoccupation with arable systems. The startling neglect of the non-arable landscape has been unfortunate since, in many societies, the ability to exploit marginal, non-arable land and forest has been critical to survival and the capacity to do so has become steadily more constrained as resources have been devoted to commodity production. Colonial rule has been particularly important in this respect. Colonialism and its successor states have brought about a transformation in the nature of the tenurial relationships between people, forest and other non-arable land. This has involved, in essence, a transition away from locally evolved man–land relations towards direct private property status or to direct state control. These changes have often involved a growing exploitation of the landscape for commodity production and a corresponding erosion in customary controls and common property rights or conventions.[1] The ecological transition has largely, although by no means exclusively, followed upon the spread of a European capitalist system over the globe with the corresponding penetration of a Western economic process beyond as well as within the colonial context.[2]

---

[1] See Garret Hardin, 'The tragedy of the commons', *Science,* 162 (1968), pp. 1243–48.

[2] For a broad analysis of the kinds of environmental changes that have followed the spread of Western industrial culture see T. Weiskel, 'The ecological lessons of the past: an anthropology of environmental decline', *The Ecologist,* 19 (1989), pp. 98–103. Weiskel does not consider the history or impact of colonial conservation.

This chapter is primarily concerned with the political economy of Western ecological systems, and the consequences of their extension to the colonial periphery, particularly in forms of forest conservation. However, it also seeks to underline the importance to the latter task of understanding the evolution of new forms of ecological control, particularly at state level, at much earlier stages in the development of the mercantile maritime states, at a time before the growing resource demands of these states were exported from Europe. While the main emphasis is here upon the political economy of colonial forest and soil controls the societal response to other major forms of ecological intervention also deserves a more thorough examination than is possible here. In particular, the gazetting of game reserves, the enclosure of common grazing lands, the draining of marshlands, the destruction of indigenous irrigation systems and the creation of new ones have all interacted in a significant way with social change, social exclusion and the dynamics of popular protest. Until recently however too little has been known about the minutiae of the relations between people and their environment to address historical problems in this fashion. Indeed, even in arable or non-forest contexts the ecological details of direct colonial intervention in the production process have received remarkably little attention.[3]

However, there is little doubt that it was in the imposition of new forms of land-designation, as between private and public and in the interruption of customary methodologies of interaction with forest, pasture and soil that colonial states (and post-colonial states effectively modelled on them) have exercised the most intimate and often oppressive impact on the daily lives and ways of production of the rural majority throughout much of the (especially tropical) world. This has been implicitly borne out by the apparent frequency of episodes of resistance to this species of colonial impact that have taken place throughout the

---

[3] There are some significant pioneers in this field, however, mainly among Africanist historians. See especially Christopher V. Hill, 'Santhal bataidars in Purnia district: ecological evolution of a sharecropping system', *Economic and Political Weekly*, 22 August 1987. For eastern Africa see H. Kjekjus, *Ecology control and economic development in East African history: the case of Tanganyika 1850–1950* (London, 1977). For a valuable micro-study see E. C. Mandala, 'Capitalism, ecology and society: the Lower Shire valley of Malawi, 1860–1960' (Ph.D. thesis, University of Minnesota, 1983).

period of the expansion of the capitalist forms of economic and political control. It is the forms of colonial ecological control, particularly 'conservation' structures and the circumstances of resistance to such control, that are the focus of this chapter.[4] The complexities of their political role, I argue, have been very much underplayed.[5] Recent studies of episodes of 'resistance', particularly by the 'Subaltern School' of Indian historians, have emphasised a largely autonomous notion of peasant resistance quite separate from the mainstream of the political economy of elitist resistance.[6] It would be easy to offer a critique of this view, in advocating a 'rounded history' that integrates elitist and subaltern approaches. Instead the dynamic I wish to draw attention to relates to the critical importance of ecological constraints in stimulating and guiding both phases of acquiescence and phases of 'resistance' to the developing interventions of capital and the colonial state in the lives of a variety of different classes of indigenous rural people and, in some instances among colonial settlers themselves. To date, because of the lack of consideration of the ecological context, the significant linkages and synchroneities, on a global scale, between these forms of resistance have been neglected.[7] This task has now been given an added incentive and feasibility both by the current environmental crisis in much of the tropics and by an emerging body of work on and understanding about the history and

---

[4] This chapter is necessarily limited in geographical scope. The emphasis here is on the British colonial context. Ideally comparable developments in Lusophone and Francophone Africa and in South America would need to be considered more extensively.

[5] However, see P. Blaikie, *The political economy of soil erosion in developing countries* (London, 1985), for a contemporary approach.

[6] E.g., Ranajit Guha, *Elementary aspects of peasant insurgency in Colonial India* (Delhi, 1983); and papers in the *Subaltern Studies* series (Volumes 1–5, Delhi, 1983–88).

[7] See J. C. Scott, *Weapons of the weak: everyday forms of peasant resistance* (New Haven, Conn., 1985); and his *The moral economy of the peasant: rebellion and subsistence in southeast Asia* (New Haven, 1979). Surprisingly, in both these major works Scott skirts the critical part played by ecological pressures in guiding peasant action. While M. Gadgil and R. Guha, in 'State forestry and social conflict in British India', *Past and Present*, no. 123 (1989), pp. 141–177, have attempted a pioneering India-wide analysis of the ecological bases of social conflict, their conclusions have been distorted by an over-narrow geographical and temporal concentration. At another level, they have not understood the nature of the environmental anxieties and political motivations behind early colonial conservation policies.

mechanisms of colonial ecological change and control. Until recently most studies have been compartmentalised by sub-continent, state or colony, particularly in the work of Stebbing, Brascamp (the pioneer in the field),[8] Tucker, Gadgil and Guha in South Asia and Stebbing and Beinart in Southern Africa.[9] In my own work I have recently attempted to stress the global common denominators of methodologies of colonial ecological control as they have developed over the three centuries since about 1640 and the synchroneity in the emergence of scientific rationales for control. It has become clear that the technical and colonial discourses of conservation have operated for much longer than is often realised, throughout the imperial context. This phenomenon alone, I think, helps and in fact demands an equivalent inspection of modes of popular response to the effects of that discourse.[10] One can now begin to expose the extraordinary vigour with which conservation programmes, in particular, were pursued after the early nineteenth century, and to understand the technical agendas and powerful motivations behind these programmes. Principal among these motives were a deep insecurity about the prospects for the long-term survival of the colonial state and a deep anxiety about the consequences of climatic change and environmental deterioration.

Both these concerns were particularly prevalent in India and southern Africa between about 1835 and 1880. From a present-day viewpoint the latter anxiety, now very familiar, but whose antecedents go back to the mid-seventeenth century, might be thought to have had its merits, particularly in view of current preoccupations with notions of

---

[8] See Brascamp's articles in *Tijdschrift voor Indische Taal ,Land en Volkekunde,* all issues 1921–31.

[9] E.P. Stebbing, *The forests of India* (3 vols, Edinburgh, 1922); *The forests of West Africa and the Sahara: a study of modern conditions* (London, 1937); Gadgil and Guha, 'State policy and social conflict'; R. Tucker, 'The depletion of India's forests under British imperialism: planters, foresters and peasants in Assam and Kerala', in D. Worster, ed., *The ends of the earth: essays in environmental history* (Cambridge, 1988), pp. 118–141. See also papers in D. Anderson and R. Grove, *Conservation in Africa: people, policies and practice* (Cambridge, 1987).

[10] See Chapter 3, also R.H. Grove, *Green imperialism: colonial expansion, tropical island Edens and the origins of environmentalism, 1600–1860* (Cambridge, 1995), and 'Early themes in African conservation: the Cape Colony in the nineteenth century', in Anderson and Grove, *Conservation in Africa*, pp. 21–39.

sustainable development.[11] Significantly, however, the conservation structures which evolved from early notions of the limitability of resources were frequently just as destructive or oppressive in their effects on indigenous societies as direct ecological destruction and appropriation of environments and common rights by private capital. The vigour and extent of the resistance movements which rose to these new forms of ecological control both deserve their own narrative and may serve as an object lesson for more contemporary advocates of conservationist prescriptions to global environmental problems.

Colonial ecological interventions, especially in deforestation and subsequently in forest conservation, irrigation and soil 'protection', exercised a far more profound influence over most people than the more conspicuous and dramatic aspects of colonial rule that have traditionally preoccupied historians. Over the period 1670 to 1950, very approximately, a pattern of ecological power relations emerged in which the expanding European states acquired a global reach over natural resources in terms of consumption and then, too, in terms of political and ecological control.[12] It is tempting to conceptualise this process in terms of the 'European system' set out by Immanuel Wallerstein.[13] However, in some respects, the notion of a European-centred system fails as an explanatory device, particularly in Western India and West Africa, where several indigenous states are now known to have developed extensive systems of ecological control and state resource monopoly.[14] Instead it is

---

[11] For a global approach to the history of ideas about climate and artificially induced climatic change and risk see C. Glacken, *Traces on the Rhodian shore: attitudes to nature from classical times to 1800* (Berkeley, 1967).

[12] For some details of this see R. Tucker and J.F. Richards, *Global deforestation and the world economy* (Durham, NC, 1983); and D. Albion, *Forests and British seapower,* (Cambridge, Mass., 1926).

[13] I. Wallerstein, *The modern world system: capitalist agriculture and the origins of the European world economy in the 16th century* (New York, 1972).

[14] For details of pre-colonial afforestation and control see K. Pelzer, *Pioneer settlement in the Asiatic tropics: studies in land-use and agricultural colonisation in Southeast Asia* (New York, 1948). The forest management systems of the Maratha state and the Travancore, Cochin and Malabar rajas are still a largely uninvestigated field. In Yorubaland a major transition in state forest control took place during the 1830s when the Ibadan state decreed that the forest belts that traditionally surrounded cities were no longer required; Toyin Falola, personal communication.

possible to postulate a periodised model which is relatively simple in structure and which, between 1670 and 1935, resulted in the incorporation of much of the forest and non-arable land of the world under two main control systems. These were developed first on tropical islands and then in India (largely in forest control) and South Africa and the southern United States (largely in soil conservation). By the beginning of the twentieth century the Indian model had become dominant, and was challenged only completely in Anglophone Africa by North American notions of soil control and a game-reserve ideology. In French Africa and South East Asia a forest system very close to the Indian model prevailed. In maintaining this dominant pattern a coterie of highly mobile scientific experts, again dominated by Indian colonial expertise, steadily grew in influence.

At least three essential kinds of motivation in the construction of colonial agendas for conservation need to be considered. Firstly, one is dealing with notions of control and with the wish to appropriate resources first for private capital and then for the needs of the state. These last two have not always constituted identical interests. In fact, in the long term the environmental concerns of the state have tended to be at variance with short-term capital interests. In this way ecological constraints have thus had an exceptional impact on what one is accustomed to think of as the economic priorities of the colonial state. Secondly, one is concerned with the emerging interest of states in preventing or localising environmental degradation or climatic change that would threaten their economic or political viability, either directly through threatening production in drought periods or indirectly through the social disorder which drought and famine might incur.[15] A third motivation, and by no means an insignificant one, relates to motives of aesthetic or ritual concern. Particularly during the period 1660–1860 at least part of the early development of colonial environmental concern was connected with the mental location of 'Edens' and 'Paradises' within various parts of the tropical landscape. At first this imposition of desired environment was limited to paradisal or utopian perceptions of tropical island environments. Later, however, such idealist and, indeed, 'oriental-

---

[15] See Grove, *Green imperialism*, ch.8.

ist', notions became bound up closely with perceptions of the 'tropical' in general and with taxonomies of natural history and concerns about species rarity in particular. During the nineteenth century the emergence of an ambiguous philosophy of game reservation combined such 'Edenic' constructions with a more blatantly class-orientated interest in retaining large animal species for exclusive European delectation, for commercial profit or for recreational hunting purposes.[16] The overarching process, however, was characterised by a process of drawing lines and boundaries. These both articulated the new assertion of control and arrogated the ecological realm to the state. In the case of the forest reserve, the case for state control was very significantly strengthened by the co-option of the arguments of scientists and early conservationists. Without massive state intervention, these arguments ran, climatic and environmental cataclysm might result. Effectively then, the increased credibility accorded to state science gave the colonial state *carte blanche* and a vast new role in claiming control and justifying its stewardship over non-arable land. By the 1890s in India this new role reached an extraordinary degree of development, with up to 30 per cent of the area of some provinces coming under forest department control. A broad sociological analysis of the impact of this process is long overdue, although not within the scope of this chapter. This kind of state intervention was highly contradictory in nature. In particular it was relatively hostile to the profit-maximising activities of private capital in timber production and to expansion in the area of arable land. Instead the state and science collaborated in reshaping the landscape according to a particular new set of 'scientific' agendas.

However, not all the motivations involved were scientific or even immediately economic. For example, it is now becoming clear that the origins of the colonial game or forest 'reserve' and the concept of the 'native reserve' were functionally and politically interrelated, particularly

---

[16] See Grove, *Green imperialism*; and J. Prest, *The Garden of Eden: the recreation of paradise in the botanic garden* (New Haven, Conn., 1981) for discussion of Edenic constructions of nature; for an analysis of the history and ideology of colonial game preservation see J. MacKenzie, *The empire of nature: hunting, conservation and British imperialism* (Manchester, 1989).

in Southern Africa, central India and the western United States.[17] Given the great expansion in the land-control ambition of the European empires during the colonial period it is surprising that scholars who have explored the symbolism of boundary-making have tended to neglect the influence of forest and land boundaries on the pre-colonial patterns of social life in forest, pasture or arable land. A part of the explanation for this may lie in the general absence of much significant research upon pre-existing systems of environmental knowledge and indigenous environmental religion, as well the general failure, by historians at least, to investigate the dynamics of the social relations between pre-industrial man and his ecological constraints. Some recent micro-studies, mainly in Africa, are notable exceptions to this general rule. These are beginning to show that Golden Age notions of pre-colonial 'common rights' and 'common property resources' are largely mythical. Instead, highly complex ecological power relations often subsisted by which those in authority sought to retain or reinforce their power in terms of their claims to particular parts of nature. These were sometimes sanctioned by particular environmental cosmologies and religious beliefs.[18] Only when this area of neglect begins to be substantially filled will one really be able to expect a thorough understanding of the social effects of the confrontation between emergent colonial ecological or conservationist systems and the social lives of the people upon whom they were imposed. Until that time, it may be suggested, discussions will normally be confined to defining the nature of colonial discourses of science, nature and conservation and to the fairly empirical reporting of episodes of resistance or non-resistance to the practical impact of colonial ecological intervention in local society.[19]

---

[17] See Chapter 3 for the working of this functional connection.

[18] E.g., Jack Stauder, *The Majangir: ecology and society of a Southwest Ethopian people* (Cambridge, 1971). An important recent attempt to investigate 'indigenous conservation' and its connections with environmental aspects of religious belief in detail is B.B. Mukamuri, 'Local environmental conservation strategies: Karanga religion, politics and environmental control', *Environment and History*, 1 (1995), pp. 297–311. See also A.H. Pike, 'Soil conservation among the Matenge tribe', *Tanzania Notes and Records,* No. 6 (1938), pp. 79–81.

[19] See A. L. Stoler, 'Rethinking colonial categories: European communities in Sumatra and the boundaries of rule', *Comparative Studies in Society and History,* 1 (1989), pp.

The Evolution of Systems of Ecological Control and Conservationism, 1200–1960

The major shift from common property to private or state control was not exclusively confined to the colonial context after 1600. The beginnings of this process can be identified very much earlier, particularly in the internal colonialisms of Britain, France and Japan. Significantly, it was in the process of conquest that the Normans imposed new notions of feudal control in England, marking off great tracts of land for the king. This imposition involved the re-inventing or fabrication of a tradition of royal tutelage over forest and waste land which had never existed in Saxon England or had only done so in the very loosest and relatively non-controversial terms.[20] Despite high rates of deforestation in sixteenth-century England, it was not until the reign of Charles I that the state attempted to intervene again so extensively in forest control. Even then attempts made by the king to secure firmer control over forests took place more for the sake of his own business interests than on behalf of state needs. Nevertheless, the increased interest shown by the state at this period in carving up and improving marshland and forest reflects a more generalised development taking place in Europe at the period in which increased appropriation of organisms, parts of the environment, society and even the individual person were signalled by a whole variety of methodologies of boundary-making and classification. In the Fen-lands of eastern England large-scale capital-intensive drainage projects were embarked upon, while new ideas about formalised and efficient ways of laying out land after drainage were developed.[21] As far as English forests were concerned the fall of Charles I marked at least a temporary end to such projects, many of which had provoked extensive political opposition at a variety of levels. In essence, the availability of capital and new market demands for raw materials meant that such programmes had to

---

134–61. In this connection, Stoler notes, quoting Memmi, that 'colonialism creates both the coloniser and the colonised'. In forest terms, this can certainly be applied. The rigidity of colonialist land-use categories was not to be found in contemporary England.

[20] J.C. Cox, *The royal forests of England* (London, 1905).

[21] R.H. Grove, 'Cressey Dymock and the draining of the Fens', *The Geographical Journal*, 147 (1981), pp. 27–38.

be transferred elsewhere. It meant, for example, that the failure of the Commonwealth and then the Restoration state to develop a forest policy internally in England (although there was a different and more colonial deforestation story in Scotland) led to the development of a huge and rigidly defined forest reserve system in New England after 1691 organised under a Surveyor-General.[22] When this system broke down after 1776 the same concept was transferred, very loosely at first, to western India.[23] In France, in contrast, where the state was faced with the same problem of strategic naval timber supply, a form of internal forest colonialism developed first under Colbert in the framework of the Forest Ordinance of 1669 with the creation of Départements des Eaux et Forêts.[24]

Until about 1770, then, the objectives of the continental systems of ecological control were strictly related to naval timber requirements and the other lesser raw material needs of the imperial despotisms. A similar rationale dictated the forest policies of the expanding Maratha system after about 1710.[25] While these objectives remained important until about 1850, other quite different and innovatory forest management considerations were also emerging in the early eighteenth century, although at first only in the early oceanic island colonies. These originated in a kind of environmental concern which had not been important in Europe.[26] The experience of introducing European plantation systems

---

[22] J.J. Malone, *Pine trees and politics: the naval stores and forest policy in colonial New England, 1691–1775* (Oxford, 1966). A parallel development took place in the Dutch context. The first formal colonial forest reserve system was set up in Java in the mid seventeenth century. In this sense, the need to find alternate sources of timber for the growing Dutch economy was even more urgent than in England or France. See P. Boomgard, 'The Dutch colonial forest system in Java after 1650' in J. Dargavel, ed., *Changing tropical forests* (Canberra, 1989).

[23] Grove, *Green imperialism.*

[24] J.C. Brown, *The French Forest Ordinance of 1669* (London, 1879).

[25] For details of this see *Report of the Bombay Forest Commission,* vol. 1 (1887), pp 22–30.

[26] Grove, *Green imperialism.* The critical importance of the colonial island periphery in promoting notions of environmental anxiety is an idea signally omitted by Keith Thomas in his survey of the development of environmental ideas at this period in *Man and the natural world* (London, 1983).

on islands such as Barbados and St Helena quickly gave rise to the realisation that rapid environmental degradation was taking place. This soon led, in turn, to the idea of preventative control, so that formal forest reservation and soil erosion prevention measures became a part of the role of the colonial state in Barbados and other West Indian islands after 1670 and on St Helena in 1709. Similar developments took place in Japan in the late seventeenth century.[27] Here too, forest protection was begun with the express purpose of preventing soil erosion. Allied to this new notion was the re-emergence among European natural philosophers and colonial settlers of a 'desiccation' theory linking deforestation with rainfall change and generalised climatic change.[28] This theory, which had lain dormant since its first formulation by Theophrastus in Classical Greece, was revived between about 1590 and 1700. It has now been confirmed as a valid theory, to some extent, by recent findings about the nature of the carbon dioxide cycle and by micro-climate studies in the Amazon basin.

After 1767 the desiccation theory provided the main motivation behind the introduction of a forest reservation system in Mauritius under the new Physiocratic regime which had been installed on the island at the behest of the Duc de Choiseul, after the collapse of the Compagnie des Indes. It was thus in Mauritius that a new kind of rationale for state forest control was first elaborated and put into practice as the earliest example of a system that was to become global in application. The system developed on St Helena also played an important linking role in this development. The East India Company first became aware of the desiccation theory in about 1784 and embarked on a deliberate pro-gramme of tree planting in St Helena to counter the climatic threat that was believed to exist. By 1836 it was thought that this programme had been successful in reversing a decline in rainfall. The observations on this subject made by Dr J.D. Hooker, later Director of Kew Gardens, became a major factor in promoting the introduction of forest conservancy in India after 1847.[29]

---

[27] R.S. Troup, *Colonial forest administration* (Oxford, 1940), p. 446.

[28] Grove, *Green imperialism*.

[29] Ibid.

The environmental consequences of a colonial agrarian system first made themselves clearly felt on islands, where the notion of widespread desiccation provided a very compelling argument for state intervention. However the logic of the desiccation argument was not applied in Africa or India until the 1840s. The relative delay in the diffusion of the technical notion of desiccation can be partly explained by the initial shortage of ecological information and by the fact that even where deforestation was very rapid, as it was in Western India between 1815 and 1840, the consequences only gradually became apparent. Instead an indirect consequence of deforestation, the silting of major river estuaries and ports, provided the first hard evidence to which scientists could point in attempts to gain state intervention.

From as early as the 1770s one can also start to trace the involvement of professional scientists with their own agendas, and with an increasingly powerful technocratic hold over the colonial state, unparalleled in Europe. Indeed, the very concept of a 'state scientist' was one that first emerged in the conditions of the colonial periphery, rather than in the European metropolitan context.[30] The combination of unpredictable physical conditions and a powerful state apparatus intimidated by the thought of social unrest meant that a relatively small number of scientists were able to wield a great deal of practical control over colonial land-use policy, although much earlier in French than British territories. This culminated, during the period 1837–47, in a process by which a handful of scientists in the East India Company medical service were able to propagandise connections between deforestation, drought and the threat of economic and social breakdown. These ideas were based largely on the writings of Alexander von Humboldt, whose work at this period was becoming frequently quoted in the new Indian scientific journals. They proved sufficiently convincing to coerce the East India Company into initiating a rigid forest conservation policy of a kind which it had, until that time, consistently resisted. An essential element of this new policy consisted in the systematic exclusion of private timber interests from the state forest reserves.[31] Furthermore, a growing alliance

---

[30] Ibid.

[31] Ibid.

between navy and medical lobbies, with their own priorities, made the case for state forest control irresistible. The mindset of the critical decade between 1837 and 1847 deserves close attention since the programme evolved at that time became a model for forest conservation throughout most of the rest of the imperial context. It was a policy which served as a cover for a complex agenda. This included aesthetic notions, species depletion concerns, public health worries, fear of famine, fear of timber shortage, fear of drought and above all fear of catastrophic regional and continental climatic change.[32] It was the ability to articulate convincingly the latter possibility (with all it meant, to borrow the terminology of Mary Douglas, in terms of death, money and time) that was most important in policy terms even though at later stages the desirability of the colonial state being able to guarantee a sustainable supply of timber for itself became more frequently voiced as a motive for monolithic forest reservation.[33] Moreover, the colonial social critique of tribal forest peoples was already becoming extensive in the 1840s.[34] When environmental damage started to be seen as a product of the agrarian systems of the forest dwellers, the environmental critique helped to reinforce existing social prejudice, and vice versa. It is no coincidence that political pressure for serious ecological controls in forest areas in India built up at the same time, in the late 1830s, as early 'tribal' anthropology began,[35] and as pioneering attempts were made to curb female infanticide and prevent *Meria* sacrifice. The development of scientific rationales for forest protection helped, too, to justify the drive to gather information on the tribes. Moreover, forest policy and tribal policy were both seen at this time as necessarily involving the geographical demarcation of 'reserves' both to exclude unwanted elements and economic activities, and to control others.

One early result of this mixed social agenda, which developed alongside simpler environmental fears, was an early preoccupation with

---

[32] Ibid.

[33] M. Douglas, 'Environments at risk', in *Essays in the Sociology of perception* (London, 1973).

[34] E.g., see John Wilson, *An anthropology of the tribes of Western India* (Bombay, 1846).

[35] Ibid.; and F. Padel, 'The evolution of the colonial discourse on the tribes of India, 1800–1947', (D. Phil. thesis, Oxford University, 1988).

critiques of shifting cultivators and their agronomies during the 1840s, a critique which quickly developed into an obsession. In part, shifting cultivation was an inherently autonomous activity whose participants were not easily amenable to social control. Local terminologies for the activity, such as *jhum* or *koomri*, were soon adopted to colonial categories. They could easily (and, from scientific hindsight, generally wrongly) be faulted in environmental terms.[36] Furthermore, particularly in the first two decades of the Bombay Conservancy in 1847–67, the activities of shifting cultivators presented a much softer political target than the far more damaging activities of timber operators with their allies in high places.[37] Even so, in these first two decades the basic needs of villagers in and near forests were taken into account far more sympathetically than was later the case. Hugh Cleghorn in particular (a medical surgeon appointed Inspector-General to the Madras Forest Service in 1856) developed a striking change of heart in his attitudes to shifting cultivation during the 1850s; so that during this period he tended to overlook or permit extant shifting cultivation, transferring his critique instead to the depredations of illegal commercial fellers, plantation owners and railway builders.[38] In general the powers of the Bombay Forest Department, which the state attempted to legitimate on Maratha precedents, were far too weak to prevent continuing and rapid deforestation.[39] It was this realisation that helped to bring about the far more oppressive regimes of the post-1865 period, when German forestry 'science' replaced the Maratha, Scottish and French methods which had been favoured earlier and which continued to be important in the Madras Presidency. The

---

[36] For a useful survey of the effects of shifting cultivation see P. Vitebsky, 'Policy dilemmas for unirrigated agriculture in Sri Lanka: a social anthropological report on shifting and semi-permanent agriculture in an area of Maneragala district', Report to the ODA, London, 1984.

[37] Alexander Gibson, appointed the first Conservator of the Bombay Forest Service in 1847, soon discovered that the opposition of timber merchants and landowners to forest conservation was so effective that he had to restrict himself to seeking controls on probably the least damaging set of forest-clearers, the shifting cultivators. However, he also pioneered the official concept of the 'village forest', a Forest Department categorisation significantly abandoned later in the century.

[38] H. Cleghorn, *The forests and gardens of South India* (Edinburgh, 1861).

[39] *Report of the Bombay Forest Commission*, vol.1 (1887), pp. 22–30.

basic infrastructure for forest conservation was in place, however, well before 1865.[40] Similar developments took place at the Cape, where the notion of the forest reserve had become a very convenient vehicle for state social control.[41] Early conservation programmes at the Cape failed when state conservationists started to promulgate the unpopular view that the activities of European farmers were as important in explaining environmental deterioration as the activities of African farmers.[42] This was a point made too by Cleghorn in connection with the activities of European planters who were, however, a much weaker lobby in India than were settler farmers at the Cape.[43]

From 1872 methods of forest conservation developed in Mauritius, the Cape and India on the one hand and Algeria on the other were taken on in one colony after another, as well as outside the colonial empires. As a result of their pioneering work in France and Algeria scientists of the French forest service were invited to advise on the forest administration of the Ottoman Empire. These experts visited and reported on :, for example, in 1872.[44] This transfer of the colonial forest control system from regional sub-bases to a global context was achieved mainly during the period 1870–1920. Some individual scientists stand out as having played a disproportionately influential part in this process: Hugh Cleghorn, D.E. Hutchins and H.H. Thompson being cases in point. Between them, they set up or reorganised the forest conservation systems of dozens of colonial territories. As early technical or 'development' consultants employed on a world-wide basis, they encouraged the imposition of a relatively homogeneous ecological ideology that lasted until the end of the colonial period, particularly in South East Asia,

---

[40] The first two decades of state forest conservation policy have been set aside in the analysis by M. Gadgil and R. Guha, in 'State forestry and social conflict'. One reason for this is that the climatic risk rationale for the precocious foundation of the Bombay Forest Department cannot easily be adapted to the simplistic nationalist critique of state forest control which these authors adopt. A more rigorous history would reveal the need for a less doctrinaire analysis than that set out by Gadgil and Guha.

[41] See Chapter 3.

[42] Grove, 'Early themes in African conservation'.

[43] Cleghorn, *Forests and gardens of South India.*

[44] J. W. Thirgood, *Man and the Mediterranean forest* (London, 1981). See also articles in all issues of *Revue des eaux et forêts,* of 1877.

throughout sub-Saharan Africa and in Central America.[45] Even the United States Forest Department owed much to the Indian model prior to the era of progressivist conservation.[46] However, although the French and Indian models of management became dominant, other colonial technical models also emerged. In southern Africa the more locally derived conservationist ideology of Dr John Croumbie Brown with his technical emphasis on grass-burning prevention and irrigation development became influential, especially in South Africa and Rhodesia.[47] After the 1920s the influence of the American dustbowl philosophy became more widespread among colonial officials, a development that can be related in part to the increased intervention of Whitehall in ecological matters, the waning influence of Indian expertise in Africa and the lack of emphasis in Indian colonial conservation thinking on pastoral and soil erosion problems.[48] However the didactic manner in which soil conservation policies were pursued in the period 1930–55 in Anglophone

---

[45] One of the first exports of Indian forest service expertise was represented by the enlistment of G. Storr-Lister in the Cape Forest Department in 1875. Cleghorn visited and gave advice about Cyprus during the 1870s. D. E. Hutchins, formerly of the Madras Forest Department, was taken on by the Eastern Cape Conservancy in 1881 and also reported on the Cyprus forests in 1889. Indian and Cape forest officials were employed to advise on policy in the following territories: Cyprus (1879, 1909,1930); Mauritius (1880, 1903); Jamaica (1886); British Honduras (1886); Tobago (1887); Trinidad (1887); Leeward Islands (1887); Antigua (1888); Malaya (1900); Southern Rhodesia (1896, 1902); Gold Coast, (1908); Uganda (1912); Kenya (1922); Northern Rhodesia (1927); Tanganyika (1930). Forest officers from India were seconded in British Honduras, Ceylon, Gold Coast, Kenya, Malaya, Nigeria, Sierra Leone, Trinidad, Uganda and Burma among other territories (Troup, *Colonial forest administration;* this is by no means an exhaustive list).

[46] See Grove, *Green imperialism*; F.B. Hough, ed., 'Report of the Committee on the Preservation of Forests', House Report no. 259, 1st Session, 43rd Congress, Washington DC, 1874. Hough makes specific reference to the precedent set by the Madras Forest Service. Similarly, Hugh Cleghorn was influential on the work of George Perkins Marsh, an early ideologue of American conservationism.

[47] The 'Forest and Herbage Protection' Acts of the Cape Colony were simply transferred without alteration to Southern Rhodesia, much as Indian Forest Law was transferred directly to Natal and the Gold Coast. T.R. Sim, conservator of the Eastern Cape and a disciple of John Croumbie Brown, conducted one of the first surveys of and reported on policy for the Rhodesian forests in 1902.

[48] For an analysis of the impact of American 'dustbowl' conservation ideologies in southern Africa see W. Beinart, 'Soil erosion, conservationism and ideas about develop-

Africa led, as had happened in India, to the imposition of land control policies which often involved a forced-labour component and other less direct forms of coercion, and policies which in political terms were even more provocative.[49]

The Social Response to Colonial Conservation and other Ecological Interventions

'Famine always lies at the bottom of an insurrection,' Louis Madelin wrote of rural France in 1789. Behind most rural resistance movements in the colonial context has lain a threat to a margin of ecological survival, a margin nurtured through years of custom and experience. However, ecological controls imposed in the metropolitan as well as the colonial states have often caused discontent among a whole variety of classes and groups and not simply among 'tribals' or 'peasants'. Indeed Sumit Sarkar's notion of a 'primitive rebellion' is very difficult to sustain in this context.[50]

Instead, many low-level movements responding to ecological trauma have, on the contrary, been highly complex in the sensitivity of their response and in the shifting nature of their allegiances. Such resistance movements have not been confined to particular classes. Rather, they have frequently involved 'baronial', bourgeois or land-owning resisters as well as subsistence resisters; and occasionally, as in Wynaad, Kerala, in 1805, or the Bombay Presidency in the 1870s, strategic alliances between the two. The connections between notions of ecological survival and threats to spiritual and cultural order or well-being have often been very significant.[51] Partly for this reason the

---

ment: a Southern African exploration 1900–1960', *Journal of Southern African Studies*, 11 (1984), pp. 52–83.

[49] There is as yet no satisfactory overall history of forest and soil conservation policy for either colonial Africa or India.

[50] Sumit Sarkar, 'Primitive rebellion and modern nationalism: a note on forest satyagraha in the non-cooperation and civil disobedience movements', in K.N. Panikkar (ed.), *National and Left Movements in India* (New Delhi, 1986).

[51] Similarly, post-Second World environmental movements in Europe, India and North America have involved a whole range of peasant/working-class/middle-class/intelligentsia alliances as well as alliances between notions of physical and 'spiritual' survival.

involvement of millenial, religious or totemic movements has often provided a central uniting influence and motivating force behind ecological resistance movements. This has long been the case. For example, in some of the earliest recorded resistance movements to imperial ecological dispositions, in the Roman Empire, the dispossession of pastoralist and peasant farmers in Tunisia by colonial plantation settlers produced its own vigorous counter-movement, inspired by a 'Donatist' cult of Christianity.[52] The material on such early movements is limited. Far more is known, however, about the social context of peasant resistance to feudal notions of forest control in medieval Europe and particularly medieval England, where population growth increased pressure on marginal common property resources. Furthermore the 'baronial' classes also found post-Conquest forest policies oppressive. In this connection, the Forest Charter of 1217 which followed Magna Carta was important in the sense that it started a process whereby the ability of the state in England to curtail customary forest rights became significantly constrained in comparison to other parts of Europe or the early colonial empires.[53] In 1215 King John was compelled to agree, by one of the articles of Magna Carta, to the 'disafforesting' of all the lands of country which had been 'made forest' during his reign. By the Charter of 1217 it was provided that all the forests which Henry II had afforested should be 'viewed by good and lawful men' and that all that had been made forest, other than his own royal demesne, was forthwith to be deforested. In accordance with this Charter special perambulations were ordered to be made before 1224–25 by twelve knights elected for the purpose to ensure compliance with the Charter.

Widespread deforestation in connection with rises in population, state-sponsored colonisation, state-building and urbanisation in many parts of the world in the early 'medieval' period after about AD1200 has frequently involved the progressive over-running of 'forest tribes' in places as far apart as eastern Germany or the Gangetic plain. For example, many of the wars between the Hindu and non-Hindu groups in India

[52] B.N. Wood, 'African peasant terrorism and Augustine's political thought', in F. Krantz, ed., *History from below: studies in popular protest and popular ideology in honour of George Rude* (Montreal, 1985).
[53] Cox, *Royal forests*, p. 6.

were specifically framed in terms of disputes about political control of forest regions, where expanding and disforesting states have encountered resistance from groups trying to prevent encroachment. In England, the early phase of resistance to the growing ecological dominance of the state and major landowners which had subsequently diminished in the wake of the population decline caused by the Black Death, only really recommenced with the abrupt liquidity of the land market occasioned by the dissolution of the monasteries. This *de facto* privatisation threatened common rights in many areas. In Huntingdonshire in 1569, for example, the extinction of woodland rights by a new owner led to several violent clashes and the subsequent intervention of the Chancellor in the dispute on the side of the common-right holders and against the landowner.[54] Such popular opposition to state intervention intensified during the period between 1580 and 1660, particularly as the richer gentry sought to impose closer control over woodlands in western England. Increases in availability of floating capital and the simultaneous emergence of the early joint-stock companies gave rise, after about 1600, to extensive land-development projects both domestically, in Eastern England, as well as in the West Indies and as part of East India Company plantation activity, all of which involved large-scale ecological and social impacts and which quickly provoked local resistance.[55] In the Fenland prolonged local resistance to the Merchant Venturers' drainage projects was a natural consequence of the considerable trauma which such schemes implied to long-established grazing regimes and common rights.[56] Indeed this opposition was so effective and prolonged, particularly in areas such as the Isle of Axholme, that it constituted a major factor in the distribution of support for the Parliamentary interest during the civil war, while the 'projectors' themselves generally supported the

---

[54] C. Marsh, Churchill College, Cambridge, personal communication. This material emerged in the course of Dr Marsh's work on the 'Family of Love' communities in Huntingdonshire.

[55] B. Sharp, *In contempt of all authority: rural artisans and riots in the West of England, 1586–1660* (Berkeley, 1980).

[56] The 'resistance' here consisted mainly in bank-breaking and widespread crop burning, as at Epworth, Lincolnshire, in 1645; K. Lindley, *Fenland riots and the English Revolution* (London, 1982).

Royalist cause. Furthermore on several occasions Cromwell himself went so far as to actively and specifically champion the cause of the commoners in the Fens. At another level, Lilburne, Wildman, and other Levellers became involved at various stages with the 'antiprojector' fen drainage resisters. Large-scale enclosure of previously commonable fens fell into the same category as ship money and other expedients which under-mined property rights and demonstrated absolutist tendencies in central government. Considerations of social justice and harmony swiftly evapo-rated if they conflicted with fiscal imperatives.[57] The problem did not end, of course, with the fall of the King. Instead, the seizure of Royalist land during the Commonwealth period provoked an early excursion into planning for state naval timber reserves alongside major rivers in the late 1640s. However, these efforts as well as related attempts to acquire closer state control over naval timber in the Forest of Dean quickly sparked disturbances among the very commoners who constituted such an essential part of the political constituency of the Commonwealth. Even the Restoration state could not politically afford to ride roughshod over this interest group. In this way, by about 1685, effective large-scale state intervention in forest control came to be abandoned domestically by the English state.[58]

---

[57] Lindley, *Fenland Riots*. Camden, in *Britain* (1637), asserted that the fenmen were 'a kind of people according to the nature of the place where they dwell, rude, uncivil, and envious to all others, whom they call Uplandmen'. Another writer in 1629 noted that the 'generality of the fen people were very poor, lazy, given to much fishing and idleness … very much against the draining because they found their conditions should be worse, which thing was about impossible' (Lindley, p. 2). Such a belittling discourse paved the way for the drainage developers to ignore the interests of the fenmen, a type of use of 'ethnological' discourse which later capitalist manipulators of landscape in the colonial context were also quick to adopt.

[58] J Thirsk (ed.), *The agrarian history of England and Wales*, vol. V.ii (Cambridge, 1985), p. 376. Riots broke out in 1680 and 1688 in the Forest of Dean even though far more parliamentary time was spent discussing the Forest of Dean than any other royal forest; C.E. Hart, *The commoners of Dean Forest*,(Gloucester, 1951), pp. 52–71, 74–5. The problem did not end there, however. A century later renewed pressure to enclose Dean for the state both for timber and coal led to episodes of active resistance culminating in the involvement of the Forest of Dean in the Captain Swing Revolt in 1831. The critical role played by this region in the Chartist agitations (for which several forest men were tried at Monmouth in 1841) can be traced back to forest grievances too. See R. Anstis, *Warren James and the Dean Forest riots* (Coalway, Glos., 1986).

Ironically, then, it was the relative success of sectional and low-level opposition to the growing ambitions of the state for internal ecological control and for land-use 'planning' that led directly to the very precocious and geographically very extensive colonial forest policy embarked on in New England by the English after 1691.[59] The fact that the French were not compelled by successful popular protest to seek such fresh resource fields at such an early date may explain much of the later superiority in British hold over global forest resources as a dynamic strategic factor. However, colonial forest policy in New England also led directly to the loss of those colonies. It stoked the fires of settler opposition and nascent separatist tendencies in direct and non-direct ways. A whole sub-culture of civil disobedience was created from about 1710 right through to 1776, in which forest regulations were continually broken by individual settler and timber interests alike, with the critical and growing connivance of the colonial courts and much of the colonial establishments.[60] In this way, grievances over oppressive imperial forest policy became, effectively, as important as any other more short-term factors in the development of the American Revolution, particularly in the way in which an entire subversion of imperial legitimacy was generated by the connivance of the legislative arm. Law-breaking, at an insidious level, had been the norm for sixty years by 1776. The revolution was thus very much stimulated by the collusion and collaboration of a variety of class and commercial interests resisting colonial forest policy.[61] British assertion of control over forests at the Cape, and then in Malabar and Burma, was a direct result of the loss of the North American source of timber supply and the consequent strategic crisis in naval demand for raw materials in the context of the wars with the French between 1793 and 1815.[62]

The French Revolution itself, in its rural and agrarian aspects, was also dynamically connected with the growing and vice-like grip of the state and its rural allies over the common ecological rights of the

---

[59] Malone, *Pine trees and politics.*

[60] Ibid.

[61] For a later account of rural American resistance to state control see J.Garentin, *Power and powerlessness: quiescence and resistance in an Appalachian valley* (Oxford, 1980).

[62] See Grove, *Green imperialism.*

peasantry. However, the class dynamics of this conflict were rather different from the American situation although the context was arguably equally colonial, a matter of the urban class interest extending a resource search out into the countryside. The effects of this process were much exacerbated by the monolithic character of Colbert's 1669 Forest Ordinance and the apparatus of control that went with it. This apparatus grew steadily in power during the eighteenth century, assisted by the growing crisis over ship timber.

The steady erosion of the element of marginal land flexibility in France during the eighteenth century dramatically increased the vulnerability of the peasantry to economic and climatic pressures. Regional fuelwood shortages became acute, while the crop failures of the early 1780s became especially significant. Both before and during the revolution incendiarism and illegal wood-gathering became widespread weapons against the growing controls and shortages.[63] In some villages in rural south-west France long-running battles over common access to marshes, woodlands and fishing rights were fought out between peasants and landlords in the second half of the eighteenth century. R.B. Rose, in his recent study of Davenescourt has shown how the originally relatively weak position of the peasantry in the *guerres des arbres* was critically redressed in the years after 1790.[64] In the long term, the degree to which the majority of the population gained in these terms from the Revolution is questionable. Initially relieved by the events of 1789–92 the Revolution eventually betrayed the ecological basic needs of the rural peasantry, particularly as urban elements used the fluidity of the new situation to further bolster their control over the countryside. Nevertheless, overall

[63] A.B. Cobban, *The social interpretation of the French Revolution*, (Cambridge, 1964), pp. 100–101. See also the allusions made to illegal woodgathering in the 1830s by Honoré de Balzac in *Les paysans* and in his letter to P.S.B. Gavault, quoted in Scott, *Weapons of the weak:* 'The rights of pasturing their cows, the abuse of gleaning grapes, had gotten established little by little in this fashion. By the time the Tonsards and the other lazy peasants of the valley had tasted the benefits of these four rights acquired by the poor in the countryside, rights pushed to the point of pillage, one can imagine that they were unlikely to renounce them unless compelled by a force stronger than their audacity.'

[64] R.B. Rose, 'Jacqueries at Davenescourt in 1791: a peasant riot in the French revolution', in F. Krantz, *History from below: studies in popular protest and popular ideology in honour of George Rude* (Montreal, 1985):

access to resources did improve, even if it was at the expense of long-term ecological balance. In fact, the evidence seems to indicate that by about 1798 the net ecological result of the Revolution consisted in an uncontrolled ransacking of forest land and mountain slopes, particularly in southern France. Soil erosion in the south-east and Basses-Alpes, already bad, became catastrophic.[65] Indeed, in the course of trying to cope with the hydraulic consequences of deforestation at this period, a whole generation of French engineers specialising in soil-erosion prevention emerged, whose writings became influential among later colonial scientists.[66]

The two revolutionary phases in North America and in France were distinctly different in context from the phases of resistance against the systems of 'scientific conservation' that were emerging in the early island colonies of Britain and France. These were based on new conceptualisations of catastrophic resource depletion, where the establishment's commitment against environmental 'crime', especially against illegal tree-cutting and over-grazing, was becoming quite marked. Thus on St Helena, as early as the 1745, transgressions against forest rules by settler common-right holders had already started to preoccupy the local government to an unprecedented extent. The government even threatened to treat such offences as illegal goat-grazing as 'capital' crimes, but was prevented from doing so by the intervention of the East India Company Directorate which at this stage did not see the logic in enforcing anti-soil erosion legislation as strongly as the St Helena government precociously did. The resulting conflicts mirrored to some extent the basic conflicts among commoners, the state and private capital which were going on in England. In the colony, however, the emerging environmental issues underlying the conflict were quite different. In October 1745 Thomas and Henry Greentree *(sic)* were arraigned for refusing to impound their goats when ordered to do so. The official record stated:

> to deter others from daring to offer the least contempt for the future
> ordered that each of the Greentrees should be fined Ten pounds ... we

---

[65] See the chapter on soil erosion in France in P. Blaikie and H. Brookfield, *Land degradation and society* (London, 1987), especially pp. 129–136.
[66] See especially J.A.Fabre, *Essai sur la théorie des torrents et des rivières* (Paris, 1797).

told them that they ought to look upon this fine as a very mild punishment for so great a crime … that disobeying lawful authority was much the same as resisting it and resisting authority was the beginning of a Rebellion which was a capital crime.

When the Directors heard of this exaction they took a critical view of the Governor's action and the island Council had to backtrack, blandly reporting to the Directors that 'we have repaid the Messrs Greentrees their fines according to your orders, as you're of opinion that the Goats are more use than Ebony they shall not be destroyed in future'.[67]

Initially, then, the metropolitan authorities themselves resisted the operation of early conservation laws in some limited contexts against the wishes of local government, if they perceived short-term profit to be thereby put at risk. At another kind of level, a comparable antagonism developed when Pierre Poivre introduced a set of new and draconian forest protection rules on the Ile de France (Mauritius), after 1767, based both on 1669 French Forest Ordinance precepts and on a coherent desiccationist philosophy. These measures encountered stiff opposition from settler landowners as well as iron foundry interests. Later, sugar plantation owners vigorously resisted state laws against forest clearance until as late as the 1850s under British rule.[68] The general point here is that, having espoused the role of environmental arbiter, the colonial state immediately found itself confronting a whole variety of classes and economic factions with varying interests in either resisting any check on resource depletion or resisting imposed methods of control in so far as they threatened customary management. While the state in Britain was, in general, not able to embark on the kinds of forest controls that evoked such bitter opposition in France and New England the vigour of the enclosure and emparking movement which it sanctioned for private landowners during the eighteenth century had analogous, although far more fragmented, effects. Enclosures of commons and parks tended to affect rights to game more than woodland rights.[69]

[67] St Helena Records; Government Diary, October 1745, p. 83. Govt. Archives, St Helena.

[68] R. Brouard, *The woods and forest of Mauritius* (Port Louis, 1963).

[69] G. Shaw-Lefevre, *The game laws* (London, 1874).

Such measures helped to criminalise a growing sector of the population, although without evoking the kinds of intensified resistance that could actually threaten the security of the state.[70] Moreover, for the state itself, opposition to ecological control was now only significant outside Britain, where colonial sources of timber were acquiring increasing importance.

At the outset of British territorial expansion in the west of India the rapid extension of political control immediately raised the issue of forest management, ownership and the social control of forest-dwellers. Some early attempts at resisting colonial forest control in this context occurred shortly after the assumption of East India Company rule. However such episodes were not entirely new since the Company had inherited a dynamic situation in which the successor states to the Mughal empire, with their growing resource and political ambitions, were already in constant conflict with forest 'tribes'.[71] More importantly, some of the successor states to Mughal rule had been quick to embark on monopolist policies towards timber resources. After annexation the intensification of imperial timber demands with the onset of the Napoleonic wars exacerbated these tensions; particularly as the British were disposed, after 1792, to allocate forests to private or to state control, ignoring any kind of customary right. While in so doing they differed little from their indigenous state predecessors, East India Company occupation quickly provoked the emergence of alliances between ruling and 'tribal' groups.[72] Thus between 1796 and 1805 Kurichians and other shifting cultivators found themselves uniting to fight a war against the

---

[70] D. Hay, 'Poaching and the game laws in Cannock chase', in D. Hay and E.P. Thompson, eds, *Albion's fatal tree: crime and society in eighteenth century England* (Harmondsworth, 1977); E.P. Thompson, ed., *Whigs and hunters: the origins of the Black Act* (Harmondsworth, 1977); J. Broad, 'Whigs and deer stealers in other guises; a return to the origins of the Black Act', *Past and Present* (1988).

[71] Chetan Singh, 'Conformity and conflict: tribes and the "agrarian system" of Mughal India', *Indian Economic and Social History Review*, 23, 3 (1988) pp. 320–340.

[72] It should be pointed out that the onset of British rule in India was not always initially to the disadvantage of 'tribal' groups. After the massive de-population of West Bengal occasioned by the 1770 famine, for example, the Santhals were able to spread out to occupy areas where they had never previously been known. How far the conditions of British rule allowed this it is hard to say.

new occupiers alongside the forces of, for example, Kerala Varma, Rajah of Kottayarn.[73] Between 1815 and 1842 the developing East India Company state on the west coast found itself continually in conflict with the Bhil tribes from Sind in the north to North Canara in the south. Control of forests thus became synonymous with the political control of dissent, leaving aside notions of resource control or conservation.[74]

Throughout the west coast of India, where the forests played a critical part in the early formulation of the scientific conservation ideology of the East India Company, programmes for resource control and conservation were increasingly frequently used to justify political controls for which no other easy rationale could easily be found. Attaching blame to forest tribes for ecological as well as political trouble-making was a logical development at this stage and one that could be used to justify far more oppressive controls than might otherwise have developed, and in particular to allow any customary land-rights to be ignored. The political 'bargain' struck by the East India Company with the Dangs Rajah can be seen in this light: Alexander Gibson, the first Forest Conservator of the Bombay Presidency, commented that 'the annual payment made to the chiefs is the ... most satisfactory outcome that could be devised to keep the peace in that wild country'.

Despite the political advantages endowed by forest control, the upper echelons of the Company were eager to contest such notions of state intervention. This helps to explain why, when the Bombay Forest Department was founded in 1847, it was explicitly justified by the Company Directors on the basis of the climatic threat posed by defor-estation, rather than on the timber-need arguments which it had consistently rejected.[75] What was more, the British fell back upon Maratha methods of forest reservation and state rights over particular timbers as part of the legal rationale for wresting control of forest lands

---

[73] P.R.G. Mathur, 'Political awakening among the tribes of Wynaad', in K.S. Singh, *Tribal movements in India,* (New Delhi: Manohar, 1982).

[74] For the strategic aspects of this policy see K. Ballhatchet, *Social policy and social change in Western India, 1817–1830* (London, 1957).

[75] Although it should be said that between 1837 and 1845 forest reserves were frequently advocated by local and naval timber agents to gain control of the forests in northern Gujerat in the Dangs and Panch Mahals districts.

back out of the landowning hands to which they had been formally granted in the opening years of the century.

During this period developments closely parallel to those in western India were taking place in southern Africa and in Algeria. To account for this simultaneity, and for the extraordinary haste with which the British and French colonial states took on their new conservation and control role in the 1840s and 1850s requires an appreciation of the way in which environmental anxieties (which were certainly a concern of the state) also provided a heaven-sent opportunity to deal with more generalised resource demands, crises of indigenous resistance and fears of loss of control.[76] Both in India and, to a much greater extent, in South Africa these fears stemmed partly from an awareness of population pressures and fear of famine. Apart from the case of Sind, all the first forest reserves in western India and the Cape were founded in close association with popular unrest and military confrontation.[77] It was also at this period, during the European crisis of 1848, that grievances against new systems of 'scientific' forest controls became part of the agenda of rural 'jacqueries' in south-west Germany where peasants and some townspeople were united by common attempts to reappropriate the wealth of forests.[78] There had been other more isolated and short-lived instances of the revival of popular opposition to state forest ambitions in England in 1830–31 in association with the Captain Swing riots[79] and in France against the new Forest Code of 1827. In the latter case opposition to the Code built up particularly in the Midi and in Corsica. In the Ariège region of south-western France peasants waged the long

---

[76] See Chapter 3.

[77] The Sind (Scinde) case is somewhat different. Here, between 1842 and 1848, forest reserves were established on the sites of hunting reserves long established by the Sindhi Rajahs. In this case formal establishment was welcomed by local farmers since they immediately gained access to pastures and arable land from which they had previously been excluded. See Capt. J. Scott, *Report on the canals and forests of Sind* (Bombay, 1853).

[78] P. Linebaugh, 'Karl Marx, the theft of wood and working-class composition', in T. Platt and P. Takagi, eds, *Crime and social justice* (London, 1981), pp. 85–110.

[79] Anstis, *Warren James and the Dean Forest Riots*. The most deep-seated and extensive part of the Captain Swing movement took place in the Forest of Dean, building on long-held resentments against the enclosure activities of naval timber interests. So too, the Forest contributed the greatest single number of transportees to Tasmania.

drawn-out War of the Demoiselles, so named because men dressed as
women to avoid recognition. Such movements can be treated as continuing and striking instances of resistance to the impact of internal colonialism.[80]

These European rebellions were a clue to what would happen a
little later in India where a German-influenced system supplanted less
formalised forest-management models after 1878.[81] There are other,
more direct, connections to be made between the historical development
of revolutionary political philosophy and the alienation of peasants from
forests during this period. In particular, Marx's first political essays and
the self-confessed stimulant to his first attempts at serious analysis of
social process stem from his concern with the criminalisation of the
peasant by new forest laws in the 1840s. The young Marx objected, above
all, to the new development of forced labour in the forest as a punishment
for forest crime.[82] It may come as no surprise, therefore, to find that the
beginnings of organised resistance to the new, monolithic kinds of forest
control can be traced to the same period, both in central Europe and in
India. Early murmurings of resistance specifically against formal forest
controls in India began as early as 1842 when the first timber contracts
with the Dangs chiefs, in Northern Gujerat, were made. From that time
onwards it is probably fair to say that almost all the major episodes of
coordinated popular resistance to colonial rule in India especially in
1856–57, in 1920–21 and the early 1930s were, almost barometrically,
preceded by phases of vigorous resistance to colonial forest control. Some
of these episodes were directly linked with the more urban-based protest
episodes, while others were not.[83]

---

[80] See Eugen Weber, *Peasants into Frenchmen* (Stanford, 1976); especially pp. 485–492,
where he applies Frantz Fanon to nineteenth-century France. For a case study of cork
workers who took over and ran their own enterprises as producers' co-operatives during
the Second French Republic see Maurice Agulhon, *La république au village* (Paris, 1970),
pp. 126–145, 305–360.

[81] See Gadgil and Guha, 'State forestry and social conflict'.

[82] K. Marx (1847), Proceedings of the Sixth Rhine Province Assembly, Third Article;
Debates on the Law of the Theft of Wood in K. Marx and F. Engels, *Collected Works* (New
York, 1975), vol. 1.

[83] For a useful recent discussion of the connections between 'Gandhian hegemony and
rural forest protest movements see Atluri Murali, 'Civil disobedience movements in

In 1851, only three years after the Bombay Forest Department was established in 1847 on a 'climatic anxiety' basis, more organised forms of resistance started to appear in direct response to the imposition of timber fees which could not be related by any stretch of the imagination to any customary system. The negotiating skills of Surgeon Alexander Gibson, the first Forest Conservator of the Bombay Presidency, successfully defused this early confrontation and it should be noted that, by and large, the forest departments founded by the Company in their brief span between 1842 (when the first reserves were founded in Sind) and 1865 were more sensitive to the possibilities of rebellion and more willing to recognise and discriminate between the different kinds of social forces causing deforestation. In the 1851 confrontation forest landowners in the Thana district of the Presidency formed a convenient 'alliance' with the Varli tribal group and actually persuaded them to march in protest into Bombay as well as stimulating agitation within the forest itself.[84] The Indian forest department system at this stage was, as yet, by no means monolithic and was able to adjust pragmatically to what was, as Alexander Gibson saw it, legitimate protest. This was at a time long before an oppressive bureaucratic framework had armed itself with a more inflexible scientific ideology of forestry. The fact that the early Forest departments in the Bombay and Madras Presidencies were run by officers of the Medical Service helps to account for this. In the Madras Forest Department, for example, founded in 1856 by Hugh Cleghorn, the senior officers of the service were all Indians until 1865, as was Chatur Menon, the planner of the pioneering Nilumbur teak plantations. The indigenous element was still significant. Furthermore, in Madras the early hostility to shifting cultivators became diluted in a significant way between 1856 and 1870 by Hugh Cleghorn's recognition that the depredations of invading lowland cultivators, timber interests and railway builders were far more destructive than the recurrent effects of

Andhra, 1920–1921; the nature of peasant protest and the methods of Congress political mobilisation', in Kapil Kuman, ed., *Congress and classes* (New Delhi, 1987). Murali asserts that, while Congress may have gained from the forest movements, their origins were relatively autonomous. While accepting the 'Gandhian hegemony' the local Congress leaders often took the lead from the autonomous articulation of local forest grievances rather than the other way about.

[84] See *Report of the Bombay Forest Commission,* vol.1 (1887), pp. 22–30.

koomri or shifting cultivation. Instead, the principal problem in the Nilgiri hills, as Cleghorn identified it in 1866, was that 'capital' was flowing into the area, largely in the form of plantation investment. This was, he thought, an inherently destructive process.

Nevertheless, in spite of this element of flexibility, the early nationalist movement in the Bombay area was able to use grievances against the forest department to motivate rural support. From about 1870 onwards the Bombay Association and the Poona People's Association actively sought out a broader constituency among the forest users and dwellers of Thana district. This meant that by the end of the decade the Poona People's Association and the new Thana Forest Association were able to act as the main spokesmen for protests against increasingly restrictive forest rules, deriving a considerable political constituency thereby. The strength of these new movements eventually impelled the authorities to set up the Bombay Forest Commission to investigate and report (in 1887) on forest grievances in a comprehensive, although ultimately ineffectual, fashion.

The steadily growing restrictions on forest rights and dispossession of customary rights particularly after the passing of the 1878 Forest Act had, in fact, ended any notions of flexibility. The rebellions in Bastar in 1876 and the Rampa rebellion in the Godavari conveniently mark the beginning of this period.[85] The incorporation of pre-colonial forced labour practices, such as *begari,* in which labour was traded simply for the right of residence, served to legitimate forest control by the reinventing of a tradition in a surprisingly insidious fashion. The history of indigenous rebellions and forest *satyagraha* against the Indian Forest Department after 1878 has been extensively documented elsewhere.[86] Existing accounts, however, have largely ignored the scarcity of forest rebellions before 1878 while simultaneously neglecting the growing complexity of these resistance movements *after* Indian independence, since when the Indian government has pursued a forest policy little different (indeed)

---

[85] See D. Arnold, 'Rebellious hillmen; the Gudem Rampa uprisings, 1839–1922', in Ranjit Guha, ed., *Subaltern Studies,* 11 (1982).

[86] See Gadgil and Guha, 'State forestry and social conflict'. See also R. Guha, *The unquiet woods: ecological change and peasant resistance* (Delhi, 1989).

from that of the colonial period. The two most potent forces in generating resistance after independence, it may be said, were the continuing and increasing restrictions placed on shifting cultivation and the sale of forest produce coupled with the alienation of tribal people from their land as a result of debt transactions. The period after 1940 seems to represent a new phase in this development, and a date far more significant than 1947. Rates of eviction increased dramatically after that time with the large-scale transfer of villages to absentee landlords.[87] Then began what one may term the 'disillusion phase'. This started when peasants and tribals realised that *zamindari* abolition would generally not benefit them and that indigenous rule did not imply any freedom in the forests.[88] The illicit peasant invasion of *zamindari* forests in north Bihar in 1946 was an important precursor of this phase.[89] In Madya Pradesh the kinds of resistance movement which first appeared during the 1920s reappeared with redoubled vigour in the late 1950s, especially under the leadership of Kangha Manjhi in 1959–62. This insurgency was quickly succeeded by the movements in Andra Pradesh in 1960–64. The latter were significant in so far as they provided a fertile ground for Naxalite agitation in the period up to 1970. With recent research it is becoming clear that the Naxalite movement itself would not have acquired momentum had it not been successful in finding deep roots in grievances against the Forest Department and its restriction on shifting cultivation in northern West Bengal, in the Darjeeling area and in the Srikukulam region of Orissa.[90] In this respect the ecological origins and rural constituency of the Naxalite movement, in terms of the way it drew upon grievances against state agricultural and forest policies, have mirrored the

---

[87] K.S. Singh, 'The Gond movements', in *Tribal movements in India*, pp. 177–83.

[88] Ibid., p. 181.

[89] See V. Damodaran, 'Betraying the people: popular protest, the Congress and the National movement in Bihar 1938–1948', (Ph. D. thesis, University of Cambridge, 1989), chapter 5.

[90] P.K.M. Rao and P.C.P. Rao, 'Tribal movements in Andhra Pradesh', in Singh, *Tribal movements in India*, pp. 354–72. See also Samanta Banerjee, *In the wake of Naxalbari: a history of the Naxalite movement in India* (Calcutta, 1980); Sohail Jawaid, *The Naxalite movement in India: origins and failure of the Naxalite revolutionary strategy in West Bengal, 1967–1971* (New Delhi, 1979).

character of both the embryonic nationalist movement in Zimbawe and the Mau Mau rebellion in Kenya.[91]

The development of the Bhil movement around Dhulia in 1972–74, led by Ambarsing Suratwanti, once again related to large transfers of land out of tribal hands and the growth in what were effectively forced labour or *begari* regimes exploiting dispossessed tribal people.[92] Over a much longer period, in Chotanagpur, the Jharkhand movement has always been closely associated with, if not entirely reliant on, forest resistance movements. In 1978–79 parts of the movement found a particular focus in resistance to the planting of teak.[93] This became central to the resistance movement and to opposition to the activities of a local Forest Development corporation typical of the kind that sprouted all over India during the period 1969–80. The concessions achieved by these last movements have generally been trivial. Their character and their agendas need to be carefully distinguished from the development of the Chipko movement.[94] Even so the central issue of local control over land and vital common property resources has been a critical common denominator.[95] Overall it is striking to observe how the Indian forestry establishment, in terms of practical policies as distinct from the politics of White Papers, has steadily strengthened the forces alienating people from their forest resources, in a forest estate being gradually whittled away by the unleashing of often blatantly corrupt commercial forces in

[91] For the ecological basis of these movements see (on Southern Rhodesia) G. Passmore, 'The native land husbandry policy', (chapter 5 of Ph.D. thesis, University of Rhodesia, 1979); G. Passmore, 'Rhodesia: a documentary record of policy failure', (unpublished MS paper); and (on Kenya) D. Throup, *Economic and social origins of the Mau Mau* (London, 1988).

[92] D.S. Kulkami, 'The Bhil movement in the Dhulis district, 1972–1974', in Singh, *Tribal movements in India.*

[93] K.S. Singh, 'Tribal secessionist movements in Chotanagpur', in his *Tribal movements in India.*

[94] Although Chipko has also concerned itself with distinguishing the relative demerits of teak as against other tree species, especially 'sal'. The much greater involvement of women in prominent positions in Chipko is a further distinguishing feature.

[95] Anil Agarwal, 'Ecological destruction and the emerging patterns of policy and popular protest in rural India', *Social Action*, 1 (1985), pp. 54–80.

the forest sector.[96] The real ecological priorities of the post-independence Indian government are perhaps best summarised by the killing of sixteen peasants in early 1984, slaughtered as they led their cattle on to pasture the rights over which they disputed with the management of the Bharatpur Wildlife Sanctuary. More recently Baiga tribespeople have continued to be evicted in large numbers from the new national parks and game (tiger) reservations in Madhya Pradesh.[97] Thus the continuing human cost of wildlife conservation in India, let alone forest conservation, has been a high one.

Forest resistance movements in India were and are largely autonomous in origin and mobilisation. However, they were harnessable by more elite nationalist formations and, more recently, by contemporary radical leftist movements. Most significantly, they have provided much of the impetus behind separatist movements in India in the post-independence period. This impetus has depended, however, on the existence of dynamic links between the rural protest movements and radical urban-based groupings. Even in predominantly arable parts of rural India, it is difficult to underestimate the critical part played by 'ecological grievances', particularly those relating to wood supply, access to grazing and local irrigation, in provoking the kind of widespread rural discontent upon whch 'national' political movements have depended for their constituency. In Bihar, for instance, during the 1920s and 1930s, peasants were caught between, on the one hand, the increasingly awkward administrative obstacles placed by the state on access to forest reserves, and on the other by the steadily more rapacious depredations of landlords encroaching on grazing lands and common rights. The striking irony is that, far from assisting the poorer peasants in their struggle to loosen this ecological stranglehold, the Congress governments newly elected to power after 1937 and again in 1946 actually connived with the landlords, at least in Bihar, in enabling the continuing erosion of

---

[96] For an account of the effects of the expansion of these commercial forces see W. Fernandes and Geeta Menon, *Tribal movements and forest economy: deforestation, exploitation and status change* (New Delhi, 1984).

[97] BBC World Service, Interview with Jocasta Shakespeare of Jersey Wildlife Trust, 28 May 1989. See also Tim McGirk, 'Going to the cats', *Time*, 10 March 1997.

common property resources.[98] This kind of political betrayal by the nationalist movement helps to explain the intensity of ecological resistance movements in the post-independence era in India.

The ecological controls originated in colonial India, particularly those developed in the name of forest conservation, have evoked similar patterns of response in most of the other territories in which they have been applied. Thus the British annexation of Cyprus in 1878 was soon followed, in 1879, by the passing of a forest law based directly on the Indian Forest Act of 1878. Indian colonial 'experts' such H. Cleghorn, B. Madan and D. E. Hutchins regularly advised on management of the Cyprus forests.[99] Australian species were imported and active reafforestation commenced. Incendiarism, which had taken place almost every year until 1965, became a regular feature of the rural response to forest reservation and planting. Forest reservation presented a strong impediment to rural pasture needs, especially for those herding goats. Repeated floods of propaganda failed to ameliorate the problem. As in India a phase of disillusion after independence about the absence of change in state forest policies sparked renewed incendiarism. To add to the problem, communal struggles between Turkish and Greek Cypriots were also characterised by the use of incendiarism as a familiar weapon of protest and conflict. One conservator, Chapman, was led to ask in 1966, 'how much longer, one wonders, will it be before the forest can be dissociated from political disturbances and before forest incendiarism ceases to be a stick to beat the government?'[100]

A remarkably similar pattern of response to forest reserve control developed in Algeria, another ex-Ottoman territory, during the colonial period. In this case the French Forest Code of 1827 was imposed almost unaltered. Here too, resistance generally took the form of incendiarism.

---

[98] See Damodaran, 'Betraying the people', ch. 2. Damodaran's conclusions are similar to those espoused by Murali in Andhra, namely that the institutional connections between the Congress and much more radical local protest movements prevented disillusion with the Congress (in actually dealing with ecological grievances) escalating into a complete break. Even the Kisan Sabha in Bihar was unable to bring itself to make such a break before independence. Political co-option therefore, allowed ecological impoverishment to continue unhindered in large parts of India.

[99] Thirgood, *Man and the Mediterranean forest* (London, 1977).

[100] Ibid.

The conflagrations of 1859, 1863, 1870, 1876, 1881, and 1892 'became literally engraved on the collective colonial memory, that is, they comprised an element of colonial political culture then in the process of formation'.[101] In Algeria, the new forest controls effectively interrupted a long-established pattern of indigenous transhumance, land use and trading patterns in forest products long established in the Beni Salah and Edough mountains. Initially Arab lands were seized and sold to trading companies, many of them English,[102] before the process was bolstered by a forest reserve system. Annual firing was already practised by the Beni Salah farmers in the course of *Kusar* agriculture and was easily adapted to more active incendiarism. The most destructive fires occurred in 1881, the turn of the Islamic century and the year of the Sudanese Mahdi. An investigative commission pointed to the influence of a revolt in the city of Oran and the French invasion of Tunisia in the same year as factors encouraging the incendiarists. The great fear of the French on this occasion, however, was that the real force behind the fires was the resurgence of Sufi agitation and Pan-Islamic propaganda. A millenarian and Mahdist influence was almost certainly involved. Behind it all, however, remained the economic attack on the Algerian way of life. As one Algerian author commented in 1881, 'the fires in our canton must be attributed to the motive of revenge against the forest companies'.[103] Simultaneously, at the other end of Africa, serious resistance to colonial forest policy began in Natal after 1882, where, once again, a version of the Indian Forest Act was put in place under the tutelage of D. E. Hutchins.[104] Under this Act the Afrians were progressively criminalised

---

[101] David Prochaska, 'Fire on the mountain: resisting colonialism in Algeria', in D. Crummey, ed., *Banditry, rebellion and social protest in Africa* (London, 1986).

[102] For example, the London and Lisbon Cork Wood Company which purchased concessions in 1865.

[103] Prochaska, 'Resisting colonialism in Algeria', p. 243. Resistance to French colonial forest policy was not confined to Algeria. In Madagascar, too, the installation of forest reserves after 1896 was stiffly resisted. The full history of these episodes remains to be written. I am indebted to Professor Maurice Bloch of the London School of Economics for this information.

[104] T.R. Sim, *Forests and forest flora of the Cape Colony* (Cape Town, 1907). D. E. Hutchins had originally been employed in the Madras Forest Service.

and 'forest crime' rose every year until 1898. Hutchins wrote that he believed that

> Forest property [sic] is similar to game, it.is widely dispersed and difficult of protection. It is easy for a Kaffir to slip into a forest, cut a sapling and sell it as a pole at the nearest canteen, as for a poacher to knock over a pheasant ... forest policy should be pursued ... against forest destruction as firmly as other moral evils are faced.[105]

Between 1858 and 1888 game reservation policies were being pioneered in the Transvaal and then in Natal, Southern Rhodesia and Nyasaland. In essence, these policies were aimed at excluding all Africans from game reserves and banning African hunting.[106] It has recently been argued that the first game reserves and national parks in South Africa effectively took on a role as symbolic vehicles for Afrikaner nationalism.[107] As a corollary of this the discriminatory effects of the reserves and their extraordinary claims over land can also be firmly be linked to nascent African nationalism. Even where this symbolism was less clearcut, as in Nyasaland, the new hunting regulations played a prominent part in evoking the kinds of grievances articulated in the first nationalist developments north of the Zambezi, and particularly in the Chilembwe rising in 1915.[108]

The increasingly political response to colonial land-use policies in Africa did not take place in a theoretical or comparative vacuum. By the early 1920s, for instance, the example of the Russian Revolution began to seep on to the political agendas of early anti-colonial struggles. Here, too, it should be remembered that actual peasant involvement in pre-1917 rebellions was primarily motivated and constrained by ecological marginality. Thus during the massive agrarian unrest of 1905–07 the illicit cutting of wood constituted the main part of mass actions against landowners.[109] Lenin had written, 'the lumber industry leaves all the old

---

[105] *Report of the Conservator of Forests,* Cape Town, 1889, p. 303.

[106] J. Carruthers, 'Game protection in the Transvaal, 1846–1921' (Ph.D. thesis, University of Cape Town, 1988).

[107] J. Carruthers, 'Creating a national park, 1910–1926', *Journal of Southern African Studies,* 2 (1989), pp. 188–217.

[108] G. Shepperson, *Independent African: John Chilembwe and the origins, setting and significance of the Nyasaland Rising of 1915* (Edinburgh, 1958).

[109] See Linebaugh, 'Karl Marx, the theft of wood'.

patriarchal way of life practically intact, enmeshing in the worst forms of bondage the workers who are left to toil in the remote forest depths'.[110] In fact truck payments and extra-economic forms of bondage had prevailed in Russia not as mere remnants from a pre-capitalist social formation but as terms of exploitation guaranteeing stability to capitalist accumulation.[111] The analogy.with colonial forest policy, especially in central India and Southern Rhodesia, was a close one. In both, erstwhile shifting cultivators and pastoralists were co-opted as 'forest serfs', and permitted to reside in forest areas only on condition they provided part of a permanent labour pool for the reserve system. In southern Africa too, as in Algeria, incendiarism became a major ecological weapon, although not one employed exclusively by African farmers. In Southern Rhodesia active incendiarism of grasslands in Matabeleland accompanied the annexation of land by European farmers and the effective agricultural and ecological marginalisation of the Ndebele. Much of the firing, however, as local officials discovered, was in fact carried out by European farmers anxious to pin blame on Africans and thereby to secure their eviction to reserves.[112] The religious importance of particular parts of the tree cover and landscape played a role, too.[113] Much opposition had been sparked in south-west India to forest policy when sacred woods were transgressed upon.[114] So too, opposition to the Matopos National Park in Southern Rhodesia focused on the religious significance of particular parts of the Matopo hills. Later, during the late 1940s, the Ndebele pursued their case against their exclusion from the national park through legislative means. The details of this legal battle, which are copiously documented, highlight the confrontation which had developed between

---

[110] V.I. Lenin, *The development of capitalism in Russia* (Moscow, 1899).

[111] See M. Perrie, 'The Russian peasant movement of 1905–1907, its social composition and revolutionary significance', *Past and Present,* 57 (1972).

[112] National Archives of Zimbabwe, GF files on 'grassfire' 1912–20; see also *Environment and History,* 1.3 (1996), special issue on Zimbabwe.

[113] Mukamuri, 'Local environmental conservation strategies'.

[114] See M. Gadgil and V.D. Vatala, 'Sacred groves of Maharashtra: an inventory', in S.K. Jain, ed., *Glimpses of the ethnobotany of Bombay* (Oxford, 1981); P.C. Hembram, 'Return to the sacred grove', in Singh, *Tribal movements in India,* pp. 87–91.

the confident and exclusionist claims of 'scientific ecology' and the basic political and religious claims of an indigenous people.[115]

After 1918 renewed fears of the consequences of drought throughout southern Africa, encouraged particularly by the report of the South African drought commission in 1922, led to a spurt of forest reserve declarations in Nyasaland and the Rhodesias designed ostensibly to protect watersheds, avoid regional climatic change and prevent soil erosion. Large-scale removal of villages from new forest reserves such as that on Dzalanyama mountain in central Nyasaland were one result.[116] At first these evoked little in the way of organised resistance. In contrast, the response to similar efforts at introducing Indian forest policies in Anglophone west Africa, and particularly to the Gold Coast and Nigeria, promoted a vigorous protest.[117] First attempts were made to install a forest department and forest legislation on the Indian model in the Gold Coast in 1909.[118] The project was an immediate failure. Most of the affected chiefs objected strongly, legally armed, as they were, by the fact of their holding far more freehold rights than did their indigenous contemporaries in East and southern Africa.[119] Only in 1928 were forest reserves established in the Gold Coast. Even then, establishment took place only after a long propaganda campaign and process of negotiation between chiefs and the state. When the Forest Department was resuscitated in 1928 wholesale concessions were made to indigenous rights, involving a strong element of local self-management. Most of the imported Indian foresters were sent home during the 1920s, appalled by the almost entirely successful efforts of the Gold Coast chiefs to torpedo their plans. They were succeeded by far more pragmatically minded and flexible military officers who were quite happy to make the desired concessions. Of course, the element of white settler agriculture was

---

[115] See T. Ranger, 'Whose heritage? The case of the Matobo National Park', *Journal of Southern African Studies,* 2 (1989), pp. 217–249.

[116] Malawi National Archives, Zomba, Malawi; Forest Department files, 1920–40.

[117] For references to resistance to forest policy initiatives in Nigeria in 1900–20 see E.E. Enabor, 'The future of forestry in Nigeria', in *The challenge of deforestation in Nigeria* (Ibadan, 1986); and A.H. Unwin, *West African forests and forestry* (London, 1920).

[118] Troup, *Colonial forest administration*, pp. 323–327.

[119] J. Brown Wills, *Agriculture and land use in Ghana* (Oxford and Accra, 1962), pp. 229.

largely absent in the Gold Coast so that political pressures to bolster conservation policies as a mask for discriminatory land policies were far less.[120] The same could hardly be said of conservation policies further south in Africa.[121] In Kenya, the introduction of a forest policy on the Indian model after the turn of the century provoked a gradually intensifying conflict between the colonial authorities and peasant farmers and pastoralists over access to lands and woods that were essential to survival in drought periods, particularly as competition from European landowners increased. The Tugen people, in particular, had become largely successful, by the early 1950s, in sabotaging many of the programmes of the Forest Department.[122] Resistance to post-1940 compulsory soil conservation and terracing in East Africa proved an even more explosive political issue since these schemes are inherently more socially invasive and geographically ambitious in conception than forest policy. Early soil conservation concepts developed in the Cape Colony in the 1860s were reinforced by North American precedents in 1920s and 1930s and then imported into Rhodesia, Nyasaland and Kenya between 1930 and 1955.[123] In each of these territories, from about 1942 onwards, compulsory soil conservation programmes, often involving forced labour and other legal sanctions, sparked determined resistance move-

---

[120] The contrast with developments in Malaysia in the same year, 1928, is remarkable. In the Trengannu rebellion of that year, sparked by new forest and land tax laws, Lebai abdul Rahman led a force of 1,000 rebels. The revolt was put down savagely after a few weeks by the colonial authorities, with many casualties resulting. This revolt marked the final stage in acquisition of full control of the Malay states by the British. For details of the rebellion see Dato Seri Lela di-Raja, 'The Ulu Trengannu disturbance, May 1928', *Malaysia in History,* vol. 12, no. 1 (1968). The brutal tradition of state suppression of forest-dwellers has, of course, been consistently reinforced in the post-independence era, particularly in Sarawak.

[121] Government of the Gold Coast, Annual Reports of the Forest Department, 1909–40.

[122] D. Anderson, 'Managing the forest: the conservation history of Lembus, Kenya, 1904–1963', in Anderson and Grove, *Conservation in Africa,* pp. 249–265.

[123] Beinart, 'Soil erosion', and 'Introduction: the politics of colonial conservation', *Journal of Southern African Studies,* 2 (1989), pp. 143–163; Throup, 'Economic and social origins of Mau Mau'; A. Thurston, *Smallholder agriculture in colonial Kenya: the official mind and the Swynnerton Plan* (Cambridge, 1987).

ments, both violent and non-violent, many of which were enlisted to support the emergent nationalist movements.[124] In each case, then, resentment against conservation controls fed directly into the embryonic nationalist movements, probably far more potently than had been the case in India. Indeed, Vail and White have recently shown how, in Nyasaland, in the political turmoil that surrounded the creation of the new Federation (of Rhodesia and Nyasaland), no other issue generated such mass resentment as compulsory soil conservation terracing.[125]

In Southern Rhodesia soil and forest conservation measures became inextricably bound up with peasant resistance and with the rise of the nationalist movement over a much longer time-scale than in neighbouring territories. Evictions and resettlement under the Land Apportionment Act in the 1940s laid the foundation for a radical peasant nationalism, which was to come fully into the open only with the guerrilla war after 1965.[126] Coming on top of resentment already aroused, the effects of the Native Land Husbandry Act, introduced in 1951, were nothing less than calamitous. The measure had been introduced in response to alarmist estimates of soil erosion losses, the result of the systematic over-populating of the native reserves. The Act demanded reallocation of holdings on an 'economic' basis, often involving

---

[124] There is as yet no useful published history of the colonial forest and soil protection programmes of Africa. An early attempt to survey the field in Africa is D. Anderson and A.C. Millington, 'Political economy of soil erosion in Anglophone Africa', in A.C. Millington, S. K,. Mutiso and J. A. Binns, eds, *African Resources* (Reading, 1990), vol. 2, 'Management'.

[125] L. Vail and Landeg White, 'Tribalism in the political history of Malawi', in L. Vail, ed., *The creation of tribes in southern Africa* (London, 1989). For details of resistance to soil terracing policies in Nyasaland and associated mass actions and riots in the wider context of the 1959 emergency in Nyasaland see *Report of the Nyasaland Commission of Inquiry* (London: Colonial Office, 1959); and W. Beinart, 'Agricultural planning and the late colonial technical imagination; the Lower Shire valley in Malawi, 1940–1960', in *Malawi: an alternative pattern of development* (Edinburgh, 1984). According to E.C. Mandala ('Capitalism, ecology and society'), the soil terracing policies were not universally unpopular; some farmers voluntarily continued the practice after independence. See also R.I. Rotberg, *The rise of nationalism in central Africa: the making of Malawi and Zambia, 1873–1964* (Cambridge, Mass., 1966), pp. 171–199.

[126] G.C. Passmore, 'Rhodesia, a documentary record of policy failure', manuscript, pp. 3-5.

wholesale movements and resettlement of population, with little regard to ancestral ties. These movements were literally carried out with the rigour of a military exercise, using army transport and personnel. Heightened regulations for destocking and conservation were vigorously imposed. The suffering and hostility to which the scheme gave rise were accentuated by a five-year plan for its acceleration, launched in 1955. It had been anticipated that those who could not be allocated land would find employment in urban areas. The threatened break-up of the Central African Federation, however, resulted in heightened unemployment, exacerbating resentment both in towns and on the land. The report of the Mangwende Commission in 1961, which had enquired into the unrest, confirmed the fierce resistance which had been mounted to 'land husbandry measures' inside one reserve. The commission found that unrest was related directly to landlessness resulting from the 1951 Act, which in some areas, because of the workings of the Act, had reached 50– 60 per cent. Widespread arson and other destruction had been provoked. The report of the Mangwende Commission led to some lessening in the rigour with which the Act was applied.[127] Despite this response Martin and Johnson, in their chronicle of the Zimbabwe African National Union (ZANU), have confirmed that the Land Husbandry Act provided the final catalyst for concerted nationalist resistance.[128] Moreover, during the period 1957–72 resistance to Rhodesian forest policy grew steadily in the Eastern Highlands, manifested mainly in incendiarism and resistance to the vagaries of a colonial soil conservation policy, the technical agendas of which were constantly changing.[129] The deeply destabilising effect of these policies on the tenants-at-will of the Forest Department helped to provide a fertile ground for the progress of insurgency from Mozambique in the early 1970s.

---

[127] Ibid., pp. 5–7.

[128] D.Martin and P. Johnson, *The struggle for Zimbabwe: the Chimurenga war* (London, 1981).

[129] J. Mtisi, 'Population control and management; a case study of Nyamukwara Valley tenants at Stapleford Forest Reserve, 1929–1971', paper presented to session on 'Conservation and rural people in Zimbabwe' at African Studies Association of the UK conference, Cambridge, September 1988.

A series of attempts were made after 1945 to introduce the kinds of soil conservation programmes which had been developed in southern Africa into both Anglophone and Francophone West Africa, and especially to Nigeria.[130] Once again the contrast with the course of policy in the white settler states was striking. Efficient activity by urban nationalist workers sent out to village areas in Northern Nigeria, particularly during 1948, quickly quelled any hopes the Colonial Office may have had for soil conservation and most programmes were abandoned by the end of the year.[131] As one Nigerian Geological Survey officer remarked when reporting his survey of Oko village in Awa division, 'Measuring the land aroused suspicion so that only rapid survey methods could be used and attempts made to elicit information from individuals were hampered by the interference of irresponsible elements from outside the village.[132] An additional reason why, arguably, imposed soil and forest conservation strategies were pursued less determinedly in the colonial Gold Coast and Nigeria than in other parts of Anglophone Africa was the growing awareness developed by the younger post-war generation of experts that indigenous land-use methods actually possessed merit in conservation terms. The protection afforded by sacred groves in Eastern Nigeria to otherwise highly erodable water catchments was noted on at least one occasion as meritorious.[133]

Such a developing sensitivity to indigenous land-use practices stands, in fact, in stark contrast to the monolithic dam-building and irrigation projects pursued, under the tutelage of ex-patriate engineers by, for example, the independent Nigerian government during the 1960s and 1970s. These projects have often involved the large-scale

---

[130] The diffusion of ideas between the colonial powers on conservation policies by this period was rapid; for a complete survey see A. Harroy, *Afrique, terre qui meurt* (Brussels,1949).

[131] To date there is no survey of popular resistance to colonial forest policy in West Africa; however, Unwin, *West African forests and forestry*, is a useful basic guide to the development of forest conservation in West Africa, providing some perhaps unwitting insights into indigenous responses.

[132] A.T. Grove, *Land use and soil conservation in parts of Onitsha and Owerri Provinces* (Zaria: Geological Survey of Nigeria, 1951).

[133] Ibid.

eviction of local farmers and their compulsory resettlement in unsuitable areas. Such schemes have themselves, not surprisingly, evoked strong local resistance in recent times by farmers who clearly understood the local ecological constraints better than state-employed 'experts'.[134] Indeed peasant communities, particularly in the colonial context, have often been made painfully aware of the superiority of their own knowledge by the sheer degree of vacillation over time in the kinds of 'scientific advice' offered for colonial and post-colonial land-use prescriptions. Pelzer records the tale of an off-duty Dutch official who fell into conversation with a *tani* working his ricefield. When the Netherlander asked the Javanese how he liked the local Dutch administrators, the peasant good-humouredly voiced his irritation at their constant interference; 'One week they come and tell us to hoe with our backsides towards the sun and the next week they tell us we should be hoeing with our backsides away from the sun.' In Java, in particular, such attitudes helped to explain indigenous hostility to government-sponsored migration schemes. However, a more general lesson can be drawn about the nature of indigenous resistance to imposed notions of land management based on 'expertise'.[135] Some of the more recent ecologically damaging and capital-intensive 'resource conservation' and 'development' projects actually owe their original concept and inception to late colonial 'development' schemes, many of which were actually put forward as sops to deflect nascent nationalist protests about low levels of local investment. The Shire Valley Project in Malawi and the Jonglei canal scheme in the Sudan have been examples of this phenomenon. In Ethiopia, the Awash Valley Development Project actually helped to bring to life the separatist movements in Tigre and Eritrea, as local pastoral regimes were dangerously interrupted.[136] While ostensibly 'conservationist', all these

---

[134] Probably the most violent episode of resistance to a 'development' project in Nigeria was that at the Bakolori Dam site in 1980. This is described in an important case study by W.M. Adams; 'Rural protest, land policy and the planning process on the Bakolori Project, Nigeria', *Africa*, 58 (1988), pp. 315–336.

[135] K.L. Pelzer, *Pioneer settlement in the Asiatic tropics: studies in land utilisation and agricultural colonisation in southeastern Asia* (New York, 1948), p. 233.

[136] M. Gamaleddin, 'State policy and famine in the Awash valley of Ethiopia', in Anderson and Grove, *Conservation in Africa*, pp. 327–44.

schemes have proved ecologically unwieldy and highly invasive to local, evolved relationships between subsistence farmers and pastoralists and their respective environments. All have evoked bitter conflicts between local people and the state.[137]

In recent years the media have accustomed us to the spectacle of indigenous peoples vigorously resisting the depredations of state forest concerns, timber developers or dam-builders on lands vital for subsistence. However, as the above account should make clear, historically resistance to other more controlled forms of ecological transition has been opposed equally strongly. Since the mid-eighteenth century the emerging discourses of natural science have played a major part in this dynamic. As they have been adopted by states in the course of the diffusion of capitalism, especially in the context of colonial rule, such discourses have been utilised to justify and promote unprecedented acquisitions of control over large parts of the landscape, above all in south-east Asia and Africa. In these regions forest reserves, game reserves and soil protection schemes have served to erode indigenous 'rights' and access to previously loosely defined or 'common property' resources. To some extent it may be possible to argue, for example in the case of India, that colonial forest conservation, as an early form of 'sustainable management', prevented what might have been an even more disastrous transition under an unbridled capitalist regime of resource extraction. However, since the systems of knowledge and even the more idealistic conservationist agendas used to justify colonial ecological control were almost entirely externally derived, their impact on indigenous peoples has been almost entirely negative. Ignoring often long-evolved relationships between people and nature, the effects of 'conservation' have tended to profoundly threaten traditional mechanisms of subsistence and thereby to threaten and alienate whole cultures from their environmental contexts. One should not be surprised, then, to find that attempts to oppose the forces of capitalist ecological manipulation have been

---

[137] It should not be thought, however, that colonial conservation ideologies have had a total monopoly in the stimulation of resistance to overbearing attempts at managing the landscape. There is a growing body of evidence to indicate that a whole series of soil conservation initiatives in Communist China have been abandoned since the early 1960s in direct response to widespread popular opposition.

frequent, although rarely effective in terms of restoring traditional ecological relationships. Equally, it is clear that the more closely one investigates episodes of rural resistance to capitalist or monolithic state ambitions, the more one is likely to uncover the political significance of the ecological element in the motivation of the resister.

Index

A

Aborigines Rights Protection Society
 164–167
 and Forestry Bill, 1908 173
 and Gold Coast nationalism 173
absentee landlordism 59
absentee landlords
 after Indian independence 211
Acacia giraffea 96
Académie des Sciences 5, 8, 9
Adu, King of Mankesim 151
Algeria 193, 214–218
American Revolution 199
Amirs of Sind 55, 80–81
Anderson, Alexander 11, 15, 130, 132
Anderson, David 35
Andra Pradesh
 resistance in, 1960–1964 211
Anglo-French Boundary Forest
 Commission 35
anthropology of tribals 191
Arbousset, T. 101–104
Australian settlement
 and El Niño 143
Awash Valley Project 221

B

Bacon, Francis 6
Balfour, Edward 21, 24, 43, 65, 72,
 73, 80, 127
Balfour, George 21, 23, 24
Banks, Joseph 15, 52, 67, 138
 and Indian meteorology 130
Barbados 6, 189
Basutoland 101
Beatson, Alexander 65, 134, 137–142
 and global climate change 138–139
 and mutiny on St Helena 140
 and rainfall measurements 137–138
Bechuanaland 20

Beinart, William 35
Belfield Commission 174
Bengal 125, 136
Bhil 204, 212
Bidie, George 20, 25
Bihar 125, 136, 213
 peasant invasion of *zamindari*
 forests 211
Black Death 197
Blandford, Henry 144
Bombay Association 208
Bombay Forest Commission 1887 208
Bombay Forest Department 74, 78,
 192, 193, 207
 and Maratha system 204
 founded on colonial science 16
botanic garden
 Aristotle's 44
 as Paradise 46–48
 Calcutta 16, 56, 68
 founding of, 1788 66
 Cape 23, 106
 Dapoorie 73
 Edinburgh 130
 information networks of 15
 Kew 125
 Kingstown (St Vincent) 11
 Mauritius 56, 61, 63
 Samulcottah 133
 St Helena
 founding of, 1788 66
botanic gardens 7, 16
 and conservationism 153
 medical surgeons and 66
botanists
 and early conservationism 153
boundaries, pre-colonial 186
Boussingault, Joseph 16
Bouton, Louis 65
Bovill, E. W. 34